MW00436291

SELF-RELIANT LIVING

PRESENTED TO: _____

ON: _____

MESSAGE: _____

_____

_____

_____

_____

_____

_____

_____

_____

_____

_____

_____

_____

_____

PRESENTED BY: _____

"A great book for the beginning homesteader! It introduces, in simple terms, the ingredients necessary to assist one's journey toward fruitful independence. This life-style requires physical work, but the rewards make the trek that much more fulfilling.

"Since we live in an increasingly-restrictive and controlled world, following this book's guidelines has great significance."

—Gordon McAllister, a happy Oregon homesteader

"Your writing style is simple, thoughtful and direct. Genius is in simplicity. It makes self-reliance quite possible and within reach of anyone with the desire. I can hardly wait to buy my big R.V. with a roof-top garden and a wind generator on top!"

—W. Scott Hale

SELF-RELIANT LIVING

Learn to PROVIDE FOR YOURSELF now
and when you retire. BE INDEPENDENT!

DR. JAMES McKEEVER
WITH
MRS. JEANI McKEEVER

SELF-RELIANT LIVING

Printed in the United States of America
First printing December, 1994

Omega Publications
P. O. Box 4130
Medford, Oregon 97501 (U.S.A.)

ISBN #0-86694-126-6 (Softback)

TABLE OF CONTENTS

This book is dedicated to the God I serve
and His only begotten Son, Jesus Christ.

This book must undeniably be dedicated to
my wonderful, hard-working wife,
editor and coauthor:

Jeani McKeever

This book is also dedicated to the ones who also
have labored so hard to bring it to you:

Jill Agar, typist and typesetting
Liz Bowman, data entry
Lloyd Darlington, proofreading
Marti Horak, typist
Wade Overdorf, shipping

This book is further dedicated to all of those who
read it and become more self-reliant by using
the information and recommendations
found in these pages.
I hope this will mean you.

—James McKeever

FOREWORD

By Don McAlvany

I had a special interest in the development of this needed book, as it is one that I have been hounding the McKeevers to write since I first heard of their intention to do so. I personally wanted to benefit from their many years of experience with this kind of a life-style, so that I can avoid unnecessary errors and can profit from their wisdom gained in living out the things they write about in this book.

As my wife and I have watched their place in the country develop over the sixteen years we have known them, we have been inspired to want to do likewise. Yet when we have visited, the things they explained and showed us were more than we could absorb in just a visit. I'm so glad this valuable blueprint of how to become more self-reliant is now documented in a plan of action that people can follow.

I too have seen the need for people in this country to become more self-reliant, and *this is the book that definitely can help you to do so!*

Self-Reliant Living offers a great deal of helpful, common-sense, intensely-practical advice. All the things that you need to know to get started on your own homestead are addressed in these pages. The repeated warnings about allowing plenty of time to put together the self-reliant retreat are especially wise. My family is certainly finding this to be the case, as we seek to move in this direction.

I appreciate the fact that attention is also given to those who want to become more self-sustaining while remaining in the city. This book is relevant to all of us today. It has a wealth of material you can use that does not appear in any other work that I have run across.

For over sixteen years, James and Jeani McKeever and myself have been discussing survival techniques, self-sufficiency, and disaster preparedness. The difference between the McKeevers and me, however, has been that I for the most part have been *talking about it* and the McKeevers have been *living it*. In this world, there are *talkers* and there are *doers*. I try to avoid talkers. In the area of physical self-reliant living, the McKeevers are *doers* and have been for almost two decades. For years James has written newsletters and books, lectured, and personally practiced self-reliant living. *He has been my personal mentor in this area.*

It is terrific to know that this kind of information is getting out to Americans in these rapidly changing times. I know that you will be richer and wiser from the profusion of constructive help offered you in these pages.

INTRODUCTION

Progressively more people are growing concerned about the government's financial situation and that the government will not be able to take care of them, particularly in their old age. When social security and welfare first started in 1935, there was one beneficiary for every 143 workers. Today in America, if you include all the government employees who, in reality, are also beneficiaries economically, there is one beneficiary per worker. When the baby boomers all retire en masse, somewhere shortly after the year 2000, my best estimate is there will be two to three beneficiaries per worker. It is obvious to any thinking person that the workers simply will not be able to support the beneficiaries at that time.

Thus, more and more people are looking toward caring for themselves during their retirement years and not relying upon the government to do so for them. They are seeking ways to be able to provide for themselves. This could mean having to provide one's own food, electricity, heating and all the other things that we have come to rely on to make our daily life comfortable.

If you throw another factor into this equation, becoming self-reliant in your life-style begins to make even more sense. Many people do not realize how fragile our distribution system is. The farmer grows the grain or the corn, and he relies on trucks to haul it to the major silos. Trucks, or trains, haul it from the major silos to places like General Mills that convert it into the food products that we later buy from the grocery store. Then other trucks or trains take these items from General Mills to warehouses or wholesalers. Still other trucks take them from the wholesalers out to the individual stores. What would happen if there was an absolute shut-down of all trucking and train operations for six months in the United States? This could happen because of labor strikes, terrorist activity, massive earthquakes or other types of natural disaster. *It is a fact that even if the trucks stopped running for just three weeks, there would be no food in most cities.* Thus, you could be forced very quickly to having to provide for yourself.

If some terrorist organization were to take out the electrical-generating plant (or several major towers) or the water purifying plant in your area, you would need to be able to provide your own electricity and water. If you look at the World Trade Center bombing and other activities of recent years, terrorism is gradually coming to the United States, and experts forecast that it will continue to increase.

The ideal way to become more self-reliant is to move out of the city to a more rural community. However, as this book indicates, there are many ways that you can become self-reliant if you are absolutely stuck in a city and cannot leave. This book covers the basics of a self-supporting life-style, addressing everything from building your home (or modifying your existing home) to raising animals. It discusses alternate ways to get your electricity—from the sun, from the wind, from water and even from wood heat. It examines ways to get your own water, including how to dig your own well.

The addresses and phone numbers of sources where you can get the needed equipment for digging your own well are listed in Appendix B, which is a small book within itself. People have told us they feel that Appendix B is worth the price of the entire book! In fact, there are other publications that give sources such as we have here in Appendix B that charge $20-$30 just for the book of addresses and sources.

In Appendix B, we also tell you where you can get wood stoves, greenhouses, the nutrients and timers needed for a hydroponic greenhouse, garden tillers, garden carts, and everything that you would need to live a self-reliant life—a life where you could provide for yourself and be totally independent and free.

We believe that in years to come, as the need to become self-reliant becomes obvious to more and more people, this book will be like pure gold in the hands of those who have it. There is a wealth of information in it.

Self-Reliant Living is not written from a theoretical viewpoint. Between my wife, Jeani, and myself, we have over forty years experience of actually living the self-reliant life-style. We have done it, and we have made mistakes. In this book, we tell you both what to do and some of the mistakes to avoid.

Once you are able to provide for yourself and not be dependent on others, nor on the fragile distribution system in the United States and not even on government or company pension plans, then you will be able to experience a peace that is beautiful. Try it! We know you will love it. You will love being able to eat food that you have grown yourself and to enjoy a life-style wherein you are able to provide basic essentials for yourself.

May God bless you as you read this book, and may it be a help to you, as we pass on the things that we have learned.

Dr. James McKeever

ACKNOWLEDGMENTS

First and foremost, I want to acknowledge my coauthor in this work, my lovely wife, Jeani McKeever. Not only did she write portions of it and provide many helpful suggestions and insights, but she also edited and proofread the book. She has been my inspiration and my encouragement. She is the perfect wife and co-laborer and I continually thank the Lord for her.

I also appreciate the outstanding work of Jill Agar and Marti Horek in typing the manuscript and typesetting the book and Lloyd Darlington for proofreading. In addition, I am very indebted to the men and women who went through the manuscript and gave me constructive feedback:

Major Lloyd R. Darlington III, U.S. Army Reserve
Scott Hale, Engineer
Mrs. Ruth Hunter, Retired Nursing Supervisor
Carl Krupp, Publisher *Self-Reliant Magazine*
Don McAlvany, Publisher *McAlvany Intelligence Advisor*
Dr. Beth McDade, Retired Dentist
Steve Quayle, Safe-Trek Outfitters
Rocky, Homesteader par excellence
John Wadsworth, Survival and Food Expert
Harry Weyandt, Nitro-Pak Preparedness Center
Walter Wirths, Homesteader

I also appreciate the prayers and encouragement of a whole host of people, especially the Omega Partners and our staff at Omega headquarters.

I also want to thank you for purchasing a copy of this book. My prayer and desire is that you would not only gain knowledge from this information-packed volume, but that you would then actually take steps to become more self-reliant.

Dr. James McKeever
P.O. Box 1788
Medford, OR 97501

Chapter 1

THE NEED TO BE
MORE SELF-SUPPORTING

In the early days of America, each homestead was basically self-supporting. People raised their own vegetables, raised chickens for eggs, and had cows for both meat and milk. These self-supporting homesteads or farms also usually had a cash crop of some kind (such as cotton or tobacco) that the homesteaders sold in order to buy items they could not raise (such as cloth and shoes).

They canned or preserved the vegetables that they grew and they stored root vegetables (carrots, potatoes, turnips and beets) in a "root cellar" for the winter. They smoked the hams from the pigs, made jerky, canned beef stew, or preserved meat using salt.

Most of these homesteads would accumulate enough food to last a year or two, so that if, for example, the bridge across the creek washed out and they could not get into town for a month, there was not a resulting hardship in their lives, for they were self-supporting. Notice that I did not say they were "self-sufficient." No one is really self-sufficient in and of themselves, for we all need other people, such as doctors, dentists, veterinarians, friends, and so forth. The term "self-reliant living" could be taken to mean that a person is relying only on himself. There is a vital and significant role that neighbors and the community can and should play in our lives.

The distribution system in America and most western countries is very fragile, at best. If *all* of the trucks stopped running for two months because of a nationwide truckers' strike, what would happen? No food would be shipped from the farms to the canneries. No canned, frozen or fresh foods would be shipped to the grocery stores. No gasoline would be delivered to the service stations. No packages or parcels would be delivered. What would happen if terrorists blew up the local water works, the local electrical-generating station and gas-distribution facility, and it took a year to get them back into operation?

I would like to ask you to pause after you have read this paragraph and take a bit of time to think through what you really would do if some or all of the situations mentioned in the preceding paragraph were to occur. Think through what you would do if the grocery stores became empty because no foods were being shipped to them. Consider what you would do if there were no gasoline delivered to gas stations. Ponder on what you would do if the local waterworks, the local electrical-generating system, gas system and sewage disposal system were all rendered inoperable, either by an act of nature or by terrorists? Realistically, what would you and your family do? I urge you to pause for a few minutes to think about life in the city under these circumstances.

I think you will agree that a wise person would like to be more independent of these fragile service and distribution systems. We would like to be less "system-reliant" and more "self-reliant" or "self-supporting."

Let me share some background with you so you can better understand why my wife and I are writing a book on a self-reliant life-style. I first tried this life-style for one year on Catalina Island. Then, after a lapse of a number of years, Jeani and I have been living it for over seventeen years continuously, as of the writing of this book. I have learned a lot during that combined eighteen years of experience that we believe will be very beneficial to you, as you consider becoming more self-reliant in the way you live. We can help you provide for yourself and rely less on the distribution systems, the government, and other conveniences.

AN INCREDIBLE YEAR
ON CATALINA ISLAND

I was in the computer business for twenty years (1954-1974) and was with IBM the middle ten of those years. Halfway through my time with IBM, I took a one-year leave of absence and moved from upstate New York with Marian, to whom I was married at that time, and our two daughters. We went to Catalina Island, which is 29 miles off the coast of Los Angeles, where we were caretakers at InterVarsity Fellowship's Camp, which is called "Campus by the Sea."

We were going to live in a cove on Catalina Island where there was neither electricity nor roads into the place, where we were planning to live off the land for a year. Many of my IBM colleagues commented that they had an inborn desire to see if they could live off the land. They were jealous that I was able to go and try it.

Had I known some of the trials and tribulations I was going to have, I may not have been so eager. But in the end, the experience and the growth far outweighed the hardships and obstacles.

The regional manager of InterVarsity Christian Fellowship flew to the island in the seaplane with Marian and me and our two preschool daughters. We landed at the dock with our suitcases. The manager pointed to a rowboat full of water in the middle of Avalon Bay, handed me a small ten-horsepower outboard motor and said, "Here's your motor, there's your boat, and the camp is about five miles north. Good luck!" Then he got back into the seaplane and left. There I was standing in my white shirt, striped tie and natural-shouldered IBM suit, looking and feeling very out of place.

We hand carried our luggage up to a small house in the city of Avalon, where we had previously arranged to spend a night about once a week. I got my family settled, put on my brand-new, unwashed blue jeans and returned to the dock.

The Avalon Seaplane Service had a boat and they were gracious enough to haul in the water-filled rowboat and pull it up by the bow-ring with their hoist, and empty the water out. With it tied to the floating dock, I crawled down, put the motor on the back and tried to start the motor. About half an hour later, with a sore right arm, I still had no luck getting it started. All the men in the crowd who had gathered around suggested that I might try a new sparkplug, so I bought one and put it in, and finally got the motor started. However, by the time I got it started, the boat was full of water again, so I had the seaplane people hoist it up once more to empty out the water.

The problem was that the back transom was not completely hooked to one of the sides of the boat, as I discovered, but in my naivety I got into the boat, drove with one hand and bailed with the other, as I headed out toward the camp. Had I known then what I know now, I would never have set foot in that boat, much less attempted to drive and bail at the same time! But God protects the stupid as well as the innocent, I guess.

I got out to the cove and discovered that all was not as had been depicted to me. There were three little cabins, none of which were winterized. In fact, the two-by-four studs only had the outside siding, and the studs were still exposed inside. There were a number of open-air dormitories for students and an open-air, large dining room and kitchen. Later I found out that the previous caretaker who supposedly stayed there all winter, left the day after the camp closed and did not come back until the day before it reopened, so he did not spend the winter out there as he had committed to do. But I had agreed to spend the winter there as a caretaker and I was going to keep my word, if it killed me.

The only kitchen in the place was the big open-air one which joined the outdoor dining room. I found a piece of asbestos and nailed it to the bottom of a table, and got a small, round kerosene heater and put it under the table. After a few days of going back and forth, I finally brought the family out to their new, magnificent home. We lived in one small, unwinterized, very cold cabin with an outhouse for the necessities of life. We cooked and ate in this kitchen, hovering around the table as we ate, with the warmth coming up from the kerosene heater underneath.

I had intended to provide all of our own food, which we ultimately did, but in that environment, especially when you are cold, the first thing you want is some adequate shelter. So we started knocking out an end of one of the other cabins, extending it to make a bathroom and kitchen, and then winterizing it. Of course, very quickly we got to the point where we needed lumber, sheet rock and many other building materials. As you will remember, there was no electricity in this cove. But there was a propane system, so we also needed a propane refrigerator, a propane stove and a propane water heater, as well as propane lights.

There was no way all this could be brought out in our little rowboat. We had to make arrangements with a man in Los Angeles on the mainland, which was not too far away, to bring over a LCT (Landing Craft Tank) that had a big bow door that lets down. (You may have seen these in war movies where the Marines land on the beach and the bow door comes down.) This man had a truck that fit into the LCT, so we loaded all the materials onto it. When the LCT came to our cove, the bow door went down and with incredible effort we got the truck off. After unloading the truck, he drove it back onto the LCT, lifted up the bow door and was gone. At this point a mere mortal would have become overwhelmed, and, since I am a mere mortal, I was overwhelmed at the task that lay ahead! However, it turned out to be fun and exciting, and we also learned a great deal.

Normally when you are building, you have an electric saw and an electric drill that you can use any time you please. However, building in a remote place like that is quite a different situation. All morning long, I would measure the lumber and mark places to cut and where holes needed to be drilled. Then after lunch I would fire up the little gasoline-powered electric generator and do all of my sawing and hole drilling in about a thirty-minute period. After that was done, I would shut off the generator and spend the afternoon nailing up the lumber I had cut and drilled. Believe me, this requires a great deal of preplanning!

After the walls were up, then came the plumbing. In those days there was only galvanized pipe, and not the convenient PVC plastic pipe available today. If a piece of pipe was 1 inch too long or too short, I would have to make a boat trip into town and get another piece of pipe. Not only did we have to plumb the hot and cold water, but also the propane. Propane was used not only for the appliances, but also for the lights. The lights had a mantle similar to a Coleman lantern that could be lit at night and would give off a very pleasant glow. When the cabin was finally completed, we indeed had a small kitchen, a stove, refrigerator, water heater, lights, *and* it was warm!

Now our thoughts could turn to providing food for ourselves. We planted a garden which was nice and productive. We hunted wild boar and wild goat for meat. We also fished and dove for abalone. We could not provide our own flour, sugar and salt, but most of the rest of the food we were able to provide for ourselves, one way or another.

We found we had to spend a lot of time doing things that are taken for granted in the city. The disposal of trash is a good example. We separated trash into three categories: the burnables, the edibles and the glass and tin cans. The burnables we burned; the edibles were taken up the canyon and put in the same place each day for the wild boar to come down to eat; the tin cans were washed, both ends were removed and then they were flattened. Weekly I would take the cans and bottles out into the ocean and dump them overboard. The bottles that floated were nice targets for my .357 magnum pistol.

Another significant consideration was medical health care. Our younger daughter fell off a slide and hit her head. She was quite woozy and we were very concerned about her condition. We all dashed for the boat and rushed her into town where they had a little, twelve-bed hospital with only one doctor. Fortunately, he was available when we got there, and took X rays and found that she had received no permanent damage. (I am happy to report that she grew to be a very lovely, young lady who acquired a degree in teaching.) But our concern regarding her accident impressed on me that access to medical care is a significant consideration.

Transportation is another important consideration. Fortunately that old row boat broke loose during a storm and was wrecked on the beach. I withdrew some of my savings and bought my own boat and, needless to say, I was much happier with it.

Later in the book, I will have more to share with you about things I learned while living in a remote cove. Many of the lessons that I learned on Catalina Island were extremely valuable when Jeani and I moved to the ranch where we are presently living.

LIVING WATERS RANCH IN OREGON

In August, 1977, my wife, Jeani and I moved to what we named "Living Waters Ranch" in Oregon. At that time, the property had an old nonfunctional sawmill, a small building that was a garage and/or shop, and an unfinished two-story house. The house had no siding on it, just tar paper with battens, and the tar paper was half hanging off. The downstairs was completed inside, but the upstairs was unfinished and totally open to the snakes, wasps, birds and bats through the open windows.

As on Catalina Island, the first concern was proper shelter. We lived downstairs and remodeled it, then completed the inside of the upstairs, which we then used as an office for the financial newsletter I was publishing at the time. It was good that the upstairs was unfinished, because we wanted to utilize passive solar heating, since the broad side of the house faced due south. We were able to put in some giant windows on the south side, which is much easier in an unfinished house than in one that already has insulation and sheet rock on the inside, so it worked out well.

Once that was completed, our thoughts turned to producing our own food, just as on Catalina. Because of the local deer population, we fenced off an area of about four acres which would contain our garden, vineyard, and some fruit-producing trees and vines. We had to make this fence 10-feet high, and that just barely keeps the deer out.

We then added some Nubian goats to the ranch, primarily for milk, but the excess of male kids also provide some meat. Soon thereafter we built a chicken house that houses a hundred chickens for eggs and meat. Then we acquired a small flock of sheep—a ram and 14 ewes—from a lady who was moving. This provided excellent meat, as well as wool. After getting our animals and garden well established, there was an area between the house and the garden that was almost a forest of pine and cedar trees. We logged out three logging truck loads of trees one year. The following year we ground out the stumps and had that area terraced. Now we have a 70-tree orchard there, but it took us a total of about six years from the time we began cutting the trees until the time we had productive fruit trees.

We later had another portion of the fenced-in area terraced, where we planted a 200-vine vineyard. There again, we found that it takes about four years from the time you plant the little sticks in the ground until you have large grape-producing vines.

We subsequently added a greenhouse so that vegetables can be produced all winter long. Our greenhouse is a hydroponic one, although a soil-oriented greenhouse would produce similar results.

There is now a small lake on the property stocked with 2,000 rainbow trout.

We freeze, dehydrate, and can excess vegetables and fruits. After the animals have been slaughtered, we primarily freeze the meat. We could make lamb and turkey jerky, and we have just purchased a hanging screened box that we can use for that purpose. We produce so many eggs that we sell the excess at a natural foods store. Since then, two other homes have been built on the ranch, one of which is being used as an office. These new homes were designed to work beautifully if we have electricity forever, utilizing heat pumps for heating and air conditioning, and simultaneously so that if there were no electricity tomorrow, they would be able to heat and cool with more natural methods.

It took us about ten years to get Living Waters Ranch into a condition where I would consider it self-supporting. Some people have 5 or 10 acres out in the country someplace, and they think that during a time of emergency they will just zip out and live there. Well, they will be in for a real surprise! They do not take into account the building materials that would be needed immediately for shelters for people and animals, pipes needed for irrigating and plumbing, and the many other things that would be needed on a long-range basis. We will address the temporary use of such a piece of property in a subsequent chapter. We will also share with you many details concerning things we have learned and how we did them, which will save you much time, energy and expense, as you move toward a more self-reliant life-style.

THE DISTRIBUTION SYSTEM

In contrast to the farmer of whom we spoke at the beginning of this chapter, who had about everything he needed on his own homestead, those who live in the city today are very dependent upon a multitude of different distribution systems.   As we mentioned, all of these systems are very fragile. For example, farmers grow grain which has to be hauled to major silos.   Trucks have to haul this to mills where it is made into flour.   Other trucks then have to haul the flour to bakeries, where it is made into loaves of bread and baked goods, which then are hauled to individual stores.   If there were an overall truckers' strike in the United States, or if because of a nuclear air explosion that radiated EMP (electronic magnetic pulses) the electrical systems of the trucks are rendered useless, very quickly that distribution pipeline would empty out and the stores would become empty.

The electrical distribution system can be disabled by the destruction of one remote tower.   Most cities have water distribution that comes from a distance.   If there were no electricity to run the pumps, the water system would dry up.

I was visiting in New York City during the first giant blackout in the 1960's and I saw the chaos that comes from a major disruption of the electrical systems. In the second New York City blackout, there was massive rioting and looting, which was not true of the first one. Cities have been getting progressively more violent.

Acts of nature can also interrupt one or more or all of the distribution systems.   For example, three weeks after Hurricane Andrew in southern Florida, there were still 1,000,000 homes without electricity.   I have video footage of people fighting over the food that helicopters were bringing into that area after the hurricane was over.

Several days after the Los Angeles earthquake of January 1994, 300,000 homes still did not have electricity. Since some of the main freeway arteries into the city collapsed, trucks could not bring food and supplies directly into Los Angeles from the north, but had to be rerouted back to the east, which added a day or more to their delivery and created a massive traffic problem. If that had been the mammoth earthquake that is predicted for Los Angeles, rather than being of the lesser magnitude that it was, probably all of the freeways and highways into Los Angeles would have been blocked and no trucks would have been able to get through.

If all of the distribution systems affecting your part of the country were shut down or eliminated simultaneously, what would your family do? Very quickly it could become very difficult to live.

I believe that the fragility of our very sophisticated distribution systems is one reason for anyone, in or out of the city, to begin to move to a more self-reliant life-style.

As violence increases in the cities, there are many who feel that a move from the city to a more rural setting would be highly desirable, and I would have to agree with that. Thinking back to John Denver's song, you might want to find that "Country Road" that takes you to your new home where you belong. However, before we specifically address moving from the city, let us first take a look at how to be more self-reliant while actually living in a city. In fact, most of the things in this book will apply and be of benefit to those who choose to remain in the city.

I should point out in the beginning that this book is **not** for those who wish to live "frontier" style. We do not talk about tanning leather and making your own shoes.

We do not discuss using horses or mules to pull a plow. We do not discuss spinning yarn and weaving cloth. This book assumes that you will live in a community where there is a cobbler, a plumber, a doctor and a variety of other skilled professionals that you would find even in a small town.

But now, let us look at the exciting adventure of being more self-reliant even if you cannot move from a city at the present time.

Chapter 2

SELF-RELIANT IN THE CITY

In the first chapter, we saw that, with our fragile economy, vulnerable distribution systems, the fickleness of nature, and many other factors, it is highly desirable to be self-reliant and not be forced to rely on other people to bring you food, water, and the energy with which to heat and light your home and do your cooking. The ideal would be to be able to move to a more rural setting with some acreage so that you could produce your own food and other necessities of life more effectively.

However, for some reason many people feel they cannot leave the city because of their job. This may be more of an excuse than a valid reason, in some cases. For example, an anesthesiologist in San Francisco tied flies for fly-fishing as a hobby. He decided to move to the country and could not find a job as an anesthesiologist, so he began a fly-tying business which ultimately provided a very adequate income for him. Anyone can move to the country if he wants to badly enough, even if it means changing vocations.

However, let's assume for now that for valid reasons one absolutely cannot move from the city but wants to be as self-reliant as possible while living there. If one lives in an apartment house or condominium he can do less than someone who owns a house with a yard. Many of the things discussed in this chapter apply primarily to those who own a home which has a yard. Let's look at some things that a city dweller may wish to consider doing.

It is important to note that many of the chapters in this book can apply equally as well to the city as to the country. These chapters can be very helpful to a city dweller:

Chapter 5 - Building Your House
Chapter 6 - The Greenhouse
Chapter 7 - Gardening and Preserving

Even though these chapters are applied basically to the country, it should be obvious that they can, indeed, help someone in the city who wants to build a house, build a greenhouse or grow a garden.

PROVIDING YOUR OWN WATER

Most cities have a water system that is frequently fed from far distant rivers or lakes. This water must be pumped up hills, through pipelines, and then into a water purification plant. After the water is purified (sometimes this is quite a job), it is then distributed into the individual homes. What could go wrong with such a system? The people who operate the water system could go on strike, which would shut down water delivery. There could be a major emergency so that the people who work for the water system would stay home to take care of their own personal property and families. There could be a terrorist attack in which the pipeline, the water facility or some link in this water system was bombed. Also, there could be terrorist activity to put poison or some type of bacteria into the water system. The electrical system could become nonfunctional so that the pumps in the water system would not work.

Above and beyond all of these possibilities, there could be a natural disaster such as an earthquake at any time. During earthquakes, water lines are frequently broken so that no water is available through the city water system. In 1971, when there was a major earthquake in Los Angeles, water in the San Fernando Valley was selling for $10 a gallon. In Hurricane Andrew in 1992, water was selling for $20 a gallon, and for a similar price during the Midwest flooding of 1993, when many of the water purification plants were contaminated and people could not drink the water coming out of their taps. In the January, 1994 Los Angeles earthquake, people had to stand in long lines to get water.

What is the solution to problems like these? It is to be able to provide your own water, regardless of the conditions. Ideally, the best way to implement this would be to have a well in your backyard that pumped water up to some storage tanks, either above ground or in the ground. In some communities it is perfectly fine for you to have your own well; in other communities it is illegal, so you would need to check the law in your location before you start to drill. You should also consider purchasing a water filter that would remove heavy metals, parasites and so forth. Sources are given in Appendix B.

There are small portable drilling rigs that you can operate yourself, if you are going down just a couple of hundred feet. Addresses of sources where these can be acquired also are included in Appendix B (also noted as *B). However, I think it is wiser to have a professional well driller come in and do the task for you. This does draw more attention to what you are doing, but it assures you that the casing will go in properly and any necessary fracturing (to increase flow) will be done in order to produce a good flow of water.

If you dig your own well, you must consider how you would get water out of that well if there were no electricity. In that event, you have two alternatives:

1. Provide your own electricity.
2. Provide for manual pumping.

The well should pump up into a storage tank, so that if you were only able to provide an hour or two of electricity a day for yourself, you could pump water up into the storage tank during that time, and then utilize it for the rest of the twenty-four hour period.

As far as providing for your own electricity, there are several regular sources of energy you can use to run the generator:

1. Gasoline
2. Diesel
3. Natural gas
4. Propane
5. Water
6. Wind
7. Solar energy

There are also some alternative sources:

8. Methane
9. Thermal steam
10. Alcohol
11. Wood

If you are going to rely on gasoline or diesel fuel to run the motor that would turn the generator that generates the electricity, then you would need to provide for storage of this fuel that meets the regulations of the area in which you live. My favorite fuel is propane. You could have a 500- or 1,000-gallon tank installed in your backyard, buy a propane generator, or get a gasoline generator converted in order to be able to use the propane. Propane is ecologically better for the environment because it burns cleaner and you do not have to keep filling up the tank on the generator.

There is a system that utilizes wind to run an electric motor which runs a pump that is submerged in your well. This system, of course, relies on an adequate number of hours of reasonable wind velocity per day. This is like the old windmills of the West, which always had a storage tank, so that the windmill pumped the water up into the tank whenever the wind happened to blow. Then the water was consumed at the user's discretion. The address of a source is included in Appendix B (*B).

There are a few 12-volt and 24-volt submersible well pumps that are run off of battery banks that are charged with solar or wind power. You would have to have a bank of photoelectric cells in order to do this. If you were going to go this route, the best type of photoelectric cells are the continuous-band type, rather than the individual-cell variety. They are easier to maintain, plus you have a high efficiency of converting solar energy directly into electrical energy.

To use water power to generate electricity, you would need a good flow and a drop of at least 10 feet in order to run the generator. This would be so unique to each piece of property, and it is unlikely to be found in the city, so we will not dwell on it, but references are listed in Appendix B that address hydroelectric generation of power.

Another way to be sure you can provide water in the absence of electricity is with a manual pump, much like the old pumps that you see in the movies which usually needed priming. However, these pumps are not suited for deep wells but only for shallow ones.

Ideally, if your property is on a slope, you can place the storage tank for the water on the high part and it can flow down by gravity to your home. However, this still requires some kind of pump to get the water up to the storage tank. In my opinion, the tank should be of at least a 2,000-gallon capacity. If you were relying on gravity flow to run your washer, the tank would need to be at least 57 feet above the washing machine.

One thing that you can legally do in just about any city is to trap rainwater. The homes on Cayman Island have only rainwater as a water source. They have a big cistern instead of a basement for their homes and all the rainwater is funneled down into that. They put a frog in this tank to eat any bugs that come in and to eat the algae.

If you trap your rainwater, discard the first gallon or two to come off the roof because of the dirt and debris that may have collected on the roof. A device called a "water switch," shown in Figure 2.1, is a convenient way to do this. You would then simply empty the bucket after the rain had ceased which would prepare the switch for the next rain.

When you lay out plans for the tank into which to trap the rainwater, be sure to consider the access to the water. You would certainly want to have an exit valve or pipe at the low part of the tank so you could fill containers conveniently by gravity.

Water that is to be collected must be filtered before it enters the tank. Such a filtering system is shown in Figure 2.2.

Water Switch

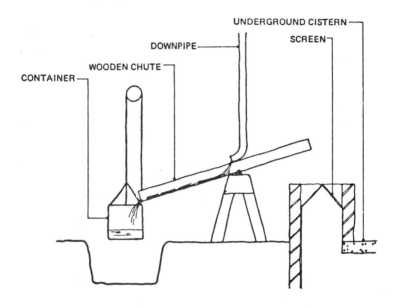

Figure 2.1

Water is the most important thing to provide for yourself if you want to become self-reliant. You can go forty days without food but only about three days without water. So this should be your number one priority if you are going to try to be self-reliant in the city.

Filtering System

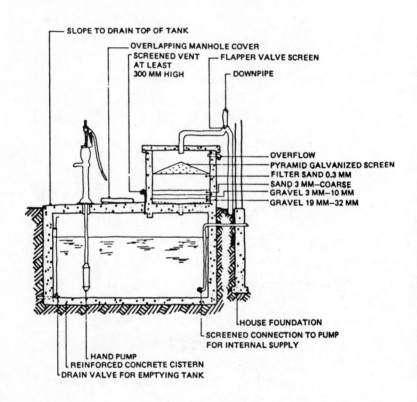

Figure 2.2

PROVIDING YOUR OWN FOOD
IN THE CITY

There are three basic approaches to raising vegetables in the city:

1. Gardening.
2. Greenhouse with hydroponics.
3. Greenhouse with soil.

Let's look at gardening first. A 50- by 50-foot
garden can provide enough vegetables to last the average
family for an entire year. Because of various conditions,
some gardens may have to start smaller. You might think
that you do not have enough land to have a garden, but if
you own your own home, you probably have the land.
You may have to dig up your back lawn and shrubs and
suffer the embarrassment of teasing by neighbors, but
there is likely room for a garden. When Jeani and I lived
in Pasadena, California, we did just this, turning about
half of our small backyard into a highly-productive
vegetable garden. We also had a tangerine tree and had
eliminated most of the lawn. It was great to be producing
many of our own vegetables and some fruit while living
in the city. We also eliminated the chore of mowing the
lawn!

If you live in an apartment, own a condominium, or
live in a retirement village, frequently there are unused
areas of land in the complex that you would be allowed to
use for a garden. If you simply do not have any land
available to you, then look around for empty land. There
is usually unused land around an airport where houses
have been torn down because of the high noise level,
empty land underneath electrical and power lines, vacant

lots and so on. Go down to City Hall and find out who owns the property and ask the owner if you can use it for a garden. If you simply cannot find any land in the city, you could find some farmer with a large farm on the edge of your city and ask him if you can use, or rent, a small corner of one of his fields.

Once you find some land, the next thing is to prepare the soil for planting. We will not get into this subject, since books on soil preparation and planting are readily available in any bookstore (B*). However, there is one form of gardening with which you may not be familiar that we will just mention. It is known as "mulch gardening" and it is one of the best methods known. A protective layer of shredded papers, old hay, sawdust or a substance of that nature, is spread across the ground to control weeds, reduce evaporation, maintain an even soil temperature and prevent erosion. This "mulch" is then separated and seeds are planted near the top of the soil underneath. Mulch gardening produces a significantly higher yield than regular gardening. Moreover, if root vegetables such as potatoes are planted, they do not have to be dug out, since they lie between the hay and the soil.

It is interesting to note that there is a revolution going on in gardening. In 1975, an organization in Northern California called Common Ground estimated that with one-fifth of an acre (93 feet by 93 feet), a person could make $12,000 a year. Their approach is "companion planting," in which compatible plants are interspersed with each other. They also describe proper soil preparation, which not only allows more plants per acre, but also creates a higher yield per plant. You may want to write for their fascinating book:

How to Grow More Vegetables
By John Jeavons
Published by Ten Speed Press
P.O. Box 7123
Berkeley, CA 94707

If you are going to provide your own vegetables from a garden, you will want to consider preserving the excess of your produce through the winter, so that you can use this food until the next garden is harvested. We will discuss various methods of food preservation in Chapter 7.

A NEW USE FOUND FOR OLD TIRES

While it won't solve the problem of disposing of all spent tires, it could be a boon to garden lovers. Tires converted to minigreenhouses makes starting your gardens safer earlier.

Protection from wind and cold is achieved by placing an umbrella-type greenhouse over each tire. The black tire provides heat to the immediate area inside the covered area and, as the tire warms from the rays of the sun, heat is conducted to the ground. Water placed in the ring of the tire warms, creating a humid atmosphere ideal for starting plants early.

Those wanting to start their own bedding plants can use this idea. Perennials, such as rhubarb or herbs, get an early start when a minigreenhouse and tire are placed over them.

The tire also acts as a mulch helping to eliminate weeds. Weed control in the area outside the minigreenhouse can be achieved with cultivation or spraying with an herbicide, while the greenhouse is in place protecting the new plants.

Two weeks to a month earlier maturity can be achieved using a minigreenhouse and tire. Even apartment dwellers with a little imagination could find room for a minigarden, growing herbs, salad vegetables, and tomatoes!

The minigreenhouses are being manufactured in Utah (*B) and will be sold through many local garden stores and tire dealerships.

In the chapter on gardening, we also mention using old tires as a convenient aid for growing potatoes.

Minigreenhouse On Old Tire

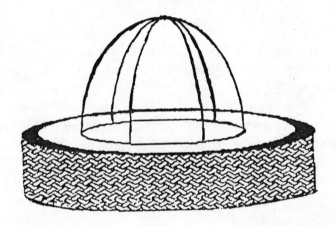

Figure 2.3

YOUR OWN FOOD FACTORY

An alternative to a garden for raising vegetables is a greenhouse. In a greenhouse, fruits and vegetables can be grown year round. The problem of preservation of the food produced in it basically vanishes, since a supply of fresh produce is continuously available. There are many advantages to raising food in a greenhouse, some of which are:

1. Protection from wind.
2. Controlled temperature (no scorching).
3. Controlled moisture (no drought or flooding).
4. Protection from airborne disease.
5. Protection from freezing.
6. No weeds.
7. No bending (you work at table height).
8. Less space used than for a garden.
9. Control over nutrients provided to plants.
10. Easy harvesting (not weather dependent).

In this greenhouse "food factory," you can utilize soil in beds or pots as the growing medium. Some greenhouses utilize soil in heavy-duty plastic sacks designed for this purpose, with drain holes in the bottom. However, many plants will require soil of a significant depth. In my opinion, a superior method to using soil for food production in a greenhouse facility is "hydroponics." In hydroponic growing, any inert medium, such as plastic foam chips, straw, 3/8-inch sterile pea gravel, marbles or sawdust, can be used to provide the mechanical support for the plants. Two or three times a day a nutrient solution is pumped onto this gravel, or other such medium, in which the plants are growing. This solution consists of water and a mixture of powdered nutrients.

One form of hydroponics floods raised beds with this nutrient solution. After about twenty minutes, the nutrient-laden water is drained so that air can get to the roots. The typical hydroponic bed is about 3 feet wide, 10 or 12 feet long, and 9 inches deep. Since the roots do not have to search for nutrients because the nutrients are brought to them, hydroponically-grown plants tend to produce bigger and nicer vegetables than those grown in the ground.

Another form of hydroponics uses pots (1 to 5 gallon straight-sided plastic pots with drain holes in the bottom), and the nutrient solution is automatically pumped into these pots for twenty-nine seconds two to four times each day. Any surplus drains out the bottom and runs on the cement floor into a floor drain.

If you want to experiment with hydroponics, you can do so very simply by using large flower pots filled with gravel and a bucket of nutrient-laden water as your basic equipment. Twice a day you would pour the solution into the pots of gravel where you have planted seeds or small plants. To carry this step further, you could have a little electric pump that would pump the nutrients from a bucket or tank up into the pots or beds. You could simply throw the electrical switch on for fifteen minutes twice a day and have the pump do the work. The pump could run off of solar panels connected to marine-style storage batteries and an inverter. The next step would be to have the pump switch run by an electrical timer (such as used on lamps and appliances), which would automatically feed the plants by turning the pump on periodically. *There is one big advantage of hydroponics: the care of the plants can be automated.*

With hydroponics you can control the nutrition and watering of the plants. If you place your hydroponic beds inside a greenhouse, you can also control the climate, plant diseases and insects. The food production from a hydroponic greenhouse garden is phenomenal. It is estimated that, in a 10- by 12-foot greenhouse, enough food could be produced for a family of four on a year-round basis. All that it would take is about ten minutes of your time per day. If you would like to have your own fresh vegetables and fruits year-round, with about ten minutes of effort a day, a hydroponic greenhouse "food factory" would be the way to do it.

If you wish to pursue this, there are two books that are head and shoulders above all the other hydroponic books that I have read:

1. *Hydroponic Gardening*, by Raymond Bridwell
   Published by Woodbridge Press Publishing Company
2. *Home Hydroponics*, by Lem Jones
   Published by Beardsley Publishing Company

A hydroponic greenhouse has the advantage that you do not have to worry about preserving the food produced. If you wanted to have tomatoes continuously, you would plant one plant, two or three weeks later plant another, two or three weeks later another, and so on. By keeping up this rotation you could have fresh tomatoes year-round. The same thing goes for lettuce, cabbage, and all kinds of peppers. Even for those who live on a farm, this type of a "food factory" is well worth considering. You can even include dwarf lemon trees and produce wonderful, juicy, thin-skinned lemons! I know some people in Oregon who grow many of their vegetables in such a greenhouse.

Plan Your Planting

If you decide to invest in a hydroponic greenhouse, once you have your greenhouse and your beds or pots ready, careful planning is necessary in order to obtain the full potential of this "food factory." Take the time to draw a diagram of your plant arrangement. For example, you will want to plant the tomatoes, cucumbers, and any other vine-type or tall plants next to the greenhouse wall, and shorter plants progressively closer to the sun-side of the greenhouse. Be sure to plant things that you *enjoy eating*, not simply things that do well in a hydroponic environment. (Incidentally, root crops, such as beets and carrots do not do well in a hydroponic greenhouse, whereas above-the-soil fruits and vegetables, such as tomatoes and peppers, flourish.) After awhile you will learn which varieties you like best, and you will be able to get your rotation going so that you can have a continuous supply of food. See Figure 6.7 in Chapter 6 for a sample layout.

We discuss the heating and cooling of the greenhouse in Chapter 6, which is devoted entirely to discussion of the greenhouse. We just wanted to introduce the subject here, as we are addressing being reliant while living in the city.

A Protein Factory

Some time ago, I ran across a very interesting article in *Science Digest* (May 1975, P.O. Box 1568, New York, NY 10019). It dealt with having your own "fish factory" in your backyard. The particular one discussed in the article, belonging to Robert Huke, is enclosed under a geodesic dome 17 feet in diameter. There is a fish tank basically stocked with catfish (the larger fish illustrated in Figure 2.4) and Tilapia (the smaller fish). The water from the tank is pumped to twin metal drums. The bacteria inside the drums convert the fish excrement to fertilizing nitrate which, through a tube, is sprayed onto vegetation. Some vegetation, like soybeans, can be shredded and put back into the water, which then circulates down a waterfall back to the fish tank and feeds the fish. Periodically the metal tanks are cleaned out, and the fertilizer is used to feed the tomatoes and soybeans. In this way a full cycle is completed.

A Protein Factory

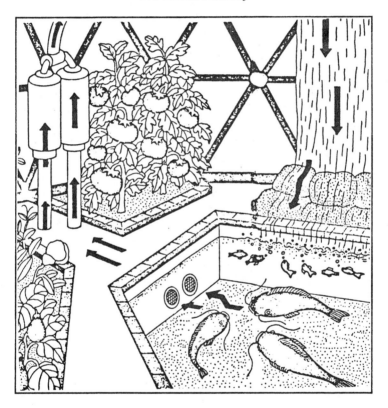

Figure 2.4

Huke estimates that he gets about 100 pounds of fish per year out of this fish factory. He chose catfish because they can be packed tightly into a small tank without eating each other. They are also good tasting. Huke estimates that building his dome cost him about $700.

Next to fish, the average city backyard would probably support rabbits better than anything else. You do not have the noise and commotion with them that you would have with chickens, goats or any other of the smaller animals. If you combine rabbits and gardening, you could have a cycle with surplus vegetables from the garden being eaten by the rabbits, and rabbit pellets being used for fertilizer.

It may be that you need to move to another suburb of your city, or else just slightly away from the city in order to have the ability to legally raise rabbits and other animals. Yet if you are tied to a metropolitan area, then raising fish, rabbits, or other edible small animals is an option that should be considered.

PUTTING MEAT ON YOUR TABLE

For those who want meat, there remain basically two ways to acquire it for yourself:

1. Hunting and fishing.
2. Raising your own animals.

If you presently enjoy hunting and fishing, these could be viable ways to provide meat for your family. They may have to become requisites rather than recreation, but the skills would certainly serve you well during any period when you needed to provide your own food.

There are many good books on hunting, but the only way to learn it is to do it. This is a way of putting meat on your table that has been used continuously since Adam and Eve. The addresses where books on this can be ordered are given in Appendix B (*B).

If you are thinking of a way to provide food for your family long-term, the normal hunting and fishing methods are not adequate. At present these are "sports" and one wants to give the game or the fish a "sporting chance." However, when one's food on the table depends upon hunting and fishing, the sporting aspect of it will soon lose its charm.

For food *production,* you want to trap and not shoot. Rather than fly fishing in a stream, which is enjoyable and time-consuming recreation, you would want to put a net across the stream and trap as many fish as possible to provide food for your family. If you look at pictures of the old Hawaiians fishing, it was always with nets. If you look at commercial fishermen today, they use nets because they know there is no way they could pro-duce adequate amounts of fish with a hook and a line. Net fishing for most people today is not legal, but if you are interested in producing food this way, you need to purchase nets ahead of time and, if possible, learn how to use them. Legally you would have to release all the fish that you catch with a net while you are learning to use it. Be careful to abide by the law.

Trapping for land animals is more difficult than trapping fish. One reason is that there are so many different kinds of traps. There is everything from leg traps and wire cage traps to pit traps and free-fall traps, to name just a few.

In some places, trapping a deer during deer season would be just as legitimate as shooting a deer during deer season. If this is the case in your county (and you should check to be sure), then you may well want to learn about trapping and try it out next deer season.

If you are considering raising your own meat, whether it be in the city or on a farm, I would recommend the small livestock such as: goats, chickens, sheep, geese, rabbits, hogs, turkeys, guinea fowl and ducks. There are many reasons why I believe these are preferable. Being smaller units, you would not lose that much if one of them were to die. Another reason is that if you kill a large cow there is the problem of preserving the meat, whereas your family could consume one of these smaller animals before it spoiled. Another factor is that smaller animals tend to reproduce faster. You can get milk and eggs from some of these, as well as meat, which provides a balance to the diet.

Especially if you live in the city and want to raise meat, small animals are the only choice that you have. In such a case, raising rabbits in an indoor building can help minimize complaints from the neighbors. You should have plenty of windows in the enclosure to let in sunlight and fresh air. A garage can easily be converted into a rabbitry. The concrete floor of most garages makes them easy to clean. You can even have labor-saving devices such as feed hoppers which can be filled without opening the cages.

The subject of animals is covered in more detail in Chapter 9.

PROVIDING YOUR OWN ENERGY IN THE CITY

We already discussed providing your own electricity, when we discussed being able to run your well pump. At that time, we mentioned in passing that if you were going to have a diesel or gasoline generator, you would need to store the fuel for it.

To be totally self-reliant in the city, you would need to be able to provide not only your own electricity, but also your own energy for heating, cooking and lighting. As I mentioned earlier, a propane tank is one of my favorite ways to store this type of energy. There are heaters designed to run off of propane, as well as cook stoves and water heaters.

Although a combination of energy sources may prove to be best in the long run, solar energy may be worth considering as a source for part of your energy needs. You can directly heat your hot water with solar energy, not using photoelectric cells which convert sunlight to electricity, but actually having the water pipes run inside a solar collector to keep your water hot. A certain amount of this hot water could also be used to heat your home. Then to generate electricity to crucial appliances and lights at night, a propane electrical generator could be utilized. This combination of solar and propane is available in every area of the country.

I believe that it is essential to have some capability for producing 110 volts, in whatever situation you might find yourself. There are so many critical pieces of equipment that only work off of 110—such as skill saws and electric drills—that having some capacity for 110-volt electricity can significantly affect your life-style. As I mentioned in Chapter 1, when I lived on Catalina Island, we had a small gasoline-powered electrical generator. While I was building the cabin, in the morning I would measure 2 x 4's that needed cutting and also mark places where I needed to drill holes for pipes. About lunchtime I would fire up the generator for about thirty minutes and do all of my cutting and drilling at once. I would then spend the afternoon nailing up all of the boards that I had cut. Having 110 volts to operate the power tools and power equipment made our life much easier.

The ideal is to have both 12- and 110-volt systems. Even our mini-motor home has both 110- and 12-volt. As far as I am concerned, a self-sufficient home should be dual-wired. We have cigarette lighter-type plugs in our kitchen. We can use 12-volt appliances in these or, with an inverter that converts 12 volts to 110 volts, we could use our 110-volt appliances. With this inverter, we could also run a small 110-volt TV, radio or even a computer. See Chapter 5 for further discussion on ways of providing electricity.

DISPOSAL OF SEWAGE
AND TRASH IN THE CITY

Most homes today are connected to the city sewer system. However, for a number of reasons, the municipal sewers could be clogged up, broken, or shut down by a strike or terrorists. In order to be totally self-reliant in the city, you would need to have your own septic tank. A septic system usually has a tank with a capacity of 1,000-2,000 gallons, wherein the waste is liquified by bacteria. Then a string of perforated pipe runs back and forth from the tank, about two feet underground, covered by drain rock, semi-permeable cloth and then soil about a foot deep. The ground absorbs the liquid waste that runs out into it from the perforated pipe. Some communities have regulations requiring you to fence off the area of the septic tank and not to have animals on it, nor to grow any fruit trees or crops there. Other communities do not have these restrictions. Check your building code when you put in a septic tank.

You also need the ability to haul off your own trash. Once you haul your own trash a few times, believe me, you will be very interested in making your trash more compact! One thing that helps compact trash is to wash out tin cans and then cut out both ends and flatten them. You can flatten other types of containers, as well. If it is allowable in your area, it helps greatly to burn everything that is burnable. You can use table and kitchen food scraps to feed rabbits and chickens. With these adjustments, all you will need to haul off will be metal and glass. Chickens will eagerly eat almost everything except citrus rinds or banana peels.

If you store your trash in bags or cans, then you are going to need a vehicle that you can use to haul it off to a trash dump somewhere. This vehicle may be a pick-up truck or an expanded wagon, such as a Suburban, but you need to know how you plan to do this and where to take the trash.

To be self-reliant while living in the city means taking time to do some of the services that are being done for you right now. Right now someone picks up your trash. It takes more time to sort your trash, to burn some, to flatten cans and haul off trash to the dump. Right now the city brings water to you. It takes time to participate in health maintenance of your own water supply by being sure that your storage tanks are clean and free from bacteria, putting in a chlorinating or ozone system to get rid of any bacteria, and so forth. Right now you go to the grocery store to buy your food. It takes time to both grow and preserve your own food.

Self-reliant living can be achieved in the city, but it is much more difficult than becoming self-reliant in a more rural setting where there are fewer restrictions on animals, buildings, wells and other things that you will need to become self-reliant in your living. So let us move on and look at moving to the country in order to make it easier to be self-reliant.

Chapter 3

A COUNTRY PLACE

There may be a place in the country in your future. There are many valid reasons why I would recommend, if at all possible, that you invest in a country property. When I say "place in the country," I am talking about a place where you can raise your own food and have some left over to sell or give away if you wish—a place where you can lead a healthful, abundant life and support yourself, regardless of what happens to the rest of the world.

One of the reasons why you may want to own a country place is that someday you may actually feel compelled to move there, as cities become progressively less desirable as places in which to live and rear children. "What is wrong with cities?" you might ask. There is much that is good about cities. However, there is also much that is not so good. The crime rates are increasing substantially; there are few cities remaining where a woman can feel safe going out at night alone. Not only is there fear of going out at night, but children are not safe walking to and from school in the daytime in some areas. Sometimes there are guns and knives in the schools, as well. Violent crimes are increasing on public transportation vehicles, and the police are not able to exert any meaningful control over this. Consequently, there is the rise of vigilante groups like "The Guardian Angels," who are trying to step in and help provide safety for citizens by taking things into their own hands.

The air quality in most cities is getting progressively worse, and this has to affect one's health and the health of one's children over a long period of time.

Cities are also highly vulnerable places. America raises an ample amount of food, but it is brought into the cities through very fragile distribution systems. If both the truckers and the railroad workers were to go on strike at the same time, the flow of food to the cities would be cut off. Since there is usually no more than about a three weeks' supply of food available in a major city, if the truckers' strike lasted several months, the city could be an extremely undesirable place to be.

Also, it is much healthier to eat food that you have grown. If you produce it yourself, you know it does not have chemicals, preservatives and colorings added to it.

Country living is a much more relaxed life, with a quiet atmosphere rather than the high level of noise found in most cities (and even most suburban communities). And, of course, if we have a nuclear encounter with Russia, and many experts feel that this remains a likelihood, the cities will obviously be major target areas. Even if one is unable to move to the country during his "working" years, he might still wish to retire to the country. I have found country living to be an invigorating, as well as healthier and richly-rewarding life-style in a multitude of ways. It is deeply satisfying to look at the food on the table and realize that you have grown it all right there on your piece of land, for example.

Last but not least, country land is a good investment. Here in Oregon, it has been going up in price at the rate of 20-25 percent per year for the last several years, and I believe it will continue to be a good investment across at least the next ten years. However, this is an investment that should not be made for the short term; it should be looked at as a five- to ten-year situation.

IS NOW THE TIME
TO BUY COUNTRY LAND?

Of course, the timing for buying any piece of property depends partially on one's financial and personal situation, as well as the current status of the real estate market. Without doing a complete personal consultation, I cannot even attempt to address your individual financial situation. However, let me make a few observations on the market for country property in general.

You may wish to schedule your vacation to include some time to drive down some country roads to find your little place in the country. Probably August would be the optimum time to buy. Those owners who wish to relocate before school starts will be getting eager to sell. Also, in June everything looks green and beautiful. By August, in many areas only the irrigated parcels will be green, and the streams that run only in the spring will be dry. Thus, you can get a more realistic picture of a property you are considering for purchase.

HOW TO GO ABOUT FINDING
YOUR PLACE IN THE COUNTRY

I have been through this adventure myself of finding a place in the country. Based on our experiences, I would first like to share with you how you should *not* do it.

The wrong way to buy a country property is to send off for some of the country property catalogs—such as *United Country Catalog* and *Home and Land* (*B)—look through them, and zoom off to look at some property. These catalogs are useful, as we will see in a minute, but this is not the way to use them.

STEP 1—PICK THE PART OF THE COUNTRY

The first thing to decide is what part of the country you want to live in and/or invest in. Perhaps you will decide that it is Montana, southern Oregon, northern Arkansas, or someplace that is within driving distance of your existing home. You will want to think that through very carefully before you finalize your decision.

You should write down your view of the future and consider whether or not it includes riots in cities, nuclear war, earth upheavals, or food shortages. Of course, the list of potential problems could go on. You will want a place in the country that will take care of you if the situations that *you* think are likely to happen actually occur. If you are thinking of retirement, you need to consider how important it is for you to have proximity to your relatives. Once you have very carefully thought through what general area your rural property should be in, then you are ready for the next step.

STEP 2—SELECT A SMALL TOWN

Let's say that you have selected the northeast corner of some state as the general area where you would like to be. The next step is to investigate the smaller towns within that area and to find one with which you would enjoy being associated.

There are a number of reasons for locating in the vicinity of a small rural town. One of the most important reasons is that there is already the right mix of skills and talents there.   There is a doctor, a plumber, an auto mechanic, a barber, grocery store operators, and so on. All the basic supplies for these various people and their trades exist there.   They usually form a cohesive unit since, in a sense, they take care of each other as a community.   Your objective is to locate a small town which you think would fit *your* purposes and needs.   Some of the characteristics that I feel are important in a small town are:

1.   Not closer than 300 miles to a major city.
2.   All the basic services exist there.
3.   At least one doctor and a dentist reside there.
4.   Preferably there is a hospital.
5.   No ghettos.
6.   Good climate (rainfall and growing season).
7.   Not flood prone.
8.   Minimal danger of nuclear fallout.
9.   Not a resort or college town.
10. Produces its own food supply.
11. Not economically dependent on anything other than small farms.
12. Not right on the coast (danger from tidal waves).
13. Not earthquake prone.
14. Has a good library.
15. Has good schools.
16. Citizens are of good character and are hardworking.
17. Not on a major cross-country highway.

It is unlikely that you will find *all* of these characteristics in many towns.   However, if the town you are considering misses more than a couple of these, you might want to skip it, because there are towns that meet all of these criteria.

You would not want to be in a small town that was dependent upon one large industry, such as an IBM plant. If that plant were to close down, large numbers of people would be out of work. Similarly, you would not want an area with a considerable number of welfare recipients. In the event that their welfare payments were suddenly cut off, they could become an angry bunch with which to contend.

Personally, I would prefer a town large enough to support a good hospital. It is good to have a doctor, but at times you also need operating facilities and sophisticated equipment that a rural doctor may not have in his office. This would require at a minimum either a very large clinic that had this equipment or a small hospital.

To me, the church situation is very important. You would want to be sure that there were groups of people with whom you were spiritually compatible. This may mean spending a couple of Sundays in a town, visiting the various churches to be sure that you are comfortable with the spiritual life there. You may also want to be careful about moving into a town that is predominantly of one religion (unless that happens to be the religion of your choice). I am not sure that I would recommend that a Southern Baptist move into a town in Utah where everyone else was LDS, for example. (In no way do I mean to pick on these two; I am just using this as an example.)

The town should be in an area that produces its own food supply. This means that there would be orchards, grain fields, cattle production, and so on. Some areas in the Midwest that raise nothing but grain are really not self-sufficient in food supply.

One other item of significance is the character of the people. Some small towns are dead and lethargic; a group of rioters could come in and take them over without a whimper. In other small towns, the people are hardworking, industrious, and they have drive and a sense of territorial imperative: they have worked hard for what is theirs, and they intend to hang on to it. I would also be concerned about the general morality of the town.

Once you have found the right small town, it becomes a matter of finding the right piece of property for your family in or near that town. Assuming that you want to grow your own food, this means that you are going to be looking for at least five acres, although ten or more acres is preferable.

STEP 3—LOOK FOR THE RIGHT PIECE OF PROPERTY NEAR THAT TOWN

Once you begin to look for the piece of property itself, the catalogs of farm property can become of value to you for surveying the area that you have chosen. The addresses for the two farm catalogs are:

The United Country Catalog   (800)999-1020
United National Real Estate
4700 Bellevue
Kansas City, MO   64112

Homes and Land   (800)277-7800
P.O. Box 5018
Tallahassee, FL   32314

As you begin to think about a specific piece of property, there are two basic approaches you can take. One is to buy some vacant land on which you can build.

The other approach is to buy a place that already has a house. Ideally, there should be two houses on the property, if you are not going to occupy it immediately. In the two-house approach, one house would be for the manager of the property; the other house would be where you could stay when you visited the place. If you have the funds to accommodate this, possibly the best alternative is to buy a place with an existing house for a caretaker and existent authorization to build a second house, one that would meet your needs. However, with either approach there are some common characteristics that are important regarding your property.

WATER IS THE MOST IMPORTANT ITEM

In looking for property in the country or in a rural community, the three most important items to look for are:

1. water
2. Water
3. WATER

Range wars have been fought over water rights. It is important that you not only have water at or near your place, but that you have the legal right to irrigate with it, for essentially nothing grows without adequate water.

If you see an ad for a property that reads, "with a stream running through it," that doesn't mean anything. But if you see an ad that reads "with stream running through it *and ten acres, irrigated,*" that is significant. You must be able to legally use the water or you will be in for years of problems and headaches.

The ideal would be to have a year-round stream running through the property from which you could irrigate and to have your drinking water come from a spring up the hill which would flow down to your home by gravity. There are not too many places like that, but they are available. It may take a lot of looking to find one, but if you can do so, you will be infinitely better off.

You may have to plumb the spring to flow into a storage tank and plumb the storage tank to flow down to your house, but that is okay, and it is well worth the time and energy to do that.

The most desirable water source, in my opinion, is a spring at an elevation higher than the house, which feeds the house and the garden by gravity. Wells are less desirable, since they require a pump of some type. Today, most pumps are electric, so if your supply of electricity is cut off, your water is too. If the property does have a well, and if this is a concern to you, you may need to put in a windmill which would pump water up to a holding tank. The holding tank could gravity feed water to your house and garden. Since a 30- to 60-foot tower for a water tank could be quite expensive, this probably implies that you are not going to want a totally flat piece of property.

SOIL AND SEPTIC PERMIT

After water, the next most important thing is soil. Unless the water supply is there, you do not even need to worry about soil. If you do have an adequate water supply, then you could have the soil tested to be sure it will produce the things that you want to grow.

Try to find a property that at least has a well and approval for a septic tank. If it does not, I would encourage you to make your offer contingent upon locating a well that flows at a minimum of 10 gallons a minute and upon getting septic approval. You may have to negotiate, but the seller should bear the expense of having both of those items taken care of while the property is in escrow. You do not want to be stuck with a piece of property that does not have an adequate well or on which the governing authorities will not grant a septic permit.

After these three items—water, soil, and septic permit—almost everything else is up to the subjective judgment of the buyer. Usually, if the property is fenced and has barns and other outbuildings on it, it is a good deal, because you cannot put in those improvements for what you will be paying for them.

If there is a house on the property and you plan to live in it, you can almost be certain that you will want to remodel it. In the city, you buy the house and take the land that goes with it. In the country, you buy the land and take whatever house happens to go with it. I have seen many people buy a piece of property and try to remodel the house. It never turns out quite like you would like it if you were building from scratch. This takes us to a further examination of the two basic approaches to a country place.

THE TWO-HOUSE APPROACH

If you buy a farm with an existing house on it, it is likely that you are going to want to build another house, if you are going to take the two-house approach. Why two houses? If you are going to be an absentee owner for a few years, you need a house in which the manager of the property can live. He can keep things in good repair, protect the property, and perhaps produce some income for you. If there is an existing house on the property, it can be used by the manager for that purpose. Ultimately, when you move to the property yourself, you can use that house as a guest house or for rental income.

You will probably want to build the second house from scratch to include all the things that you would like to have in your retirement home. If you are concerned about nuclear war, it should have a root cellar that could also double as a fallout shelter. If you do not like to saw and chop wood, it could have south-facing passive or active solar heating.

You could also build into the new house some form of electrical generation, whether it be a wind-driven generator, a hydro-electric generator, or a propane-electrical generator. This new second home could be used for vacations, holidays, and even weekends away from the city until you retire or make the decision to occupy it full-time.

THE VACANT LAND APPROACH

Purchasing vacant land is also a viable alternative, but the approach is quite different. In this situation, you would buy the land, perhaps fence in a portion of it, and possibly put up one or more of the outbuildings, such as a barn. You could then plant an orchard, which would not reach full productivity for four to five years. You could rent out the fenced-in pasture to someone in the community, and thus provide a little income.

During the years until you are ready to personally occupy the land, the fruit trees could be maturing, the property would be increasing in value, and you could visit there occasionally in a mobile home or travel trailer.

After the fencing, the next thing we would recommend doing would be to build a barn of the type shown in Figure 3.1. One wing of it could be used for chickens, tools or something of that nature. If you have a motor home, you should be able to drive it under the other wing.

Practical Shed Barn

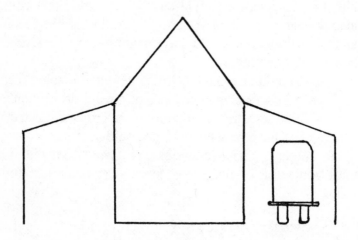

Figure 3.1

Once you got ready to move there, you could put a motor home or a small mobile home on the property to live in, while you were building your permanent home. At the end of the construction of your home, you could either sell the mobile home (likely for about what you paid for it, if you bought a used one), or you could use it for a guest house or a rental.

The advantages of the vacant land approach is that you can do exactly what you want with the property and you do not have to worry about any existing structures.

Also, you can usually take this type of approach with a smaller capital outlay on the front end.

STEP 4—NEGOTIATE FOR THE PROPERTY

As you begin to look around the small town of your choice for the right piece of property, I would not try to narrow it down to just one. Select a minimum of three or preferably four or five properties that you like. This way you do not become emotionally involved with a single piece of property and make unnecessary concessions.

As you begin to negotiate on the various pieces of property, you will find that one begins to emerge as the best bargain and the best opportunity for you both from an investment and a security aspect.

If you have difficulty negotiating, it is well worth the expense to bring along a friend who is good at negotiating at this stage. It can save you many thousands of dollars above and beyond your friend's travel expenses.

THANK GOD I'M A COUNTRY BOY!

As I said in Chapter 1, Jeani and I live on a 70-acre ranch in southern Oregon. We have planted about an acre with fruit trees. We really enjoy raising our own food. I thank God that He has allowed me to be a "country boy," as the song says.

As soon as you move to the country, you are going to feel the same way. There are many new, fun things to learn. Even the mistakes can be fun and the source of much amusement for years to come! You will enjoy turning up the soil, planting seeds, and watching them grow into edible food. If you choose to raise poultry, for example, you will experience the joy of raising a bunch of baby chicks to frying size. Then you may take a day to kill and dress maybe twenty of them to put in your freezer (or hire someone to do this for you). What a good feeling it is to know that the food you are eating was produced by the work of your own hands! There is a sense of independence, satisfaction, health and vigor that one just cannot get in the same way living in the city.

If you are concerned about making a living, in towns that have 30,000 to 39,000 population, businesses often come up for sale, and there are many opportunities for starting new businesses. If you are good with gardening and trees, maybe starting a nursery is the thing. If you are good with mechanical things, maybe starting a tractor sales agency for one of the new Japanese four-wheel drive diesel tractors is for you. Maybe a business in solar energy, hydroponics, and wind and water energy is needed in the community of your choice. Perhaps there is something else that you have longed to do and are good at, and this would be the opportunity to do it. It has been proven that *if you do what you enjoy, you will succeed and prosper.*

WHETHER OR NOT TO HAVE ANIMALS

Whether or not you wish to raise animals is a major consideration when deciding how big a place to buy. If you are a vegetarian, you can probably get by on 1 or 2 acres. However, if you intend to raise animals, you are going to need to add 5 or 10 additional acres to produce food for the animals. You need to decide whether or not you want to have animals *before* you begin looking for property.

One of the things that we have found from experience, and would recommend to anyone, is not to get any animals during the first year after you move to a farm or ranch. You have plenty of other things that will require your attention that first year. Another recommendation would be that you carefully evaluate whether it is really worth the investment of time and money for you to try to produce your own milk.

The concept of a homestead with a milk cow grazing outside may be beautiful in theory, but it is very different in real life. In the first place, cows have to be bred once a year (freshened) and have a new calf in order to produce milk. This means that, if you want to be self-sufficient, you would have to keep a bull as well as a cow, just to do the annual breeding. If you want milk year-round, you would need to have two cows. Also, they should be milked twice a day, seven days a week, and "cowsitters" are even more difficult to find than babysitters. If you really would like to produce your own milk, we would definitely recommend goats rather than cows (more on this in Chapter 9).

We sell goat's milk and fertile eggs and have found that the market for eggs is better than the market for raw milk. Moreover, eggs are easier to package than goat's milk. Thus, you could easily produce some extra eggs and trade them with someone for some of his surplus milk.

For meat, as I mentioned, we recommend the smaller animals, such as sheep, goats, rabbits and chickens. This way, if one animal dies, you would not be losing the significant investment that you would lose if a cow were to die. Also, smaller animals are easier to handle by various family members and easier to doctor.

THE LAY OF THE LAND

It is desirable to have some flat land to use for gardening and hay production. However, it is equally desirable that you have some elevation somewhere on the property so that you can place a water tank about 60 feet above your home. The land should be a south-facing slope so that you can use passive solar energy to heat your home. That is so you can have the south side of your house almost all glass so that the winter sun hits it and heats much of your home through passive solar energy. A cross section of the ideal land and home is shown in Figure 3.2 on the next page.

But there is more to consider than just water, animals and the lay of the land.

GOOD NEIGHBORS

If you found the piece of land that you want (and you are willing to take whatever house happens to go with it), it is wise to spend some time meeting some of your neighbors. If you are a very conservative Christian, for example, and all of your neighbors are people who smoke marijuana and worship Buddha, there could be some conflicts. On the other hand, if you are a free flowing-spirit and all your neighbors are super-conservative, straight-laced and rigid, then you, too, could have some problems. The more compatible you are with your neighbors, the happier you are going to be. This will be particularly true during some of the tough times that are forecast by economists and followers of trends and that are prophesied in the Bible. Neighbors are going to need to be able to work together and help each other.

One Possibility of an Ideal Site

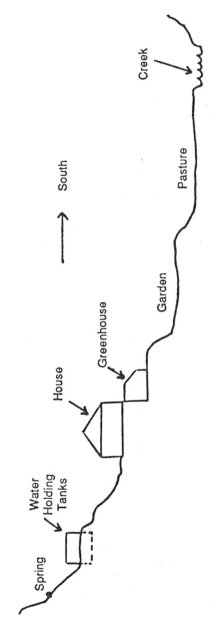

As an alternative to a spring, a well could pump up into the water tanks.

Figure 3.2

There are some areas of the country where the existing residents resent outsiders moving in. For example, in Oregon, many neighborhoods resent people from California moving in. They claim that they simply run up the property prices and contaminate the environment. This may or may not be true, but you need to ascertain if your neighbors are welcoming you or are hostile and dubious about you purchasing and moving into "Brown's old place."

Not only are your neighbors important, but it is important that you have adequate local services.

THE LOCAL COMMUNITY

I once knew a group of Christians who tried to move out from the city and form their own community. They were wanting to find a medical doctor who would move out with them, a plumber, a carpenter and people with various fundamental skills. They never were able to find a group of people who all wanted to move and had the right mix of skills. To me, this is an idealistic and unrealistic approach. You need to buy property near a community that already has a hospital, plumbers, carpenters, electricians, veterinarians, automobile repair people and all the basic services upon which you will rely.

When I lived on Catalina Island, there was a twelve-bed hospital and only one doctor on the island. If he was off the island for a visit to the mainland, the residents were basically left without medical services. To me this is below the acceptable minimum for medical services. You should look for a community with a significantly-sized hospital and a number of doctors before you decide to buy in that area.

If you move out rurally, you can probably do much of your own plumbing yourself with the new PVC pipe, for all you do is cut it and glue it together. However, when the water heater or the furnace goes out, you will need a qualified plumber or repairman to come in and fix those kinds of items. Therefore, ideally you want a community where there are at least two plumbing companies, so that you would not be at the mercy of one of them.

The same thing would be true of automobile repairs. You want a community with at least two automobile garages that are competitive with each other.

Many of the appliances that you need for your home and land you can buy from catalogs. However, it would be nice to have one or more stores that sold furniture, washers and dryers, stoves, refrigerators, video equipment, and so forth, so that you could go in and examine these items instead of ordering them blindly through a catalog.

To me, churches would be an important consideration. I would want to know that there was at least one church that believed roughly as I did, with whom I felt as though I would fit in. Whatever religion you might be, this would be a consideration, to be sure that there was a compatible religious community that could help you grow.

Of course there are a whole host of retail services, such as grocery stores and drugstores, that your community should have. You do not want to have to drive a hundred miles to go get a prescription filled, so double check that there is an adequately-stocked pharmacy in the area where you are contemplating purchasing property.

SUMMARY AND CONCLUSION

We have seen that a place in the country is desirable both from an investment and a security point of view. It could provide security for retirement or security as a place to live in the event that cities become unbearable.

We discussed the fact that now is as good a time as any to actually purchase a place in the country. We then looked at the four steps involved in finding a place in the country:

1. Locate the area of the United States in which you would like to have your country place.
2. Find a desirable small town within that area.
3. Look for the right piece of property (properties) around that small town.
4. Negotiate on three or more of these pieces of property until you find the best bargain and the most suitable property.

We discussed at the important characteristics of a piece of rural property. The three most important are:

1. water
2. Water
3. WATER

Next in importance are soil and septic approval. If the place is fenced and has outbuildings, that is an added plus to the property.

We also looked at a number of other important items in moving to the country and looking for property.

1. Realize that you are going to buy the land as your primary concern and take whatever house is on it.
2. Look for land that has some flat area and also has a south-facing slope which is high enough that you could put a water storage tank about 60 feet above your home.
3. Make sure you have good, compatible neighbors.
4. Make sure the community has adequate medical facilities, retail stores and services such as automobile repair garages, plumbers and so forth.

Begin to do your thinking, planning, and investigating early, so that during the summer you can actually go out and walk around some of the properties around your chosen small town.

Once you make the decision of which piece of property to buy, you are likely going to be living with it for the next ten to twenty years or more, so make the choice carefully. It is better to take a little extra time and choose the right piece of property, than it is to get something on impulse and later regret it.

All the time and energy you spend developing that property will be wasted, in a sense, if later you find out that it is not the appropriate piece of property for you, and you have to sell it and move on. Therefore, be sure to choose your place in the country with care.

Once you have purchased your country place, you need to realize that it is going to take time (probably years) to get it into the shape you want it in.

Chapter 4

IT TAKES TIME, TIME, TIME

Let me outline for you a scenario that is typical of some people. They live in the city and they own 5 or 10 acres somewhere out in the country, usually undeveloped. Their feeling is that if the city were to become an undesirable place to live, they would simply move out to this acreage, become instantly self-sufficient, and live happily ever after.

I wish I could endorse this type of thinking, but unfortunately I believe it is naive and truly an impossible dream. I have found by personal experience and by observing others that it takes five to ten years to develop a piece of raw land into a self-sufficient, self-reliant place to live.

I had been with IBM for ten years and had been a financial consultant for twenty years, when we moved to our present location in the country. I was used to receiving a project, flying in, getting it done and over with, and then moving onto the next. When Jeani and I moved to a ranch in Oregon, I still had the same attitude, but was I in for a surprise!

THE DEVELOPMENT OF
LIVING WATERS RANCH

When we moved here to a 70-acre ranch, which we named Living Waters Ranch, there was a partially-completed, two-story home on the property. The downstairs was livable and the upstairs was totally unfinished. The property had a 20-foot wide stream running through it and an irrigation system and a water system of sorts. The lower pasture was fenced in where a previous owner had run some cattle.

It sounds almost ideal, doesn't it? In some ways it was a wonderful piece of property to begin with, but it lacked so many other things that we needed for self-reliant living.

After working extremely hard on this place for a year, we had barely made a dent in all of the things that needed to be done. All of a sudden, I had to come to the realization that this was not a project I was going to fly in and do overnight; rather, this was probably a ten- to twenty-year project. Looking at our finances and time limitations, we realized that we were only going to be able to do one or two major projects a year. Let us briefly look at a few of the things that initially required vast amounts of our time and energy.

THE ORCHARD

We wanted to have fruit trees on the property, but there was a small forest of good-sized pine and cedar trees where we wanted to put in the orchard. First we had these logged off and sold three logging trucks full of trees. But, of course, the loggers left all of the tree tops and residual scraps scattered everywhere, and it took us about a year to cut all of that up into firewood and get the area cleaned up. Believe me, that is *work*!

Next we needed to have the stumps ground out so that we could plant an orchard. So the following year we contacted several stump removal people who ground out stumps, but most of them would not come out because our land was too rocky. We finally found a company that would come out, so that year we had the stumps ground out.

Two years had already gone by, and we knew from reading the Bible that fruit trees have to be in four or five years before you can really expect any harvest from them. Yet even with the stumps ground out, the area still needed to be terraced, for it was on a slope. So the following year, we had a caterpillar tractor (cat) come in and terrace the future orchard area. By the time we found a good, reliable person to drive the caterpillar tractor, it was late in the summer, and too late to plant trees.

Then on the fourth year, we got some small fruit trees about 4 feet high, which the nursery trimmed down to about 2 feet high, that we planted. About three-fourths of them grew, but some died and had to be replaced the following year—the *fifth* year. As well as apples, pears and plums, we put in some nectarine, peach and cherry trees, which we discovered really do not grow well in our climate, so those subsequently had to be removed and replaced.

I am happy to report that we now have about a 70-tree orchard, but it took us nine to ten years to get to the point where we could enjoy the wonderful fruit from our trees.

We also put in two almond trees, which turned out to be the wrong kind. These were the very hard shell almonds that you can only break with a hammer, rather than the paper shell ones that we normally buy in the store. We did not replace those; we have simply lived with them. However, the two pecan trees we planted died.

There were three old apple trees on other parts of the ranch, as well as one old pear tree and two plum trees. We were able to enjoy fruit from these trees from the beginning, but all these old trees were in bad shape from neglect, when we first moved to the property. We needed to have a professional pruner come out and get them into shape so they could produce, and produce well.

Then, lo and behold, we discovered there were worms in our apples! In contacting the local agricultural society, we were told that we had to spray with some type of insecticide in the fall, and again two or three times at the beginning of the year. We had a major decision to make: whether we wanted to go the insecticide route or live with the worms. We later decided that a few worms were not so bad. (After all, apple juice could use a little protein in it!)

We discovered there was a disease called "leaf curl" which killed two of the trees in our new orchard. We now know that if "leaf curl" begins in a tree, we absolutely must spray it. There is no choice, or the tree will die. When they are leafed out, the trees need to be checked at least weekly, if not more often, to be sure that they do not have "leaf curl."

If there is a freeze after the fruit trees blossom out, there is the danger that you will lose all those blossoms and, basically, the fruit from the harvest that season. You have a couple of choices to prevent losing all the blossoms: putting in kerosene heaters scattered around your orchard or having a high overhead sprinkler system that you run all night when the blossoms are likely to freeze.

We never have put in either one of these systems; we just pray like mad when we hear frost is coming, and, up until now, the Lord has given us a good harvest each year, although some years it is much better than others.

As perhaps you are beginning to appreciate, a simple statement like, "We'll put in an orchard over here," can lead to an enormous amount of work over many years. One thing we found is that you should dig a very large hole when you put in a small tree, because the loose soil around the roots will help the early development of the tree. You should also keep weeds out from around the base of the trees and you should fertilize them periodically.

Then comes harvest time. When you harvest multiple bushels of apples and pears, what do you do with them? You could keep a few of them in the cooler, but that does not take care of the bulk of them. We chose to buy an apple cider press in order to be able to squeeze the apples into apple juice. Most years we get about 100 gallons of apple juice, which we freeze and then enjoy throughout the entire year. Some of the fruit we have made into jams, jellies, and apple and pear butters. Some we dehydrate.

Our experience has been that pears do not last very long. You have about a two-week period when you need to pick them and do something with them or they will soon get overripe and begin to rot. They also make great juice (similar to apple juice.)

Plums will keep a little longer than pears. You can pick them over a period of several weeks and enjoy fresh plums for about a month, which are absolutely delicious.

But soon we discovered that planting an orchard created a new problem....

FENCES, FENCES, AND MORE FENCES

The area where we had cleared the tall cedar and pine trees was not fenced in. We realized that the deer would love to come and nibble the delicate foliage off of our tender new trees, as well as the fruit that would come later, so we had to build a 10-foot high fence around our orchard area (which we lovingly call "the deer fence"). While we were at it, we also enclosed a portion of the old pasture with this 10-foot high fence which we intended to use for a garden. Another portion of fence closed in the old apple trees and an area which was ultimately to become a vineyard (more about that later). These were the first of many, many fences that we had to put in.

When we got sheep (more about sheep later), the area that we now call the "middle pasture" was unfenced, and we had to fence it in so the sheep could be contained there. However, that fence could be lower for livestock, since we were not concerned about keeping the deer out of that area.

Incidentally, you can raise two or three times as many sheep if you have two, three or four different pastures for them. You can let them be in one pasture for a week, and then move them to the next while you let the grass in the first pasture grow for two or three weeks. Then when you bring the sheep back to it, there will be a good growth of new grass there for them, and you can let the other pastures rest and produce new growth.

However, to move the sheep from one pasture to the other, we had to go through the garden area. Thus, we had to build two fences to make a driveway through which they can run, so they would not use our garden as a salad bar (which they did one year when they pushed a gate open and got in there!). There were also other cross fences that we had to build over the years which are too numerous to list.

Several years later, we planted a 200-vine vineyard within this 10-foot high fenced area, and it prospered quite well. We decided to try another vineyard across the road, which was in an area a little higher in elevation and received more sun. The first thing we had to do was have a "cat" come in and terrace the area for us, and remove some of the trees. Then we had to fence it in so our goats could not get at the grapevines, since our goats roam wild out on the hillside. (Goats are fenced *out* of areas where you do not want them to be, not fenced in. In fact, we have an automatic gate on our property that we lovingly call the "goat gate," to keep the goats out of the area around the buildings.)

Later we decided that we would like to be able to run the sheep on the other side of the road up the hill, so we had a huge area fenced in so that we can keep them over there for a couple of months in the spring when the grass is high.

Then we built a volleyball court which had to have a very tall fence around it, both to contain the ball and to keep the animals off of the court. We had to fence in an area for the goats around their barn. It seems like we are continually in need of a new fence for some reason. The simple ones we put in ourselves, but we have had a fence company of professionals come out and build the more complicated ones for us.

Believe me, if you are developing a piece of property, you are going to build fence after fence after fence! And that takes time, money and energy.

In order to grow a garden, orchard, and vineyard within our 10-foot-high fenced area, and also to keep our pastures green, we had to have an irrigation system, so on to the water and irrigation system. Watch out for this one—it is a tremendous amount of work!

THE WATER SYSTEM

Before we discuss the irrigation system for water to help grow vegetables, fruit and hay, we should look at the water system proper that feeds the houses. The existing water system when we arrived on the ranch was poor to totally inadequate. There was a black plastic irrigation hose that came from a spring up the hill that fed just the house during the winter. There was a small, Sears pressure pump with which the previous owners pumped water from the 20-foot wide creek that runs through the property, for a month or two during the summer. They used this for both the house and the irrigation system, such as it was.

They had previously run their spring water into a wooden tank lined with visqueen (plastic), but this was in total disrepair and we were not able to use it. During the winter, they would leave one outdoor faucet running full blast all the time when the weather was below freezing, so the water would not freeze in the pipes. Our first winter, although we had been told about this, we thought a trickle would do, which it did not. Our pipes froze and we found ourselves carrying water from the creek in buckets one day! This is certainly good motivation to improve the water system!

Where in the world do you start on such an anti-quated system, and what do you do? Let me jump ahead and state that we now have five sources of water. One is from the creek that runs through the property; one is from the lake that we built; one is from the spring up on one side of our property; another is from an upper reservoir that we built in connection with another spring; and then we dug a manual well. Water is so very important that we wanted to have various sources to be able to get at it.

The first thing we did was to have a backhoe come out and dig a 16- to 18-foot hole, into which we placed a culvert 4 feet in diameter that had been perforated at the bottom. This well has a good flow, and from a direction that is a couple of hundred yards from the stream. If necessary we could draw water from this well with a bucket, as they did in the olden days.

Another year, we redid the system that pumps out of the creek and we built a small pumphouse. The water from this goes up to two 2,000-gallon tanks, from which it subsequently flows back down to the house by gravity, as needed. As mentioned earlier, in order to run a washing machine, this water source needs to be at least 57 feet above the level of the washer. For all but a couple of months each year, water runs down by a pipe from a spring into these tanks. When the spring dries up for about two months, we pump the water up from the creek into these tanks. This way, at any time, we have at least 4,000 gallons of water stored in these tanks available to us for use by gravity flow.

However, one note of caution here is that if someone were to leave a garden hose running, it would totally drain these tanks overnight, and the next morning no one would have any water. In a self-reliant situation, you are highly dependent upon each other and everyone living on the property should be instructed as to the importance of caring for the water supply.

There was an area on the ranch, a swamp with mosquitoes, that we erroneously thought was totally on our property. Later we found out that it is partially on BLM (Bureau of Land Management) property. The creek overflowed into this swamp about every second or third year and it was a mess.

Thinking that we would beautify this area and provide a home for wild ducks and geese to light while flying north and south, we dug this area out and formed a small, about 2-acre pond (we call it a lake). However, our input system was inadequate and after a couple of years the creek overflowed into it so much that it totally filled up the lake with debris. We then had to call in a "cat" and excavate once more. We then built a very sophisticated input source from the creek with an iron input gate that raises from the bottom, so we can totally control the flow into the lake. It is from this lake, which we put in for fire fighting and aesthetic purposes, that we can also do our irrigation.

The reason I would like to emphasize fire fighting is that we had a log cabin here on the ranch which caught fire and burned to the ground. We called three different fire departments and none of them would come, because we were out of their district. So subsequently we built our own fire-fighting system based on the lake, from which we can pump into our fire-fighting system. At each of the three buildings on the property, we have a "firehouse" which has 150 feet of firehose and so forth.

The last element of our water system, which took years to develop, was to put in an upper reservoir. We dammed up a creek that ran from one of our springs so that the reservoir now holds 40,000 to 50,000 gallons. The 4,000 gallons we had stored in the tanks would only fight a fire for about five minutes, so it was totally inadequate. So this upper reservoir, from which water could flow down by gravity even if there were no electricity, is another, secondary, source of water for fighting fires. It can also be used, somewhat, to provide drinking water to one of the houses.

To redo the water system, dig the well, build the lake, build the upper reservoir and replumb everything involved took about ten years. That does not even count the irrigation system.

THE IRRIGATION SYSTEM

When we arrived, there was an irrigation ditch on the property that had not been utilized for years. The primary irrigation the previous owner had for their one pasture was sprinklers, but these were scattered at random and did not give anywhere close to a total coverage.

We started by installing an irrigation system in the garden, where we lined up two sprinklers about every 60 feet. Thus, we ended up with the 2-acre garden area divided into five sections, wherein we could control the amount of water that was sprinkled on each section.

Next we tackled the old, lower pasture. We totally removed, revamped and replaced that entire sprinkling system, so that we would get total coverage.

Then later we also had to irrigate the new vineyard. We have table grapes along the fences and, in the rest of the vineyard, we have some varieties of grapes from which some people make wine (we make grape juice.) So irrigation sprinklers were needed there too. When we fenced in the middle pasture as a separate pasture area, it too, had to be irrigated. We did this by putting in sprinklers with extra-large rainbird heads around the perimeter of the pasture. These are set to cover a 180-degree area and they get good coverage. This way we do not have sprinklers and irrigation pipe out in the middle of this pasture.

Some years later, we built a second vineyard area across the street up the hill, and we also had to provide irrigation sprinklers for it. It seems like we are forever adding to our irrigation system or one of the sprinkler heads will cease to rotate, and we will either have to repair it or replace it. Expanding or maintaining the irrigation system, as needed, seems to be an ongoing task.

At first, with our irrigation system, we had to switch valves manually in order to run the water to the portion of the ranch that we wanted to irrigate at a given time. Fortunately (praise the Lord!), we now have an automatic timer and solonoid valves that turn on the water to irrigate the various areas designated, according to our preset timing. We have been so blessed by this excellent labor-saving device that I wish we had had it from the very beginning!

One of the things I mentioned that we irrigate is our garden, and that is something we should discuss further.

THE ROCK GARDEN

In order to have a garden, we first had a man come in and rototill a portion of the pasture. This area had never been used for anything but a pasture. Consequently, we would run across rocks that were sometimes as big as a foot and a half in diameter, which Jeani and I laboriously carried over to the fence at the edge of the garden. Every year the rocks seem to get smaller, but there still are hundreds of them that we have to remove every year after replowing.

The soil in the garden is river bottom soil and very rich. However, we supplement this every fall by putting the animal droppings (and old straw) we clean out from the goat and sheep stalls onto the garden and plowing it under. We have a very prolific and productive garden.

Yet, sometimes the way different crops produce is confusing. For example, one year we would get an abundance of fantastic corn, and perhaps the next year our corn would be puny and very unfruitful. We are still working on this problem.

Another problem we have had with the garden has been pests, like porcupines, that would come in and eat the tops off of lettuce, cabbages, and so on. Even marigolds do not even bother them—they just eat the tops off of those, too, and ruin everything! We finally got rid of all the porcupines, but not without effort and some losses in crops.

To some degree, your garden will be a trial and error project, because each location has a different climate and soil. Therefore, some plants will grow well in your area, and others will not. It takes several years for you to experiment with planting a variety of types of seeds before you find out which seeds thrive and excel in productivity in your climate and soil.

Although there is a lot to learn about gardening, it is one of the really fun projects possible with country living. The satisfaction of eating foods you have grown yourself is really tremendously rewarding.

As I mentioned earlier, if you do not already know how, you will want to learn how to preserve the excess produce from the garden (can, dehydrate or freeze), so it will keep and you can enjoy it throughout the year. Acquiring these valuable skills also takes some time and practice.

There are many other things that we could discuss that require a great deal of time, such as learning how to take care of and benefit from animals, building your home, and so forth. But I hope this chapter has helped you see that it takes time, Time, TIME, **TIME** to take a raw piece of land and make it productive and suitable to your needs. Even if there is already a home on it, it still will require much time, because you will need to customize that property to the needs and goals of yourself and your family.

It is interesting to note that in the process of developing the land into a self-sufficient, self-reliant place to live, the people doing the work are becoming self-sufficient, self-reliant people.

ONE POSSIBLE APPROACH

If you have some land in the country that you think you might need to occupy if life becomes less desirable in the city, I would like to repeat a suggestion as to some things you can do now, so that when you do move there, your life can be much easier.

The first thing would be to fence in an area and plant some fruit trees and grape vines. As we mentioned, it takes about four years for these to mature and begin to produce fruit. If possible, dig a well or tap into a spring or a city water system so that you have water available for irrigation. You can set your irrigation system up on a timer that waters these trees and grape vines for you regularly during the summer.

The second thing I would suggest would be to build a barn of the type that was shown in Chapter 3 (Figure 3.1). The center portion of the barn could be used for storing a tractor or other equipment. The left, shed part of the barn could ultimately be used for a chicken or goat house, and the right portion should be large enough to drive a motor home in under cover. Alternatively, you could put a small, easily-movable house trailer there, in which you could live until you were able to actually build your own home.

As we suggested earlier, if there is already a house on the location, you might want to consider renting it out to someone who would be caretaker and subsequently building your own house on the same property. However, you *must* check the zoning laws to be sure you can build a second residence on that property. Where we live, we can only have a house on every 20 acres. Thus, 40 acres would be required in order to build a second home on the property. This varies from state to state and county to county, so be sure to check before you buy your property, if you want to build a second dwelling.

SUMMARY AND CONCLUSION

In this chapter, we have endeavored to make you aware of the fact that it takes a great deal of time to convert raw land, even land that has been used for cattle, into a functioning place for self-reliant living. It takes time to build fences. It takes time to put in a water system. It takes time to put in an irrigation system. It takes at least four years after you plant an orchard to have much fruit from it. Similarly, it takes at least four years after you plant a vineyard to have a grape crop from it. The garden area needs to be worked over and rocks and other hindrances need to be removed. Adequate irrigation (drip, flood or sprinkler) needs to be installed.

I would estimate that the minimum amount of time in which all of this could be accomplished would be about five years. Ten years or more would be more likely, particularly if you add animals into the equation and the building of a new home on the property.

Just keep in mind that it takes time, Time, TIME, to do these things. Please do not underestimate the task.

As we said earlier in the book, when purchasing property in the city, you buy the house and take the land that goes with it. However, in rural areas, you buy the land and take whatever house goes with it. It is very likely that you are not going to be happy with the house that is there and you are going to want to build your own. Having built several personally, I could write an entire book on building your own house. In the next chapter, we will look at a few of the significant considerations to entertain as you begin to develop your own "home sweet home" in the country.

Chapter 5

BUILDING YOUR HOUSE

As with most of the topics in this book, this chapter would apply to someone building a home on a city lot or in the suburbs, as well as to someone building a home in the country. Many of the principles are the same. But it applies even more to someone buying a small amount of acreage—whether on the outskirts of a city or metropolitan area or in a more rural setting—and building a home from scratch.

In many ways, buying a piece of property with an existing home on it and with the legal ability to build a second home has two advantages. If it will be awhile before you live on the property, one option would be to rent out the home to a caretaker at a reduced rent in exchange for his caretaking of the property. Then when you decide to actually occupy the property, you could live in that existing home while your new home is being built.

Another alternative would be to have a motor home or a house trailer that you could park on the property and live in while your house was being built. For many people, this would be quite cramped quarters and they would not be comfortable with this living situation. However, if you are used to camping and "making do," then this would be a viable alternative.

SITE SELECTION

Selecting a site for your new home on the property you purchased is a very key and critical decision. Ideally, your building site will be on a south-facing slope such that the broad side of the house will face south. The reason for this is that you will want much of the south side of the house in glass so that you can make use of passive solar heating much of the year.

Another consideration in site selection is the water supply. As we mentioned in an earlier chapter, your water tank needs to be 57 feet above your washer to have enough pressure to run the washer. Thus, the house would most likely need to be located on a somewhat lower portion of the property than your water tank. Otherwise, you would have to go to the expense of building a tower for the water tank. The reason for the water supply to be that high above the house is so that water can flow down to the house by gravity.

Do you remember seeing the old windmills in the midwest? Usually adjacent to them there is a tower with a corrugated iron tank on top of the tower. However, these towers are usually between 10 and 20 feet high, not at the 60-foot elevation that you would need for adequate residence water pressure.

One thing you would want to avoid in choosing a site would be having it on a flood plain with a creek or river running through nearby that occasionally floods. You could check with old timers in the area to see how high the flood water had ever come on a particular site on which you are considering building.

One consideration for the site selection, which would be important to some people and not important at all to others, would be the defensibility of the site in the event of attack by a bunch of looters or some other violent group of people. The defensibility of the home would also be a consideration in designing the floor plan. This subject is covered in Appendix C, in case it is of interest to you.

Some people desire to have their home in an area where it cannot be seen from the main road, while to others this is not an important consideration. If this is significant to you, then you will need to consider the fact that a road must be cut through trees to get back to the house, or perhaps the road will have to go over a hill that will conceal the house from the main road.

One thing that many people find significant in site selection is that it is desirable to have the home near the garden and the barn, if animals are to be raised. However, be sure that the house is not downwind from the barn!

The cross section shown on the next page (Figure 5.1), repeated from Chapter 3, gives one possibility for an ideal site.

Once the site has been selected, there are many things to be considered and decisions to be made before actual construction can begin.

AN UNDERGROUND HOME
OR AN EARTH-BERM HOME

The ground underneath your home is approximately 55-60 degrees Fahrenheit year round, once you get down past the first several inches, which of course will be hotter in the summer and colder in the winter. If your house had dirt piled up against cement walls on three sides, then it would tend to be that same 55-60 degrees year round.

One Possibility of an Ideal Site

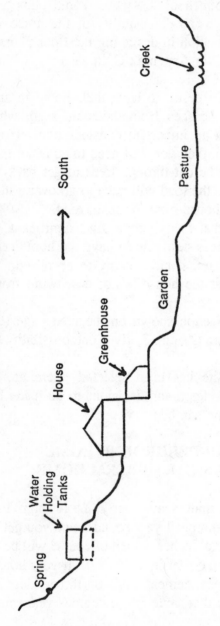

As an alternative to a spring, a well could pump up into the water tanks.

Figure 5.1

Perhaps you recall going down into a basement even during the middle of the summer and finding that it was nice and cool, even though the outside air temperature was hot. The reason a basement remains cool is because the dirt transmits its temperature to the cement walls, which then transmit it to the air inside the basement. The same thing would happen in an earth-berm home.

In an underground home, you would want the side facing south to be mostly glass and of course have the doors. The other three sides would be piled up with dirt. There would be a cement roof with a slight slant for any ground water to run off. This roof would be covered by two to three feet of dirt. This is considered to be an underground home and, for pennies a year, it can be heated and cooled with very little effort, or one could even live in it without any additional heating or cooling. The Indians in early America lived in caves and cave dwellings which had the same type of stable temperature. The only fires they had were outside the entrances with no heat inside the dwellings.

In order to have an underground home, the site needs to be appropriate and the desire to have an underground dwelling should be strong. An example of an underground home is shown in the drawings in Figure 5.2. The front view shows that the wall would extend beyond the house to act as a retaining wall when the dirt is pushed up against the end of the house. This is designated in Figure 5.2 as "A."

An earth-berm home, on the other hand, has the earth against three sides of the bottom floor but another story or two of the structure is on top of that, rather than it being covered by earth. This has some of the advantages of an underground home, but the temperature is not as stable because the roof is not covered by earth and it is

An Underground Home

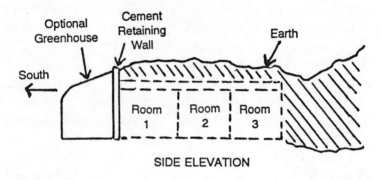

SIDE ELEVATION

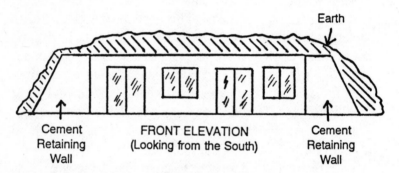

FRONT ELEVATION
(Looking from the South)

Figure 5.2

not as fireproof, since the ceiling of the bottom floor is not cement but wood, in most cases. Yet it does have advantages over a structure that is entirely on top of the ground.

One advantage is that one could have a root cellar, which could also be used as a fallout shelter, off of either side or the back of the earth-berm bottom story. The upper stories would also be more light and airy than the bottom story which has earth on three sides. An example of an earth-berm house is shown in Figure 5.3a and Figure 5.3b. These two stories do not include a basement. A basement could also be used as a fallout shelter, if a portion of it had a cement ceiling.

To me, one great advantage of an underground or earth-berm home is the lack of effort required to maintain a comfortable temperature.

My preference for the walls of either an underground house or an earth-berm house would be prestressed concrete walls or poured walls. However, if one chooses to use cement blocks and have them filled, my recommendation is that when the wall is halfway up, you have your cement contractor fill that portion of the wall. Then, when the wall is completely up, have him fill the top portion. I have seen too many instances where the wall was completely up and the attempt was made to fill it, but the filling simply did not run all the way down to the

An Earth-Berm Home

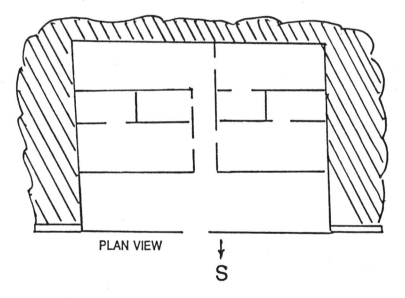

PLAN VIEW

S

Figure 5.3a

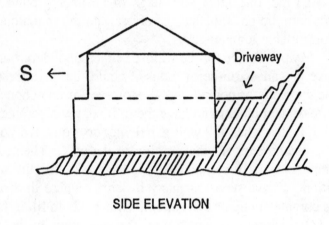

SIDE ELEVATION

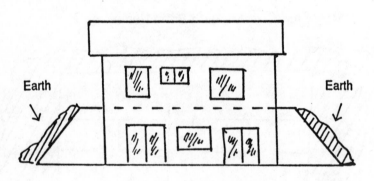

FRONT ELEVATION

Figure 5.3b

bottom, even using the heavy vibrators to facilitate the flowing of the cement.

ELECTRICITY IN YOUR NEW HOME

Before discussing various ways to generate electricity, which you will need to do if you are going to indeed be self-reliant, we first need to look at the two types of electricity in which you would be interested. Of course you are going to want to wire your house normally with 110- and 220-volt circuits, as would be done in any house. While you are wiring these, it is desirable to go ahead and wire in, or at least block in, a transfer switch which would automatically kick on a generator if the power from the outside power company fails. If this is done at the time of the initial wiring, it is much less expensive than attempting to retrofit a transfer switch and a generator.

You do not necessarily have to have a generator installed at the time you install the wiring to the transfer switch, although it would be desirable. However, at a minimum, it would be wise to run the wires to the area where a generator would be located at a later time. We will talk about different types of generators shortly. If wires are not run, at least run two or three empty conduits (3/4 inch to 1 inch) to future generator sites. On the front cover is a picture of me (James) with our 12.5 KW propane-powered generator and the transfer switch.

The other thing that you may well want to consider, which I recommend, is also wiring your house for 12-volt electricity. In some out-of-the-way well-ventilated closet, you could have a bank of 12-volt batteries (of the trickle-charge type) which would feed this 12-volt circuitry. You could have a light in each room connected to this 12-volt system. I recommend actual 110-volt-type fixtures which have an on-off switch on the fixture itself. Then use 12-volt bulbs in them that look just like regular 110 bulbs.

In addition, in your kitchen, you could have several of the female-type cigarette lighter receptacles into which you could plug 12-volt appliances. You could also have an "inverter" which will convert the 12-volt DC current into regular 110-volt AC (*B). You could charge this bank of batteries when the wind blew or when the sun shone (solar) and have stored electricity that could be used twenty-four hours a day.

For this 12-volt system, you can use the same type of wire that you use for your 110-volt wiring. It is a little heavier than necessary, but it also provides less resistance, which is good.

During normal times, you can keep the batteries charged by using a trickle charger plugged into the regular electricity to charge the batteries. However, if you are going to be self-reliant you would eventually need an alternate source for charging the 12-volt batteries, such as a wind-powered generator or photovoltaic cells, which convert sunlight to electricity. The new sheet type are superior to the old style and they are also cheaper; thus, they are recommended. The addresses of where these can be obtained are found in Appendix B (*B).

Let us assume that we have the house wired with both 110-, 220- and 12-volt as well. We have already mentioned how to charge the 12-volt batteries. We now need to turn our attention to providing the 110-volt power to the regular circuits.

We always consider the ideal case first. The ideal would be to have the electricity generated by water, through some type of turbo generator. For this, you would need an ample flow of water and a drop of at least 10 feet. A 5-gallon-per-minute flow with a drip (head) of

200 feet or a 100-gallon-per-minute flow with a 10-foot drop will give 80 watts of continuous power. This is approximately 2 kilowatts per day.

If a property has flowing water with that much grade, this would be my number one choice for a way to generate electricity. It is constant, has no pollution and it is quiet. If you are considering purchasing land, this would be one thing to keep in mind. It is possible that there is a stream on the property that could be dammed up to give you the appropriate drop. If there is a stream coming through the property that slopes down enough, water could be directed off at a higher level into a trench or channel that slopes down less than the stream. The channeled water could then be dropped back into the stream at a lower elevation.

There are books listed in Appendix B that I would recommend for further pursuit of the subjects of wind and water electrical generation. However, very few places have this type of adequate water flow, so other methods of generating electricity must be considered for the majority of the people who wish to become self-reliant.

A generator is turned by an engine, in most home applications. The engine can be powered by gasoline, diesel or propane. Diesel generators are very noisy and smelly, but diesel fuel can be stored far easier and longer than gasoline. So between gasoline and diesel, a diesel-powered electrical generator would be preferable.

However, as far as I am concerned, the superior method is to use a propane-powered engine that turns the generator. The propane burns clean, it is easily stored and the engine runs quietly. Most places that sell generators can easily convert a gasoline generator so that it can be powered by propane. It is a minor modification.

The size of the generator to acquire depends on how

much you want to run off of it. If your home is heated and cooled by a heat pump that is powered by electricity, normally this would not be included in items that the generator would power. Usually, the generator would basically power the lights and plugs of the home, plus possibly the hot water heater. If you have a propane-powered electrical generator, it is more economical and better to use a propane-powered hot water heater, so you do not have to worry about that extra load on your electrical generator.

In times of emergency, you could power up the generator for one or two hours in the evening and do all of your drilling, cutting, milling of wheat, mixing of dough and the other functions you need that require electricity. You could then use other sources of light and heat for the remainder of the evening.

In an earlier chapter, I mentioned that when I was on Catalina Island, I would spend the morning measuring lumber for places to cut and holes to be drilled. Then after lunch I would fire up the little, gasoline electric generator and I would then do all of my sawing and hole drilling in about a thirty-minute period. After that was done, I would shut off the generator and spend the afternoon nailing up the lumber that I had cut and drilled.

If long-term lighting (as opposed to emergency lighting) is to be powered by a 12- or 24-volt DC system, the lights should be "PL" fluorescent, because they are more energy efficient and do not flicker. With the "PL"-style light bulbs and the direct-current, low-voltage electronic ballast, it is now possible to have high quality lighting while using very little power. PL lights draw five times less energy to give the same amount of light as an incandescent bulb. A 5-watt PL light equals a 25 watt incandescent bulb. A PL bulb has a 10,000-hour life, which is about ten times longer than a regular light bulb. Socket adapters are available to allow the PL socket to be installed in place of a regular socket in a table lamp (*B). Using PL lights will greatly reduce the amount of solar panels required where solar-powered lighting will be used.

Electricity is one item that is very significant. It is the major thing that separates modern man from the typical rural farmer in early America. With it you can achieve so much more in a short period of time. It is quite a chore to drill holes in wood with a hand brace and bit, to make all of your saw cuts with a hand saw, and to use a hand mill to grind wheat into flour. It can be done, but electricity will make your life so much easier and is therefore a major consideration for self-reliant living.

Wind-Powered Generation of Electricity

All generators utilize some type of motor to turn the generator, which generates the electricity. In the case of nuclear power, this motor is a steam engine, the steam being generated by the heat of the nuclear reaction. But any kind of engine will do—including gasoline, diesel and *wind-powered* engines. The wind-powered system has something that is unique in that it runs sporadically. Sometimes it runs very fast; sometimes it does not run at all. Therefore, there must be a way to store the electricity generated so that it can be used whenever desired, even when there is no wind.

Normally a wind electrical generator will charge 12-volt batteries. There would be a large bank of these in a well-ventilated area (as mentioned earlier), the number depending on how much electricity you want to store. These batteries are usually mounted on shelves up a wall. If you are using a 12-volt lighting system, it can be hooked directly to this bank of batteries. If you want a 110-volt system, the 12-volt direct current can be converted by using an inverter to 110 alternating current. By proper wiring, you can have the same bank of batteries run either system.

The two basic classifications of wind machines are recorded on page 178 of *The Homebuilt Wind-Generated Electricity Handbook*, by Michael Hackleman:

> A wind machine is an aeroturbine; as the word suggests, it's an airdriven turbine. Mechanical energy from the wind....
>
> ...there are two classes of aeroturbine: the vertical and the horizontal axis machines. And they're pretty well defined by the name. The vertical axis machine rotates about a vertical shaft (or axis) and the horizontal axis machine—yep, you guessed it—rotates about a horizontal shaft. The sail-wing, wind-sail, prop-types, Chalk turbine, farm water-pumpers, Dutch windmills, are all horizontal axis machines. The Savonius rotor, Darrieus rotor (alias "egg-beater"), and the hybrid-types are all vertical axis machines.
>
> —Earthmind, 5246 Boyer Rd.
> Mariposa, CA 95338

As can be seen in Figure 5.4, there are many types of horizontal axis wind machines. These all have to turn into the wind in order to take advantage of it. The ones with a vertical axis are able to receive wind from any direction. Thus, a vertical axis machine might be more appropriate if the wind is quite variable in your area. If there is always a prevailing wind from the same direction, a horizontal axis machine would be preferable.

Horizontal Axis Wind Machines

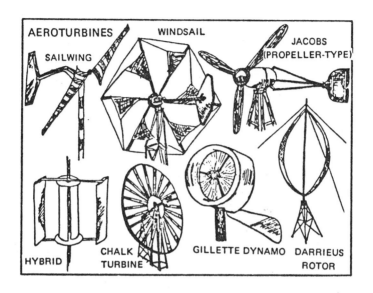

Figure 5.4

Figure 5.5 shows a large vertical axis wind-powered generator, built in Scotland at the beginning of the century, and a smaller vertical axis (S-type) windmill that is in common use today (from pages 64 and 71 of *The Autonomous House—Design and Planning For Self-Sufficiency* by Brenda and Robert Vale, published by Thames and Hudson, London).

For most situations, the horizontal axis wind machine is very adequate and a bit more efficient than the vertical axis one.

Vertical Axis Wind Machines

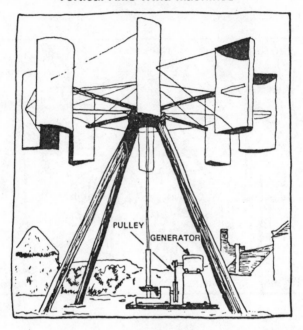

Figure 5.5

THE ROOT CELLAR
AND/OR FALLOUT SHELTER

The subject of fallout shelters was discussed in detail in the book *Preparing for Emergencies*, another book in this "Preparation" series (*B). Therefore, we will not go into detail here. Suffice it to say that I consider a root cellar (which could also be used as a fallout shelter) to be an essential for rural self-reliant living. The root vegetables (carrots, beets, potatoes, turnips and so forth) need to be stored in a cool place where they will last all winter long until the next harvest.

A simplistic root cellar can be created by digging a 6-foot-wide trench about 6 or 8 feet deep, putting boards across it, and placing some of the dirt that was dug out back on top of the boards. A slanted door can provide access. Bins or shelves can be built inside to hold the root vegetables. If this is also to be used as a potential fallout shelter, then cots, water, a means of waste disposal, some type of lighting and food other than root vegetables, such as freeze-dried no-cook food (*B), should be stored in the root cellar as well.

Needless to say, life would be much more comfortable, if a root cellar were built connected to an earth-berm house, and it had a cement floor (with a drain and a toilet), nice 12-volt lighting and other amenities (see Figure 5.6). Again, I would refer you to the book *Preparing for Emergencies* for our discussion on how such a room can become a "happy room" that is used regularly by the entire family.

A Root Cellar In
An Earth-Berm House

Double Row of Cement Blocks Filled—18"

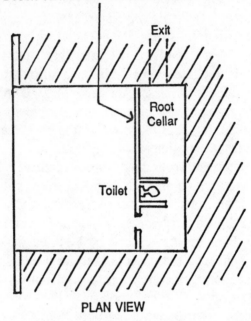

PLAN VIEW

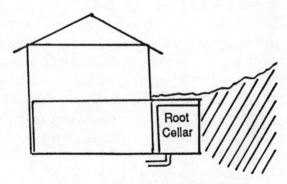

CROSS-SECTION ELEVATION VIEW

Figure 5.6

HEATING AND COOLING THE HOME

Any good, self-reliant home should be built as though it were going to have electricity forever and, simultaneously, as though there were going to be no electricity starting tomorrow. You could have a heat pump to heat and air-condition the home or you could use electricity to cool the home and heat by wood or propane. These things are well known and need not be discussed further here.

However, the capability of heating or cooling the home without any electricity requires that some things be done at the time of construction that will make this relatively easy. These things can be retrofitted into an existing home, but it is much harder.

Let us first start with the cooling aspect of the home. The rooms in most homes have doors and windows which stop 1 to 2 feet from the ceiling. The hot air trapped in that top 2 feet has no way to get out. Even if you opened all the windows, this heat is still trapped.

A natural solution to this problem is to build in "input vents" near to the floor and "output vents" right next to the ceiling. Then, when you have those vents opened, you will get a natural convection with cool air coming in at the bottom of the room and hot air being forced out of the vents at the top of the room. If possible, the input vents should be larger and located on the windward side of the house.

The details of these vents are shown in Figure 5.7. The vents could be filled with foam rubber when they are not in use and covered with an attractive wood cover, held in place by strong hidden magnetic clasps or Velcro. The outside, of course, should be screened and ideally have some type of metal louvers.

Natural Convection Using Vents

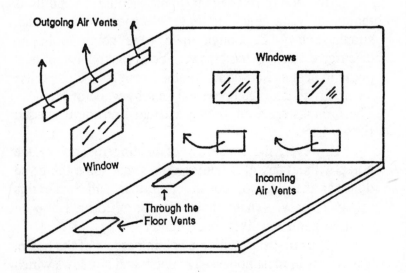

Figure 5.7

Similarly, heating without electricity would most likely be by wood. If it were a two-story house, you could put the woodstove on the downstairs floor, but you would need vents through the floors so that the heat could come up to adequately heat the upper story. Again, these vents could be filled with pieces of foam rubber when not needed. A floor grill could be placed over the vents on the upper floor, and a ceiling vent could be used on the ceiling of the lower floor. When wood heat was needed to heat the entire house, then the foam rubber could be removed and the upstairs floor vents opened to allow the heat to rise upstairs. These through-the-floor vents are also shown in Figure 5.7.

As we look at heating the home, let us start at the beginning. There are three basic methods to consider with regard to space heating, independent of public utility systems:

1. Solar
2. Wood burning
3. Wind-generated electricity

In considering the use of solar energy to heat your home, it is obvious that it will be much easier to utilize if you are building a new home than if you are trying to "retrofit" solar heating into an existing structure. The main motivation for installing solar heating, as far as I am concerned, is not economics but independence. Solar heating will tend to make you less dependent on the utility systems.

There are two basic types of systems in solar heating: passive and active. In a passive system, one does not have the pipes and pumps that are involved in an active system. The simplest form of a passive system is to have all of the south side of a house glassed in (see Figure 5.8), and perhaps no windows on the north side. While the drapes are open all day, the sun shines through the glass. This heats the air in the room, the furniture and, if there is a thick concrete floor, it heats the floor. In the evening the drapes are shut (or a movable insulation is placed across the inside of the windows), and the heat is slowly released from the furniture and floor to keep the house warm all night.

Another passive system also utilizes a glass wall on the south side, but drums of water are stacked inside, and the end of each of these that is next to the window (sun) is painted black (Figure 5.9). All day these drums collect

South-Facing Window
As A Solar Collector

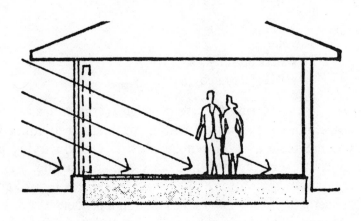

Figure 5.8

heat, which they release during the evening and night. These are but two of the many variations on passive systems. The nice thing about them is that if the electricity went off, they would still work.

Another advantage of the passive systems is that they are more easily installed in existing structures. For example, one could fairly inexpensively add another window to the south side of one's house—or more ideally, several giant floor-to-ceiling windows. However, this will only heat rooms on the south side of the house. This leaves something to be desired, unless the house is built as a long narrow structure running east and west, so that every room has a southern exposure. This means that most houses will probably require an active system.

**Passive Solar Heating
Using Drums of Water**

Figure 5.9

There is a huge variety of active solar heating systems. All of them consist of four basic components:

1. Collection
2. Transportation
3. Storage
4. Distribution

There is some type of a collector, usually placed on the roof, to convert the incident solar radiation into usable thermal energy. The collectors are usually metal boxes with glass or plastic covers. The interior of these gets very hot and pipes are run through them. In the simplest case, water is circulated through these collectors and becomes hot. This water is then stored in a hot water tank. Air is heated as it is passed around the hot water tank. The hot air can then be moved through ducts to heat the house. Thus, we can see the other components of the system—that of transporting the hot water to the storage tank and the distributing of the hot air through the house. Such a system normally requires an electric pump, and also an auxiliary heat source in the event of a large number of contiguous overcast days.

In an integrated system, the heating of the house and of the hot water would be combined into a single system. This can be seen in Figure 5.10. In the house pictured in this figure, hot water is circulated, whereas in some solar systems, hot air is circulated. We will not attempt to get into a comparative evaluation of these systems, but will leave that for your individual investigation. One good book on this subject, that unfortunately is now out of print, is:

Designing and Building a Solar House
By Donald Watson
Published by Garden Way Publishing

You can likely still locate it in some libraries or a number is given in Appendix B of a company that can help you locate out-of-print books.

An Integrated
Solar Heating System

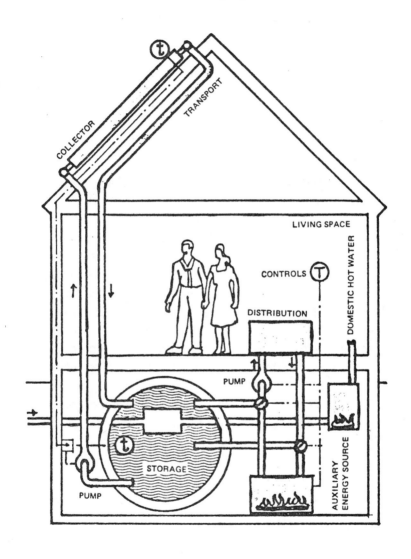

Figure 5.10

As a supplement to solar heat, one could have wood-burning stoves in many of the rooms. Another alternative would be to have supplemental heat by hot water radiators, the water being heated by wind-generated electricity.

One significant consideration when thinking of space heating is the temperature of the space that you need to heat. For example, in an underground home the air is roughly 55 degrees summer or winter. This means that air conditioning in the summer is unnecessary and heating in the winter is minimal—the temperature has to be brought up only a small amount.

By no means are all underground houses ugly. Jack Strickler, a retired assistant vice-president of the engineering division of Bell Aircraft, built his own underground house on Camano Island, Washington. He initially designed a wind system to generate electricity used to heat water. (He then stored energy generated by his windmill in hot water, as opposed to batteries.) At that time, his heating bill was less than $30 per year! He has made some modifications since then and, as of 1992, his total electric bill for all energy costs was $50 a month. This included heat, light, cooling, hot water, running a freezer and so forth.

Jack collects his own water for household use. He has a plastic-lined, V-shaped pit, of about the same dimensions as the house, to collect rainwater. This pit has a cover. He has about 26,000 gallons stored. His total construction cost was between $17 and $18 a square foot, for a total cost of between $25,000 and $30,000. A view of this energy-efficient home is shown in Figure 5.11. If you are interested in this, he would be happy to answer any questions you might have about it. You can contact him at:

An Energy-Efficient Underground House

Styrofoam-backed doors are closed for the evening on Jack and Billie Strickler's "modern-day sod house" on Camano Island. The flat roofed home is banked with dirt on three sides for insulation, but the patio doors across the front let the sunshine in. When the sun gets thin, the inner sliding doors are closed to trap the warmth.

Figure 5.11

John F. Strickler   (206)652-2102
20420 Marine Drive, N.W., #22
Stanwood, WA 98292

Two older books that I would highly recommend in connection with heating are:

New Low-Cost Sources of Energy for the Home
By Peter Clegg
Published by Garden Way Publishing

Complete Book of Heating with Wood
By Larry Gay
Published by Garden Way Publishing

The first book is educational, as well as being a catalog of available equipment for solar, wind, water and wood power. Unfortunately, both are out of print, but they are available in some libraries.

While we are on the subject of heating the home, we should discuss the significant difference between an open fireplace and woodstove. An open fireplace, even with hot air conducting log supports, is still a very inefficient means of heating a home or even a room. You would utilize an enormous amount of wood in even attempting to do so and, even then, there is no guarantee that it would really do the job.

It is lovely to look at and to sit in front of a fireplace, but if one is going to use a fireplace for serious space heating, we would recommend a fireplace insert that sticks out at least 6 to 9 inches in front of the fireplace proper. Usually these fireplace inserts have a fan that will help conduct the heat out into the room. The glass door enables you to watch the fire through it, similar to watching a fire in an open (but heat-inefficient) fireplace.

Even better than a fireplace insert for heating a home by wood is a stand-alone woodstove. There are innumerable models of woodstoves. With some, in addition to heating your home, you can also do at least rudimentary cooking on them. Others are designed for room heating only. On any of these, you can get an upper hot air chamber that will fit onto the stove pipe that will give you additional surface area for heating the room. Regardless of what type of stove you get, you will want to get one that will combust all the fuel and the resulting gases as fully as possible. Chimney fires, and sometimes the destruction of homes that they can bring, are frequently caused by wood-burning devices that incompletely burn the wood and the resultant gases.

Whether you choose a fireplace insert or a woodstove, you want to be sure that it is installed by a certified woodstove installation expert.

Both the fireplace inserts and some woodstoves can come with glass fronts or glass doors on the front. If viewing the fire is highly desirable from your perspective, then these types of stoves can partially replace the warmth and glow of a fireplace, while providing you with efficient heat production.

THE SEPTIC SYSTEM

We will discuss the septic system, outhouses and trash disposal in Chapter 11. Suffice it to say here that you will need a septic system approval before you can get a building permit.

THE FLOOR PLAN LAYOUT

To actually discuss the details of a floor plan would require an entire book by itself, since the needs of each family differ widely. The floor plan will also vary depending on the site, the view, and whether or not you decide to build your house completely above ground or partially underground.

The main advice in this area is to let the floor plan follow the functions of the family, rather than trying to squeeze the family into some preexisting floor plan. For example, if the lady of the house spends a great deal of time in the kitchen and the family congregates in that area, then it should be a large, pleasant, well-lighted room. If one of the men of the house does a great deal of carpentry, then a workshop should possibly be included, either in the house or in an adjacent building. If the wife does a great deal of canning, then a pantry would be highly desirable. If you have small children, having a rumpus room might be important to you. Start off by writing down all the functions that you need, and then combine these into rooms to see how many rooms you really need. Then design your floor plan from that.

Now let us look at some specific things that you should consider when you are building your home, especially if you are going to be your own contractor and hire subcontractors to lay the cement, to do the framing, the plumbing, the electrical wiring, and so forth. Whether you are your own contractor or you hire a professional one, the following section addresses some specific considerations.

THE ACTUAL CONSTRUCTION

The first McKeever rule of construction is:

It will always take longer to complete the building and it will cost 20-30 percent more than you think!

I have never seen a building yet that did not take longer to construct than anticipated, so allow an extra month or so on your time schedule.

The next McKeever rule is:

Use 2 x 6's for studs.

If you are using stud construction, you can use 2 x 6's on 2-foot centers rather than 2 x 4's on 16-inch centers. The lumber cost is not that much more, yet your insulation will be 30 percent greater and the structure will be stronger.

Get A Building Permit

Be sure to get a building permit! Even if you are in an area where the need for building permits is questionable, the building permit is your friend. If the contractors or subcontractors do not do the proper job, the building inspector will make them tear it out and do it right. As an individual, you do not have that type of leverage over the subcontractors, so let the building inspectors do the dirty work for you.

Invariably, there will be changes to the construction as you go along. These take time and also cost extra money, so the better planning job you do at the beginning, the cheaper your construction will be and the faster it will proceed. So plan, plan, plan, plan ahead.

No Need to Finish Closets

It costs about $200 to finish the inside of a closet, including sheet rocking, taping and plastering, painting and so forth. Why finish the inside of a closet? It is easier to use if you leave the studs sticking out on the inside. You can build nice little shelves between the studs and you can also drive nails into them to hang things on. Isn't there someplace else you would rather spend $200 or $300 than on finishing the inside of a closet? If a typical house has four closets, then you could easily save at least $1,000.

Metal Roof

Consider using a metal roof. It is slightly more costly than a shake or asphalt roof, but it is there for a lifetime and will not need to be replaced or repaired. Plus it provides fire protection against forest fires and sparks from people's woodstoves landing on your roof.

The Root Cellar

If you include a root cellar as part of your floor plan, make the door to your root cellar a heavy metal door (some people who are extra security conscious have even used bank vault doors) to protect it from fire and intruders. Also consider having an alternative exit out of your root cellar (even ground squirrels have a back door to their holes).

For the root cellar, you will need at least a 1-foot thick cement roof. You need to shore up underneath this like you would in a mine. Along the walls you would nail 2 x 4's up under the lid (which is 1¼ inch tongue-and-groove plywood). Put vertical 2 x 4's underneath this at 2-foot intervals, with a 10-inch 2 x 4 plate under each vertical 2 x 4. Right down the center you would have a double 2 x 4 on edge, supported by double 2 x 4's with a 2 x 4 plate under these. The 1¼ inch plywood lid then will support the 1-foot thick cement that you will pour. If you wish to have an interesting ceiling in your root cellar, you can throw a few rocks and pebbles on the plywood, cover this with visqueen (plastic) and pour your cement on top of that. It creates a very striking texture in the cement.

After the cement dries, you can then use the 2 x 4 braces and the 1¼ inch plywood to build shelves and bins in your root cellar, and even beds and a kitchen counter, if desired.

If you are building an earth-berm or underground house, you will want to paint the outside of the cement walls with tar and then put on felt (like that used to cover the outside of a house over the plywood), starting at the bottom and overlapping it by at least 6 inches. Then place perforated drain pipe along the bottom of the walls and cover it 2 to 3 feet with drain field rock. Cover the drain field rock with a semipermeable cloth (called hardware cloth) that will let water down through it but not dirt, and then back-fill the rest with dirt. Of course, these perforated pipes need to drain out to an area away from the house, just as the rain gutters and downspouts do.

If you are going to cover the lid of the root cellar with dirt, you will want to have a slight slant on it and give it the same tar and felt treatment as described for the outside walls of an earth-berm house.

SUMMARY AND CONCLUSION

We have just hit the highlights on building your own home, whether in the city or on some rural property. We discussed site selection for the house, considering that it should be south facing, near a garden and barn area, and possibly defensible.

We looked at having dual voltage in your house, with both 110 volts and 12 volts. Regardless of the best laid plans of mice and men, there will be times when the 110 simply is not working. It is so nice to be able to have 12-volt lights in every room of the house. We discussed ways to recharge 12-volt batteries, as well as to generate the 110 voltage for your regular system.

We also considered having all or a portion of the house covered by dirt for help in heating and cooling and also defensibility.

We touched briefly upon having a root cellar which could also be utilized as a fallout shelter. This is desirable, even if you think there will never be a nuclear exchange, simply for the storage of the root vegetables through the winter.

The main portion of the house which we have not discussed is the greenhouse. That is such a large subject on its own that it will be the topic of the next chapter. With a greenhouse, you can grow your vegetables year round, have no weed problems, and it can all be run by automatic timers and thermostats. It is one of the least labor-intensive ways to grow fresh, wholesome vegetables and fruits year round.

Chapter 6

THE WONDERFUL GREENHOUSE

A greenhouse can be utilized in either the country or the city. Thus, the information in this chapter would apply equally to those who intend to remain in the city and those who intend to move to a smaller, rural town.

A greenhouse is not essential to self-reliant living. By and large, most of our forefathers did not have greenhouses. However, they raised enough food from their gardens, fields and the animals during the summer season (or growing season) so that it would last them through the entire winter. Then they spent a great deal of time canning, smoking and preserving in other ways, the abundance of the harvest, so that they would be able to enjoy it until the next harvest. (It is interesting to note, however, that George Washington and Thomas Jefferson had elaborate greenhouses and root cellars.)

One thing the majority of our forefathers did *not* have during the winter was fresh, salad-type vegetables. They had fresh root vegetables, such as carrots, beets, potatoes, since these could be successfully stored in a root cellar after harvest, but they did not have fresh lettuce, tomatoes, bell peppers, and things of this nature.

This is where a greenhouse comes in. A greenhouse can provide you with an abundance of salad fixings and other vegetables (such as green beans and cucumbers) all year long. You may wish to shut your greenhouse down for a month or so in the summer when your garden is in full production, but for the remainder of the year, it can provide you with your own ever-ready salad bar!

Another advantage of a greenhouse is that it is weed free! Weed seeds simply do not blow into the enclosed glass structure. Thus, you do not have the weeding problem you have in a garden. The plants are also protected from deer, raccoons and other wildlife, which is a decided advantage.

Still another advantage is that the vegetables can be grown on tables that are approximately 2 feet high. If you set up your greenhouse in this fashion, then you will be picking beans and tomatoes at waist height, rather than having to squat down or kneel down in order to pick your produce.

If a plague of something like locusts ever came over the land and devoured all outside gardens, a productive greenhouse could be a very valuable thing to have, since the locusts would not be able to get into your greenhouse and you could retain that food productive area even in the midst of such a plague.

One thing that I have found is that the greenhouse is a very therapeutic place to be. It is nice after a hard day's work to go out there and spend a few quiet minutes examining the plants, picking a few vegetables and perhaps seeing how the new seedlings are coming. It is very relaxing and brings one back close in touch with the soil.

THE LOCATION OF THE GREENHOUSE

Wherever the greenhouse is located on your property, you will want the longest side of it to face due south, so that it can take full advantage of the winter sun which comes from that direction. (We are writing this book for the northern hemisphere, so our friends in South America, New Zealand, Australia and Africa will have to reverse all such directions.)

Since heating and cooling the greenhouse is a major consideration, which we will discuss next, the ideal would be to have the long side of the back of your house facing south and, then to build the greenhouse, in a sense, like a shed roof area coming off the back of the house. The ends of the greenhouse should be solid with glass louvered windows. Along the southern, lower edge of the greenhouse, you would want to have some material that would retain heat through the night. We will discuss the reason for this when we discuss heating the greenhouse.

A simple diagram of a greenhouse built onto the backside and the south side of a structure is shown in Figure 6.1.   Later in the chapter, we will enhance this

Greenhouse on South Side

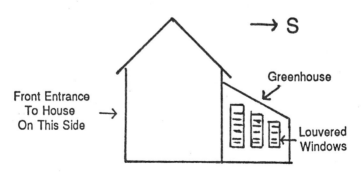

Figure 6.1

diagram to point out other things, but for now we want to give you a simple idea of what we are suggesting.

I realize that some site locations simply do not allow for this type of greenhouse, since the front of the house faces south. Individual decisions must be made, but it is possible to put the greenhouse across half of the front of the house, or on either end, using the end of the house as one end of the greenhouse and building a solid back. This does not require much more construction material than having the greenhouse on the back of the house on the south side, but it is harder to heat, since there would be less of the house adjacent to the greenhouse.

Others may decide to have a free-standing greenhouse. I would caution against greenhouses that come in a kit and are glass or plastic all around. These are very difficult to heat in the winter. If you build a free-standing greenhouse, you are going to want to take the same type of approach as described above, having the sides or ends solid with windows, the back solid, and something on the lower south side to collect heat. Building a free-standing greenhouse is much more expensive in construction material and it also requires more energy to keep it hot in the winter. With that said, let us move on to discuss the heating and cooling of the greenhouse specifically.

HEATING AND COOLING
THE GREENHOUSE

Many books address the topic of heating the greenhouse. And that is, indeed, an important subject. However, I feel that it is just as important to be concerned about cooling the greenhouse during the summer, if you expect your plants to survive and not fry in the hot summer weather. Both the heating *and* cooling should be considered at the time the greenhouse is constructed.

Hopefully, the primary way that your greenhouse will be heated is by solar heat. However, it is possible that auxiliary types of heat may be required. Let us discuss solar heating first.

What is needed for solar heating is to have the back wall of the greenhouse (which is solid) made of some kind of material that will absorb and retain the sun's heat and then release it all night long. Brick is an excellent medium for this. Cement tends to be a very poor medium. If you use cement, be sure to paint it black. Ugh! What a terrible color! But you would need to do so to help that wall absorb the solar heat.

Along the front edge of the greenhouse, you could place some metal 50-gallon barrels filled with water and painted black and put lids on them. A row of these right next to the glass on the south side on the floor would serve to collect heat all day long and then give it off during the evening. This is shown in Figure 6.2.

Barrels To Collect Heat

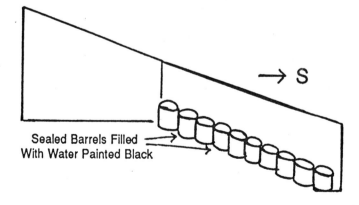

Figure 6.2

Obviously, if you had a ten-day snowstorm, your solar heating is going to go out the window (or not come in the window, as the case may be). Therefore, you will need to have some auxiliary source of heat, either small electric heaters or small propane heaters. The advantage of the electric heaters is that they usually have their own thermostats on them. Or you can have a special thermostat that will control anything that you plug into a particular socket. The type of these thermostats recommended is found in Appendix B. This type of thermostat can not only control heating devices, but also cooling devices, such as a swamp cooler or a water cooler.

There are other potential sources of heat for a greenhouse, which we will discuss later—such as using rabbits, a jacuzzi or a hot tub—but for now we will leave the heating side of the temperature-maintenance equation and turn to the cooling side.

As we have said, one thing we strongly recommend is to have each end of the greenhouse (the solid ends) fitted with louvered windows with outside storm shutters and, if necessary, inside wooden shutters (see Figure 6.3). In the summer, these windows can be opened on each end. When you do that, it can be like a wind tunnel coming through the greenhouse, which can certainly help in the exhausting of excess heat during hot summer months. A picture of us in our greenhouse is shown on the front cover. You can see one of the louvered windows behind us.

Another highly effective feature to include in a greenhouse is a roof opening that is controlled by a thermostat. When the temperature gets too hot, sections of the roof about 9 inches wide by 2 or 3 feet act as vents that automatically open up and let the hot air out.

Louvered Windows

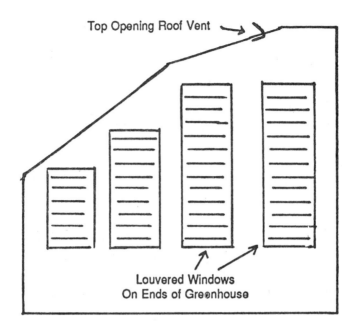

Figure 6.3

During the summer, you would want to remove the black barrels, because you will not want that extra heat absorption; adequate cooling is more of a consideration in the summer. As an alternative to barrels, you can take 4-inch sewer pipe, which is black, put a cap on one end, fill it with water, glue a cap on the other end, and have stacks of these along the south side of the greenhouse. They work just like the black barrels for absorbing solar heat. But whatever you are using as solar collectors during the winter, be sure that those are removed when the heat of summer comes.

A MULTIPURPOSE GREENHOUSE

An interesting possibility presents itself in designing your greenhouse. You can elect to provide an area on the upper level where you can have a ping-pong table or do exercises or dancing. Exercise equipment, such as a stationary bicycle, weights or a Nordic Track, could even be set up there for your convenience in inclement weather. In the winter when it is raining or snowing outside, this is a wonderful place to go and spend some time close to nature, while still remaining warm and cozy indoors. This option allows the greenhouse to be an enjoyable recreation area, as well as a productive source of food.

If your greenhouse is big enough, you can also have a jacuzzi or hot tub in part of the greenhouse. When we built our greenhouse, we ran copper pipes from the jacuzzi at a distance of 1 foot apart all through the cement floor of the greenhouse and then back to the jacuzzi heater, so that whenever the jacuzzi is on, we have 102 degree F water flowing through the floor. This makes it nice and toasty warm and helps with the heating all night long. Plus, when the jacuzzi timer shuts off, we have 800 gallons of 102-degrees-F-temperature water that acts like a huge heat source all night long. It also increases the humidity, which the plants like.

Of course, if you are going to do something like this, the copper pipes have to be laid into the floor at the time the cement slab is poured. You will also want to put insulation underneath these pipes, so that the heat does not go down into the ground but up into the cement slab. A plan or top view of a multipurpose greenhouse is shown in Figure 6.4.

A Multipurpose Greenhouse

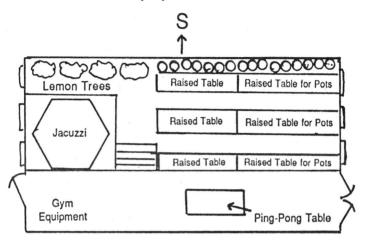

Figure 6.4

Believe me, a jacuzzi or hot tub is a welcome addition to any greenhouse. Even if you can not afford one initially, designing your greenhouse with space allowed for a hot tub, and the copper pipes in the slab, will allow you the option of adding one when it fits into your budget. In Appendix B, we give a source for hot tubs that are heated by wood rather than propane or electricity. Not only does it help to heat the place, but it is fun to sit in the jacuzzi and see snow falling on the glass roof of the greenhouse while you are all cozy and warm.

By including an area where you can play ping-pong, exercise, dance, sit and visit or enjoy some other form of recreation of your choice, then you have really made the greenhouse not only a food factory, but a fun, multi-purpose area that the entire family will enjoy.

THE GREENHOUSE
CAN HELP HEAT YOUR HOME

If proper forethought is given, you can utilize your greenhouse, especially during the fall and springtime, to help heat your house. Between the house and the greenhouse, you would want to have a series of low vents through which the cold air from the house could flow down into the greenhouse by convection. Then you would want to have a number of high vents where the hot air from the greenhouse would flow back into the home by natural convection. During the winter and the summer, these vents can be stopped up with foam rubber and an attractive wooden covering.

Natural Convection Vents

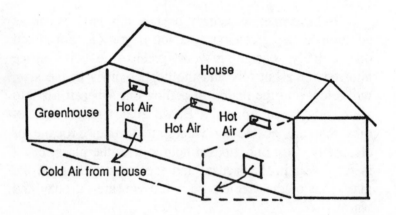

Figure 6.5

In our home, we have two lower vents approximately 2-feet square going out into the greenhouse, and we have four upper vents approximately 9 inches by 18 inches that bring the warm air back into the house. This makes use of the same principles we discussed in the last chapter when we talked about vents for natural air conditioning. These high and low vents between the house and the greenhouse can be seen in Figure 6.5.

RABBITS, FISH AND VEGETABLES

Normally we think of a greenhouse as only furnishing vegetables for us, and possibly some fruits. Indeed, it does an excellent job of this. However, you can make your greenhouse more of a complete ecosystem in a number of ways.

One way is to use rabbits. Rabbits produce an enormous amount of heat. The rabbit cages can be located either inside the greenhouse or around the outside, possibly with some vents into the greenhouse.

Also, the rabbit pellets could be used for fertilizing the greenhouse plants and the excess vegetation in the greenhouse, such as tomato leaves, overgrown parsley or cabbage leaves and so forth, could be used to feed the rabbits. Thus, you would have a complete ecological cycle.

A very similar thing could be done with fish, if you have an adequate flow of fresh water that can continuously flow into and out of the fish tank. Fish would also eat the excess vegetation, as you place it into their water, and fish droppings can be used for fertilizer. A diagram of one combination is shown in Figure 2.4 in Chapter 2.

Again we must emphasize that if you are planning to add fish or rabbits to make a complete ecological cycle in your greenhouse, this needs to be given some forethought before you begin to design and construct your fun and productive greenhouse.

HYDROPONIC SYSTEMS

There are some greenhouses that use soil as a medium of planting, although this is getting progressively more rare with the development of the outstanding method of managing a greenhouse with hydroponics. A hydroponic system is one in which the plants are planted into a sterile medium. The sterile medium could be anything from washed pea gravel to finely broken up phonograph records, or any inert substance that could support the root systems of the plants. However, the best planting mix that we have found is one-third vermiculite, one-third perlite, and one-third peat moss.

Water which contains all the needed nutrients is flushed onto the plants several times a day, bringing with it everything the plants need to grow. This water is subsequently drained off so that the roots can get air, which they also need.

There are two primary types of hydroponic systems that we have used which are typical of the primary hydroponic systems in general. The first system is to have beds filled with pea gravel into which the plants or seedlings are planted. These beds are flooded twice a day with the nutrient solution which then drains back into holding tanks for recycling back onto the plants at a later time. We used this system for several years successfully, but it had several major disadvantages, from our perspective. First, it was just about impossible to move plants from one bed to another, which, believe me, you will want to do in a greenhouse. The other was that the holding tanks for the nutrient solution would tend to get contaminated with algae and so on. In general, it was just messy.

The system that we now utilize and prefer uses the planting mix that we described above, which is placed into pots (the black, heavy plastic pots like a nursery uses) of various sizes (see Figure 6.6). (We primarily use pots that are 10 and 12 inch in diameter.) The nutrient-laden water is pumped into them twice a day during the winter and four times a day during the heat of summer. Any excess water simply drains out the holes in the bottom of the pots and runs out the floor drain in the greenhouse. By using these individual pots, it is easy to move plants around at will, and it eliminates much of the mess and difficulties we had with the other system.

With our current system, we have a large, approximately 300-gallon holding tank of water into which we add the nutrients. The water is pumped out by sump pump through half-inch PVC pipes which later feed into half-inch black irrigation pipes. These black pipes are punctured at desired intervals and tiny black feeder hoses are placed in the holes and thus come off of each main line and into each individual pot. We have been very happy with this system and do not hesitate to recommend it.

The automation of your greenhouse watering, made possible with a good timer, is a great time-saver and certainly reduces greenhouse care to a minimum. It also allows you to take vacations without worrying about your greenhouse getting watered. You will need a special timer that allows you to run your pump for a few minutes or seconds (*B).

We water our greenhouse plants 29 seconds from two to four times a day. By manually turning on the water about once a week, we can check to see if any hoses are stopped up or if any feeder hoses have come out of the pots and need to be reinserted. Frequently, simply

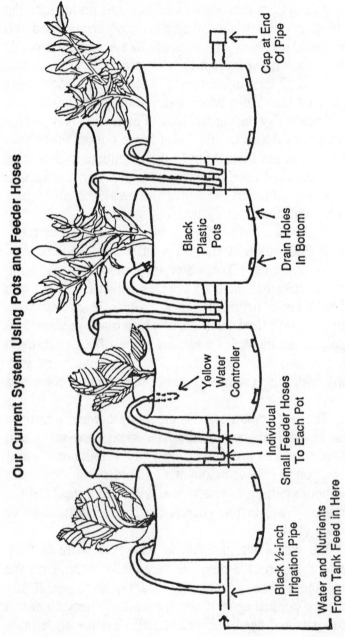

Our Current System Using Pots and Feeder Hoses

Cap at End Of Pipe

Black Plastic Pots

Drain Holes In Bottom

Yellow Water Controller

Individual Small Feeder Hoses To Each Pot

Black ½-inch Irrigation Pipe

Water and Nutrients From Tank Feed in Here

Figure 6.6

pulling off the yellow water regulator, which is at the end of each feeder hose, and putting it back on will unclog a plugged pipe. These yellow plastic waterers on the end of each hose can be set on one of four possible options to allow the desired amount of water into the pot, as this varies depending on what you have planted. If one pot is not in use, the center position allows you to shut off the flow from the feeder hose going to that pot.

The type of nutrients that we recommend and the timer and plumbing system that we use are described in Appendix B (*B), with appropriate addresses given there.

WHAT TO PLANT AND WHERE

Let us start with the question of "where" to plant. You will want to have your shorter vegetables, such as lettuce, cabbage, and chives (all short plants) on the southern-most side of the greenhouse. In the middle, you will want the medium-height plants, such as bell peppers and parsley. Then near the northern wall, you will want the tall, running plants, such as tomato vines, climbing cucumbers, climbing green beans, and so forth.

By planting the shortest ones to the south and the tallest ones to the north, the sun can adequately get to every plant. If you did the opposite, the tall plants would shade the shorter plants and prevent them from getting the optimum amount of sun.

In your garden, plants put out roots looking for nutrients, whereas in a hydroponic greenhouse you are bringing all of the needed nutrients to the plants. Therefore, a huge tomato vine in a greenhouse may have only a small ball of roots, as opposed to the extensive root system that the same plant would develop outdoors in a garden. You need to realize this, because root vegetables consequently do not do well in a greenhouse. In a hydroponic greenhouse, if you plant carrots, beets, and turnips, you will get huge, gorgeous green leafy tops and little bitty carrots, beets or turnips, so avoid root vegetables when planting your greenhouse, unless you are using soil as a planting medium.

To some degree, which of the above-ground vegetables you do plant will depend on your own taste and preferences, as well as the actual available amount of sunlight in your location. We have already mentioned some of the vegetables that generally do well in a greenhouse environment. In our greenhouse, we also have five dwarf lemon trees which produce huge, thin-skinned, extremely-juicy lemons year round. This is something you may or may not want to consider adding, depending on your tastes.

One thing we discovered that does *not* do well in a greenhouse is corn. It simply does not develop the way it should, because it just does not get enough hours of sun per day during the winter.

As long as we are on this subject, you need to be aware of something concerning tomatoes. Tomatoes out in the garden will naturally fertilize themselves, as the wind blows the pollen from the blossoms around. However, in your greenhouse, you do not have any wind. Some commercial greenhouses have people who daily go along with small vibrators grabbing hold of each plant; the shaking provides the opportunity for pollination to occur. We have found that an easier and superior method is to use a leaf blower, like the type you use out on your lawn, and to turn this on each of the tomato plants two or three times a week so that they will fertilize themselves.

Lemon trees are a different matter. They need bees to fertilize them. Even a leaf blower will not help.

Therefore, we take a very small artist's paint brush to go around and dab each blossom, moving the pollen from the male blossoms to the female blossoms, and back and forth. This fertilizes the lemon blossoms. (If you ever wondered what it feels like to be a honey bee, this is your chance to find out!) Most of the rest of the vegetables take care of their own fertilization and you do not have to be concerned about it.

A sample layout of a typical greenhouse planting arrangement is shown in Figure 6.7.

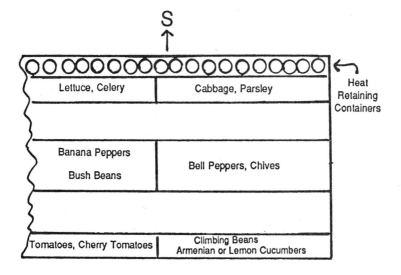

Figure 6.7

Humans give off carbon dioxide as we breathe, which would kill us if we remained in a small enclosed space with no air circulation. Plants give off oxygen, and it would kill them if it stayed around the plants, so you must provide air circulation. Even in the winter, we run the exhaust fans four to six hours a day.

Summarizing hydroponic greenhouse planting is easy. Avoid root plants and plant foods that you like. The only other thing to remember is to plant the short plants to the south and the tall plants to the north. Then enjoy watching your plants thrive in their ideal greenhouse setting.

However, there is one thing that you do need to be aware of and give some attention to, and that is pest control.

PEST CONTROL IN THE GREENHOUSE

By far the biggest problem in a greenhouse is control of pests, such as aphids, white flies, spider mites and so forth. Out in your garden, there are natural predators that eat these pests and keep them under control. I do not know how in the world they get into the greenhouse in the first place, or how they maintain their life there, because we cut down all of the greenhouse plants once a year and fumigate the place, but these little pests still reappear and persist in being a periodic nuisance.

There are two approaches that you can take to pest control, and we have found neither one to be totally successful. The first one is to use natural predators. You can buy ladybugs which will eat aphids and not harm your plants, but we have not had any luck in getting the ladybugs to reproduce themselves, and so we would have to keep reintroducing ladybugs every month, if we wanted them to continue to control the aphids. Other kinds of natural predators are required to take care of some of the other potential pests, such as white flies and spider mites.

If you choose to go the route of using natural predators to control the pests, then you can *never* spray. If you do, you will kill the good predators along with the pests. And if you see one species of pests beginning to get out of hand, you will have to hurry to get predator insects that will control them. This is a very valid approach to controlling greenhouse pests; you just need to realize what is involved.

The other approach is with sprays. We are not talking about the bad sprays that environmentalists are against. Basically, you can spray with liquid soap and water. The soap gets on the pests and dries them out and causes them to die. However, most garden shops have an insecticidal soap which has a tiny bit of insecticide along with the soapy mixture which seems to do the job even better. This can be placed in a specially-designed plastic spray container that you screw to your garden hose in the greenhouse. When you depress the lever, it automatically mixes the water with the designated amount of soap to spray on your plants.

If you go this route, in the winter you can probably spray just once or maybe twice a week. It is during the winter that these pests have a slow growing season. However, they thrive in hot, dry weather. The extra moisture and humidity from spraying also serves to clog up the pores of spider mites, which love a dry, hot greenhouse, and therefore helps to keep them in check. When the weather turns hot, you may find yourself spraying every other day or—in some cases, if you have a string of very hot, sunny days—possibly even daily.

These pests all tend to hide on the under side of the leaves, so a normal spraying operation from above does not take care of them. You have to get the nozzle down underneath, so that the bottoms of the leaves are hit with the spray. Some sprayers have an adjustable mouthpiece that you can set specifically for spraying under the leaves.

Pest control is the biggest negative to a greenhouse, but from our experience, the effort required to control the pests is well worth it, when you realize all of the benefits and enjoy eating delicious, fresh, home-grown vegetables all winter long.

PLANTING BEDS OR TABLES

If you are going to use planting beds filled with pea gravel or some other inert substance, you will want to have them a minimum of 6 inches deep, but preferably closer to 9 inches. In building them, if you use 1 x 10 wood for the sides, 1/2-inch or 3/4-inch plywood for the bottom supported by 2 x 4's on edge underneath the plywood, you will have sturdy beds. These would normally be raised approximately 2 feet off of the floor. If one bed overflows into another, the second bed would be slightly lower, with an overflow pipe connecting the two beds together, and the lower bed would drain into the nutrient-water holding tank below. A pump would pump the water into the upper bed for fifteen minutes twice a day. As we said earlier, this is the system we used at first. A diagram of this is shown in Figure 6.8.

If you use the system that we are using currently where the plants are placed in pots, buckets or bags, you have two basic choices. One choice is to have these pots sitting on a cement floor so that the excess runs down the

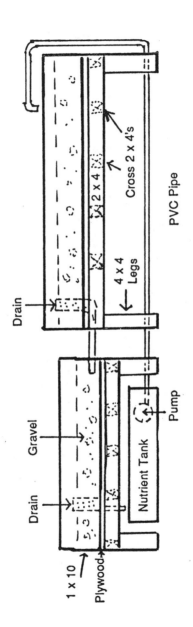

**Hydroponic Planting Beds
And Nutrient Tank**

Figure 6.8

cement into a central floor drain. Or the floor could be of
rounded river rock, so that the nutrient water that drips out
of the bottoms of the buckets or bags would sink into the
soil below the river rock.

However, it is easier if these plants are raised about
two feet off the ground for ease in maintenance, trimming,
and harvesting the fruit and vegetables. We have ex-
perimented with various types of tables and have found
none of them to be totally satisfactory. However, we will
give you the best of our experience and wisdom, and let
you do your own experimenting from there. The trouble
with raised tables is that the plants shed leaves and other
biological material on the tables that is then difficult to
sweep or wash away with a hose.

We tried flat tables made with 4 x 4 legs and 3/4-
inch plywood to form the top of the table, on which the
plants set, which was supported by 2 x 4's on edge. This
was unsatisfactory because the water that dripped out of
the bottom of the pots ran in all directions.

We then tried slanting the plywood table tops so that
the water would run off on the side nearest the floor drain
and we could, to some degree, wash the leaves in the
direction of the slant. This was far better than the flat
beds, but it still left much to be desired, because the water
would begin to grow algae on the plywood, and it would
be messy and difficult to work with.

We have now gone to having 1 x 2 slats on 6-inch
centers over the 2 x 4 frame for our greenhouse plant
tables. This works better than the plain plywood top, but
the leaves of the plants still get looped over the 1 x 2 slats
and they tend to stay there, even with hosing, until they
dry and fall apart. Even with this small disadvantage,
these tables with 1 x 2 slats are by far the best method
that we have seen or used. The slats are turned on edge,

as can be seen in Figure 6.9. Having the plants raised off the floor in this fashion certainly does make it easier to work with them.

Slatted Greenhouse Plant Tables

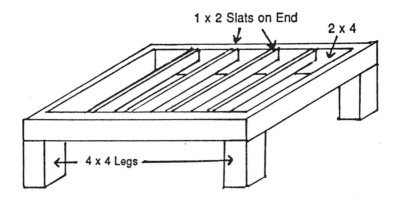

Figure 6.9

ROTATION OF PLANTS

Unlike the garden, where you tend to plant most everything at once, in the greenhouse you can have a regular rotation of the plants. For example, you can plant a couple of tomato vines now, a couple more in three or four weeks, and so on. If you have six pots of tomato plants, for example, then these would be in continual rotation, so that at all times you would have at least one or two plants producing ripe, luscious tomatoes.

It is not advisable to plant the seeds directly in the pots or directly in the pea gravel, if you are using that type of bed. You need to start the plants outside of these pots or beds and then after they are about 3 inches tall, transplant the young plants into the pots or beds.

We have used a number of methods for starting seeds. We have used the peat moss balls that come as flat disks, which when soaked in water, expand to a round seedling starter the shape of a large marshmallow about 1½ inches high and covered by a netting to hold the soil and roots together. The cheapest and easiest thing that we have found is to utilize the four-place, light-plastic planting trays that are available at most seed stores. We use regular potting soil or plant starting mix in them, poke a hole the appropriate depth in the center of each one with a chopstick, and then plant the seeds in these.

One of the things that the seeds need in order to begin to germinate and to grow is warmth underneath them. If you place them on an electric blanket or on the deck of a jacuzzi, they will sprout much faster. Then after the seedlings come up, they need to be thinned out. We plant approximately three seeds per square, to help ensure successful germination. We will cut off the two weakest-looking seedlings and leave the strongest one and allow it to grow and flourish.

Ideally, a greenhouse would have seeds in some degree of sprouting almost continuously. What we said about staggering your planting of tomatoes would apply to bell peppers, lettuce, cabbage, herbs, and other plants as well, so that you would always have a continuous supply of new plants. It is a difficult thing when you first plant to only plant 25 percent of the greenhouse. There is a tendency to want to "fill up all the pots." But resist the temptation, and a few weeks later plant 25 percent more.

Then a few weeks later, plant some more, such that it is at 75 percent of capacity. Then a few weeks later, you will fill up the rest of the pots. Shortly after that, the first plants that you planted will be ready for harvest. In this manner, you will utilize the prime production and these older plants will be ready to be replaced by new plants once again.

There is one exception to this continual rotation principle if you do what we do. Every August, when our garden is in full production, we take out all of the plants, except the lemon trees, and we fumigate the greenhouse with bug bombs to try to kill all of the bugs. We then fumigate once more five days later to catch any of the eggs that have hatched in-between time. Then, in August, we begin our replanting of new seedlings (for the first 25 percent of the greenhouse). In that way, those initial plants will be ready to start producing just as our garden is finishing up and giving us its last produce in September or October. You may or may not want to do this annual changeover. Again, it is part of the rotation of plants.

WHERE TO BUY
READY-MADE GREENHOUSES

You can buy glass, preferably glass with two or three layers (thermopane glass), put up wooden rafters, attach the glass to it, and build your own greenhouse. But if you do this, the biggest problem will be at the places where the two pieces of glass overlap. You can take care of this simply by sliding the lower piece of glass about 1 foot up under the upper piece (giving a 1-foot overlap). The water coming down on the roof would then run from the upper piece onto the lower piece, and there would not be enough capillary action to cause the water to run up.

Then you would just have to be sure to seal the areas where the glass meets on the sides. We built our first greenhouse this way.

To some people, this is too much of a challenge. It was for us, on our second greenhouse. This time, we bought a prefabricated greenhouse, with which we are very happy. The addresses and recommended companies for greenhouses are given in *B. When you finish reading this book, you can turn to that appendix and send off for their catalogs, which they will be most happy to send to you.

SUMMARY AND CONCLUSION

As we pointed out at the beginning of this chapter, a greenhouse is not essential to self-reliant living. Our forefathers lived without them. However, they also produced an abundant harvest each year and took a great deal of time in preserving it, so it would last all winter and spring, until the next harvest.

Yet there are some wonderful benefits of having a greenhouse. In December and January when there is snow on the ground, imagine eating big, juicy, luscious red tomatoes so delicious that you do not even need to use salt on them, while everyone else is using pale, pink "tomatoes" that they buy at the supermarket. Think of how nice it would be to be able to go into your greenhouse and pick lettuce and cabbage for a tasty fresh salad, and perhaps a few sprigs of parsley to garnish the plates or to include in a salad. A greenhouse can provide you with tasty, fresh salads all winter long, as well as a continual harvest of green beans, peppers of various kinds, cucumbers and other fresh foods. The benefits are well worth the effort!

The greenhouse can be run almost automatically. The thermostats can control the heating and cooling of your greenhouse. The timers can control when the nutrient water (water into which you have added all the nutrients the plants need) is pumped onto the plants and how long the pump will be on. With the temperature control and the feeding of the plants automated, you could go away for a week or two or longer, and your greenhouse would continue. The only thing that would require some human intervention, if you do not use natural pest control, would be someone to spray the plants with soap and water as needed, depending on the time of year.

We have discussed the need for the greenhouse to be facing south. You can utilize solar energy for much of the heating of it, but when you have a series of rainy or snowy days, then you must have an auxiliary source of heat, such as a small electrical heater or a small propane heater. We also talked about using rabbits for heat, or a jacuzzi as a heating source.

Cooling a greenhouse is just as important as heating it. A thermostatically-controlled opening in the roof is one highly-recommended method for cooling, along with the use of louvered windows at each end of the greenhouse.

As we turn from the consideration of a simple greenhouse to a more complex one, we have seen that we potentially could include everything from a ping-pong table, to an exercise area, to a jacuzzi in the greenhouse, making it a fun recreational area for the entire family, as well as being a useful and productive food factory. We could even have a complete ecological cycle, utilizing rabbits or fish.

We discussed the advantage of hydroponic growing, where the plants take the nutrients from the water-nutrient mix being pumped to them, rather than trying to get their nutrients from a bag or bucket of soil. With a hydroponic system, you can bring to them a perfect nutrient mix, whereas with soil, you will frequently have various types of deficiencies. You are going to have to pump water to the buckets of soil anyway. Why not add the nutrients to the water while you are at it and make life easier for both the plants and yourself?

Personally, I would not want to have a greenhouse that was not hydroponically run. With hydroponics, everything can so easily be put on timers, so that you can go away for a week and come back to find the greenhouse still in good shape. However, you could also put the watering on timers in a soil-based greenhouse to minimize care.

We discussed not planting root vegetables, such as carrots and beets, and planting the short plants to the south and the tall plants to the north.

The big problem with a greenhouse is pest control. We saw that natural predators, such as ladybugs, can be used or you can control the pests with a soap spray.

The effort put into a greenhouse will richly reward you with better health from eating fresh vegetables year round and having a sanctuary where you can go and just relax after a hard day's work. It is very therapeutic, similar to being in an outside garden.

Let's now put on our old clothes and walk down to the garden together, another important facet of self-reliant living.

Chapter 7

GARDENING AND PRESERVING

There are many elements that go into making up a good garden: the soil, good seeds, adequate water, sunshine and air. Most people do not think of all these elements when they go to plan and plant their garden, but they are all important and each one needs to be considered.

For example, there are various types of soil, and sometimes a certain type of soil is better for some plants than for others. There are many different ways to water a garden, from overhead sprinklers, to drip irrigation systems, to subsurface watering, and each of these has advantages and disadvantages.

Let us begin our discussion of a garden by first considering its location.

THE LOCATION OF YOUR GARDEN

If you are a city dweller and have a normal-size lot, the location of your garden has probably already been predetermined for you. It is most likely all or part of your backyard. On the other hand, if you have just purchased a piece of property in a more rural setting, then you have a number of choices as to where you could locate your garden. Of course you would want to locate it where the soil is the richest. As a general rule of thumb, the darker the soil, the richer it will be, so it would be a good idea to dig around a few places on your property to find where the soil is the darkest. Normally, this would be in more of a river bottom area or on the lower portion of your property.

Since sun is important to your garden, in selecting the site, you would also want to consider how sunny the location is. For example, if there is a row of tall trees running north and south, and you have the option of planting a garden either to the east of these or to the west, you would want to plant your garden on the west side of these trees, so that it would get the full afternoon sun.

In addition, you would want to have your garden located in a place with good drainage, so that if there were a sudden, intense rainstorm, the excess water would be drained off.

Once you have decided where your garden is to be located, you need to spend a little time investigating the most important element in your garden itself, which is the soil.

TESTING AND PREPARING THE SOIL

You can take a sample of your soil to the agricultural extension of a university or of the state in which you live, and usually they will test it for free. They will let you know if it is missing any of the significant elements of good soil. If your soil is lacking something, they could give you some guidance as to how you could remedy the deficiency. It may mean sprinkling calcium potash on the ground before you plow it up.

Speaking of plowing your garden, if you are looking at virgin ground that has never before been plowed, then in most parts of the country, you need to be prepared for rocks—little, big, and large ROCKS.

Here at Living Waters Ranch, when we first plowed up our garden, which had previously been a pasture, we had to carry out lots of big rocks, some of which were about a foot in diameter, as they were unearthed by the rototiller. Gradually through the years, the size of the rocks fortunately has diminished, yet we still have a certain number of rocks to get rid of each year that the plowing turns up.

Also, the very first time you plow up virgin ground, you are going to want to go over it, and over it and over it. It is advisable to plow it in one direction and then to replow it in a direction 90 degrees different from the original plowing. Any of the clumps of grass should wind up finely pulverized before you consider it ready for planting.

If time is available, spreading black visqueen over the garden site and leaving it down three to six months will "sterilize" the area and kill grass, weeds and seeds. Water it well first, then cover it.

Another alternative for killing the grass and the weeds that may currently exist in your desired garden spot is the use of a chemical solution called "Round Up." This kills the vegetation that it encounters but it does absolutely nothing to the soil. If you use this, it should be applied at least one week before the plowing, and there should be no rainy days in between. If we were to start a garden over again from unplowed ground, we would certainly use Round Up, but we did not know about it back in the days when we first plowed our garden area.

Once you have a freshly-plowed garden—whether you achieve this with a tractor in the country, a rototiller in the city, or you turn it over by spade for a small garden—freshly-turned soil smells beautiful, looks nice, and is ready to be planted with the seeds.

SELECTING THE SEEDS

You can go to a local store, such as a Grange Co-op, and buy your seeds. However, these will all be hybrid seeds. Let me explain what "hybrid" means. Suppose you plant hybrid cantaloupe seeds, for example, and they produce large, delicious cantaloupes, so you decide to save the seeds out of those tasty cantaloupes to plant the following year. If you do so, you will probably wind up with baseball-sized cantaloupes that next year. Hybrid seeds were designed to produce well for just one season. They will not reproduce themselves in the same deluxe fashion as that first crop.

Those who want to become truly self-reliant are now returning to using seeds that are not hybrid. The original fruit or vegetable is not quite as big as the hybrid fruits and vegetables to which we have grown accustomed, but you can use the seeds from your produce year after year to produce the same quality of fruits and vegetables. By growing non-hybrid, open-pollinated vegetables, the seeds produced are a little better acclimated, more resistant to disease and local bugs, and they get stronger year by year.

There are some major and potentially-disastrous things happening in the world of vegetable seeds, the kind of seeds that most people buy in the spring to plant their gardens. The first major area of concern is that a number of large conglomerates are buying up all of the seed companies. Thomas J. Porter, Jr. reported the following:

The seed business is a growing concern, but the number of old-time, family-owned seed houses is declining.

Recently, nationally known seed companies such as Burpee, Ferry-Morris and Northrup-King have been purchased by conglomerates and multinational corporations.

Giants such as International Telephone and Telegraph, Atlantic Richfield, Celanese, Upjohn, Purex, Sandoz and a growing list of other large firms are jumping into the seed market.

Most recently, Amfac, a multibillion dollar sugar, food and hotel conglomerate based in Honolulu, purchased the Gurney and Henry Fields seed companies.

—*Pittsburgh Post-Gazette*
(date unknown)

If the control of the seed business came into a few hands, in many ways, those people could control the food production of the world.

Your response might be, "That doesn't bother me. I will just save my own seeds." Unfortunately, that will not work. As we said, almost all of the seeds produced by the seed companies are hybrid seeds. That is, they have taken two or more generic seeds and interbred them. These hybrids produce either sterile seeds or seeds that will revert back to one of the original strains or worse. The example given earlier about cantaloupes is from our own experience. One year we had a cantaloupe that we had purchased in the store which was especially large, sweet and lush, so we saved the seeds from it. We dried these and planted them, but they produced little bitty cantaloupes about the size of apples! This is typical of what you can expect with second-generation hybrid seeds.

Another problem with these hybrid seeds is that they are not resistant to disease and insects, as were the generic (also called "heirloom") seeds and varieties of vegetables. Tom Minehart had this to say about the problem:

> Raleigh, N.C.— Famines are "inevitable" in the next few decades because variety has been bred out of seeds for the world's major food crops, scientists at North Carolina State University say.
>
> "It's beyond quick fixes," says Gene Namkoong, professor of genetics and forestry. "Once you lose your genetic base, you can't recapture it. Major famines are inevitable—even with zero population growth—within 50 years."
>
> The problem is "genetic wipeout," says Major Goodman, professor of statistical genetics. Extinction of hundreds of grain varieties and the loss of their inherited traits has made major crop failures certain, he says.
>
> But the threat could be reduced if scientists act now to save varieties that still exist, he says.
>
> The U.S. Department of Agriculture's top researcher dealing with the issue says the scientists' assessment is "over-exaggerated."
>
> "There are areas in the world where the germ plasm of crop plants is endangered in terms of genetic diversity," says Dr. Quentin Jones, of the department's Agricultural Research Service. "But we have a lot of germ plasm in gene banks now."
>
> Germ plasm is the living matter in a seed, the part that contains the genes.
>
> Most U.S.-grown [seed] is based on three genetic varieties, says Goodman, who has the only seed collection of all 250 major corn races still in existence.
>
> Development of other such collections is vital because the seeds hold the inherited traits that would be needed to

help crops survive new diseases or changing climate, he says.

Because most corn has been bred for high yield in a specific environment, climatic changes or a new pest could wipe out the entire crop, he says.

Namkoong says 12 crops provide 95 percent of the world's calorie needs. In corn, one-third of the genes come from four inbred varieties. The problem is worse in wheat, soybeans and other crops, he says.

—*Orlando Sentinel* (date unknown)

To help solve these and many other related problems, there is a growing, grass-roots (no pun intended) movement to go back to the generic, heirloom seeds of our forefathers. Information on how to obtain these non-hybrid seeds is in *B.

When seeds from the best of your non-hybrid crops are saved each year and replanted in the next year's garden, a natural resistance to insects will build up normally. They will inherit characteristics inherent to surviving well in that environment and each year they will improve genetically by natural means.

Open pollination (pollination by natural means, such as wind and insects) of two varieties of non-hybrid seeds, which would then produce hybrids in your garden, can be prevented with some attention to where you plant vegetables that are likely to cross-pollinate and by rotating your planting. For example, certain types of corn will easily cross-pollinate (producing hybrids). You can avoid this by planting different varieties a few weeks apart, so that their pollination times are staggered. With squash, you can avoid planting varieties next to each other that you do not want to cross-pollinate.

If you want to pursue saving your own seeds, it is worth noting that not all plants complete the life cycle in one year or produce seeds each year. Plants are either annuals (they go to seed each year), bi-annuals (they produce seed only in the second year) or perennials, such as asparagus and rhubarb, that grow back each year. Root vegetables, such as carrots and beets, are bi-annuals and they will not give you seeds the first year. If you leave some of them in the ground, they will get pithy and will send up a flower stock and will go to seed the next year.

We can foresee some difficulties ahead in the continued use of the vulnerable, hybrid seeds being put out today by the seed companies, which are progressively being more controlled by giant conglomerates. You might want to take this matter into consideration and possibly plant part, or all, of your garden with the old, hardy varieties of seeds which were geared for long storage, since back in those days there was little refrigeration and few greenhouses. The vegetables then were dryer and denser than today's hybrid vegetables. If you decide to move in this direction, you could also be a "seed multiplier" by saving and distributing some of these hardy generic seeds.

WATERING SYSTEMS

Earlier when we talked about buying a piece of rural property, we said the three most important things were water, Water, WATER. The reason for this is that nothing will grow without water. In a garden—as in a hydroponic greenhouse—you must bring the water to the plants. There are various ways of doing this, each with advantages and disadvantages.

If you use a system that sprinkles from overhead, whether it be hand held, moveable sprinklers, or sprinklers on fixed posts, you have the advantage of simulating rainfall. This is the option that most small gardeners will utilize, at least initially.

However, it is difficult to get even water distribution in this manner, particularly with rotating overhead sprinklers, such as the rainbird. With overhead sprinklers, in places you will have some overlap, where you will get excess water, while other places will only get the outer fringes of water from just a single sprinkler. Also, if you are not careful, water from a heavy overhead sprinkler can beat young tender plants to a pulp, destroying them before they have a chance to even begin to mature.

If water scarcity is a problem, then one should also realize that overhead sprinkling is by far the most wasteful, inefficient method of watering a garden.

However, taking all of these things into consideration, if you plan your overhead sprinkling system well, with an eye to be sure that all the areas of the garden are covered approximately the same amount, and you have a very adequate water supply, then this is probably the easiest system to use and there is nothing wrong with using this type of a system. We have used rainbird sprinklers successfully in our garden for years, just being careful not to overwater, particularly when the seedlings are young and tender.

People in the nation of Israel initially developed the drip irrigation method of watering. This type of watering system has long pipes running along each row of vegetables, with little feeder tubes going over to the base of each individual plant and dripping water specifically right at the base of that plant. This has the advantage of being the most efficient use of water. In addition, the water tends to soak deeply into that one small area, causing the plant's roots to go down deep, which is desirable.

The disadvantage is that when you are hoeing or rototilling the weeds from around the plants, these hoses get in the way. Thus, if you are going to use this method of watering, you should use some type of a mulching system for weed control rather than relying on hoeing.

Subsurface watering systems actually apply the water beneath the surface of the ground rather than on top of it. Usually these are utilized by commercial growers. In most cases, this would not be a viable alternative for the home gardener.

The bottom line is that plants need adequate water. This is an absolute must. However, you also have to be careful not to give them too much water. The famous Irish potato famine earlier in this century was not caused by a drought; rather it was caused by too much rain. The roots of the plants need to breathe, as well as needing moisture and nutrients. This is why earthworms are welcome in a garden, as they burrow subsurface holes in the soil that allow air to get to the roots of the plants. It is better to give your garden a major watering once or twice a week, and then let it dry out between the waterings, so the roots will have a chance to get air as well.

WHAT TO PLANT

Up until now, we have discussed the location, the soil, the water, and heirloom versus hybrid seeds, but we have not discussed *what* you are going to want to plant in your garden. One of the things you need to consider is the growing season where you live. If it is a shorter growing season, then plants that take longer to mature should be omitted from your garden. But the main thing is that you are going to want to plant things that you and your family *like to eat*.

If you are going to be self-reliant, however, you also want to give attention to planting things that you can preserve by freezing, canning or dehydrating, as well as foods that can be stored in the state they were in when they were harvested, to last through the winter until the next harvest. We have already mentioned that root vegetables—such as carrots, beets, potatoes, Jerusalem artichokes, and turnips—can be stored for almost a year in proper root cellar conditions where they are kept cool and dry.

There are some plants that will grow through part or even all of the winter, depending on your climate. In fact, you can have a winter garden. This would include the cabbage family, peas, pea pods, broccoli and cauliflower —anything that thrives in a cooler temperature. You may wish to section off a small area of your garden that you reserve for your winter garden vegetables. There you would plant vegetables that do well in cooler weather that you would not plow up in the fall, but you would leave through the winter.

Once you get a good freeze, that will end your winter garden too, but frequently that will be two or three months after the rest of the garden has ceased producing. In areas of the country with a warmer climate that do not get below freezing temperatures, you may be able to keep your winter garden going much longer.

Winter squash are not root vegetables, but they were marvelously designed by God with the capability of being stored through the winter. Winter squash include numerous varieties, such as hubbard squash, acorn squash, and pumpkins.

We discovered an interesting thing one year about zucchinis. We had a lot of very large zucchinis that we decided to try to store through the winter. A few months later, when Jeani went to cut one of these open with the idea of using it to make some zucchini bread, it was too hard even for her electric knife to get through. Thinking it may be no good, she gave it one last chance and decided to bake it. Afterward, she was amazed when she sliced it open—it was a rich orange color inside, like a pumpkin! We learned that year that when zucchinis finally get ripe, that is the color they turn! The pulp can then be scooped out and used just like pumpkin or other winter squash, including for "pumpkin" pies! Most zucchinis are eaten green; this is why people are not familiar with their true ripened color.

Jeani has found that some of the easier things to can (in jars) are tomatoes, tomato sauces, relishes, and fruits, such as peaches and pears. Easy vegetables to dehydrate that do well through the winter include zucchini, tomatoes and green beans. Corn, peas and beans lend themselves well to freezing. We will have more to say about preserving foods shortly.

We plant a combination of seeds and seedlings in our garden. If you have a greenhouse or someplace appropriate to start seedlings before it is warm enough (or, in our case, dry enough) to plow and plant your garden, you can get a head start on the growing season this way. We find this especially helpful with tomatoes, peppers, eggplant, cabbage and broccoli. Some of these seeds are so small that it is easier for them to get a good start in the fine soil you can provide them in seedling trays, versus out in the garden, although both ways are viable. Also, when you do plant your tomatoes and peppers, for example, they are weeks ahead of where they would be if you planted the seeds directly in the garden.

Many gardening stores will have some seedlings available for purchase around planting time, if you are unable to plant your own. However, to be self-reliant, it would be preferable to learn how to grow your own seedlings.

There is no need to start larger seeds that germinate quickly, like squash, beans, peas and corn, as seedlings. They do great planted directly in the garden. Soaking these seeds overnight can help them to germinate faster in the warm garden soil.

One recommendation we would make would be to plant bush beans rather than pole beans. Pole beans will require the extra step of adding stakes and strings or poles for the beans to climb on. You can plant pole beans beside corn and they will climb the corn stalks, but we find bush beans preferable and much less trouble.

As you can see, when deciding what to plant, your thinking must include, not only what is fun and enjoyable to eat during the summer while the garden is producing, but also what will last you through the winter until the next harvest time, either by storing it in a root cellar, or by canning, freezing, or dehydrating it.

You may possibly want to plant some marigolds in various places throughout your vegetable garden to keep away some of the pests and insects. There is a book out on companion planting entitled *Carrots Love Tomatoes*. This book deals with which plants do best when grown in close proximity to each other. Obviously from the title, carrots and tomatoes do well when planted next to each other. (The addresses where you can get this book and others on companion planting are given in Appendix B.)

When planting corn, it is important to be aware that corn plants have to fertilize each other. Therefore, you would not want to plant just one long row of corn. Rather, it would be desirable to plant several short rows of corn adjacent to each other, in a block or square area.

Also, remember that you are not planting just enough corn to eat the delicious corn on the cob as it comes fresh out of the garden during the summer, but you want to plant a significant excess, so that you can cut it off the cob and freeze it or dehydrate it for use during the winter. The same thing would apply to many other vegetables as well; you would want to plant an excess, so that you would have ample surplus for the wintertime when your garden is no longer producing.

There is a theory that bears looking into, the theory of "The Nutritional Density of Foods" pioneered by John Wadsworth. Here is what he has to say concerning this:

> Too often today our focus on food is relative to calories and fats rather than nutrition. We are learning something about the bad choices but little about the good, better and best choices.
>
> By understanding the relative nutritional density of foods, we can make the best choices in what we eat.
>
> Example: "An apple a day keeps the doctor away." But is it the best choice? By studying comparative nutritional density of foods we find that the cantaloupe is a far better choice. Both are good but look at the difference. The cantaloupe has fewer calories (50), versus (80) for the apple, more iron, fifty times the vitamin A, ten times the vitamin C, more folacin, thiamine and riboflavin and more of virtually every other nutrient than the apple. Likewise, spinach and bok choy are significantly better than lettuce.
>
> My studies of nutrition and foods in other cultures has led me to conclude that many of these cultures base their cuisine on best nutrition. The oriental stir fry dishes with bean sprouts, bok choy, spinach, broccoli, peas, asparagus along with fruits such as kiwi, mandarin oranges, plums and apricot were ingeniously concocted with foods

showing the highest nutritional density. The same is true of the Italian and Mexican cuisines.

Some of the poorest people in the world, living on some of the worst land have the best health, eat the best food, from the smallest space, using the least amount of energy and time.

The application for provident living, disaster preparedness or caring for the poor and needy has tremendous implications. You can obtain better health from less food for less cost, from less space, in less time, with less effort. Conservation is enhanced in all aspects. Making a tortilla versus bread is a good example. The tortilla takes two minutes, the bread one and one half hours. Energy, time, effort are saved but nutrition remains the same. Stir fry dishes provide similar savings. A complete meal of vegetables, noodles, meat and legumes is served in about seven minutes from one pan using minimum energy. Compare this with cooking potatoes in one pan, beans in another, corn in another and meat in the oven. Consider not only the savings in energy, but the amount of water and human energy to clean up the latter cooking method.

Nutritional density provides a guide for what we plant in our gardens. It allows us to yield the highest nutrition from the smallest space using the least amount of water and human energy. Plants like broccoli and bok choy and spinach can be clipped and grow back for multiple harvests unlike potatoes and corn that yield a single crop. The cantaloupe is not only 6 times more nutritious than an apple, it can be grown in about 100 days as compared to 6 years for the apple tree.

Understanding the relative density of foods helps us prepare transitionally for emergencies. Foods which provide the highest nutrition the fastest, using the least amount of energy and time would be selected early in a disaster. The supplies of wheat, beans, salt and sugar are reserved for the long term and are complimented with nutritional foods and seasonings.

—"The Nutritional Density of Foods, Theory and Application"

Some of the initial work on this concept was done by Dr. Roy E. Vartabedian (who worked with Dr. Ken Cooper, the father of modern aerobics) and was presented in his book *Nutripoints* (Harper Paperbacks). Nutripoints are a way of measuring the total nutritional value of a food, including all of the vitamins and minerals contained in it. The higher the nutripoint value, the more nutritious the food. Many Americans have a lack of energy because of a lack of minerals. Therefore, it would be advisable to raise and eat foods with the higher nutritional content.

Dr. Vartabedian's table of foods with a higher total nutrition are shown on the next six pages.

John Wadsworth thinks that the seeds to plant would be those that grow the fastest, require the least amount of energy, are the cheapest and provide the greatest amount of nutrition. I would certainly agree with this. He and I together feel that it also is wise to plant vegetables and fruits that "keep on giving."

For example, if you plant corn, once you harvest the ears of corn, it is all over. But if you plant broccoli, beans or tomatoes, you can keep picking as long as the growing season lasts. The same thing would be true with spinach, romaine lettuce and cabbage. You can harvest some leaves from each plant and within a few days the plant will have replaced those leaves. Thus, you have a renewable food source rather than a one-time shot, like you have with an onion, a beet or a carrot. Of course, we do plant and enjoy carrots, beets and corn, but we are also careful to plant plenty of the "renewables."

Nutripoints of Food

VEGETABLES

Turnip Greens, Cooked	1 cup	79.0
Spinach, Raw	2 cups	75.0
Bok Choy, Raw	1 cup	72.5
Mustard Greens, Cooked	1 cup	62.0
Beet Greens, Cooked	1 cup	56.5
Spinach, Cooked	1 cup	53.5
Broccoli, Raw	1 cup	53.0
Watercress, Raw	20 pieces	52.5
Lettuce, Romaine	2 cups	47.5
Asparagus, Fresh	8 stalks	44.0
Peppers, Sweet Red	2 whole	42.5
Swiss Chard, Cooked	1 cup	42.0
Collard Greens, Cooked	1 cup	42.0
Cauliflower, Raw	1 cup	40.5
Brussels Sprouts, Cooked	1/2 cup	40.0
Cabbage, Common, Raw	1 cup	39.0
Broccoli, Cooked	1 cup	38.5
Kale, Cooked	1 cup	38.5
Green Pepper, Raw	2 whole	37.5
Cauliflower, Cooked	1 cup	37.5
Chicory Greens, Raw	1 cup	35.5
Carrots, Raw	1 whole	35.5
Lettuce, Butterhead	2 cups	34.0
Mushrooms, Fresh	1 cup	32.5
Asparagus, Canned	8 stalks	32.5
Okra, Cooked	1/2 cup	31.0
Tomato, Fresh	1 whole	30.0
Carrots, Cooked	1/2 cup	30.0
Radishes, Raw	1 cup	29.0
V-8 Juice	6 oz.	28.5
Squash, Baked	1/2 cup	26.5
Okra, Raw	1 cup	26.0
Kohlrabi, Raw	1 cup	24.5
Beans, Green, Cooked	1 cup	24.5
Scallions, Raw	10	24.0
Vegetables, Mixed	1/2 cup	22.0
Celery, Raw	8 stalks	20.0

Nutripoints of Food

FRUITS

Cantaloupe	1/4	29.0
Guava	1 whole	21.0
Papaya	1/2	20.5
Strawberries	1 cup	19.0
Currants, Black	3/4 cup	19.0
Mango	1/2	17.5
Kiwi	1 whole	17.0
Litchi	6	16.0
Mandarin Oranges	1/2 cup	15.5
Honeydew Melon	1/4	14.0
Plums	1/2 cup	14.0
Orange	1 whole	13.5
Apricots	3	13.5
Tangerine	1 whole	13.0
Grapefruit	1/2	13.0
Blackberries	1/2 cup	13.0
Fruit Salad	1/2 cup	13.0
Carambola	1 whole	12.5
Raspberries	1/2 cup	12.5
Orange Juice	6 oz.	11.5
Peach	1 whole	11.0
Casaba Melon	1/4	11.0
Apricots, Dried	6	11.0
Grapefruit Juice	6 oz.	11.0
Watermelon	1 cup	10.5
Prickly Pear	1 whole	10.0
Kumquat	6	10.0
Fruit Cocktail	1/2 cup	10.0
Nectarine	1 whole	10.0
Cranberries	1 cup	10.0
Loquat	5	10.0
Boysenberries	1/2 cup	9.0
Passion Fruit	2	9.0
Pineapple	1/2 cup	8.0
Cherries	10	7.5
Banana	1/2	7.5
Persimmon	1 whole	7.5
Cranberry Juice	6 oz.	7.0

Nutripoints of Food

GRAINS

Wheat Bran	1/2 cup	26.5
Wheat Germ	1/4 cup	12.0
Crackers, W. Wheat	8	9.0
Oat Bran Cereal	1/2 cup	7.0
Bread, W. Wheat	2 slices	6.5
Amaranth, Pilaf	1/2 cup	6.5
Muffin, W. Wheat	1	6.0
Flour, W. Wheat	1/4 cup	6.0
Shredded Wheat	2/3 cup	6.0
Puffed Wheat	1 cup	5.5
Pancakes, W. Wheat	4 sm	5.5
Quinoa	1/4 cup	5.5
Oatmeal	1/2 cup	5.5
Rice, Wild	1/2 cup	5.5
Bread, Diet	3 slices	5.5
Bread, Multigrain	2 slices	5.0
Amaranth	1/4 cup	5.0
Tortilla, W. Wheat	1	4.5
Roll, W. Wheat	1	4.5
Bread, Roman Meal	2 slices	4.5
Bread, Triticale	2 slices	4.5
Bread, Pumpernickel	2 slices	4.5
Rice, Brown	1/2 cup	4.0
Bread, Rye	2 slices	4.0
Muffin, English	1 whole	4.0
Bread, Wheat Germ	2 slices	4.0
Flour, Rye	1/4 cup	4.0
Tortilla, Corn	2	4.0
Spaghetti, Hi-Pro	1/2 cup	4.0
Pita Bread, W. Wheat	1	4.0
Noodles, W. Wheat	1/2 cup	4.0
Waffles	1	4.0
Bread, Raisin	2 slices	4.0
Bagel, W. Wheat	1 whole	4.0
Rice, Spanish	1/2 cup	4.0
Bagel, Pumpernickel	1 whole	3.5
Macaroni	1/2 cup	3.5

Nutripoints of Food

LEGUMES

Bean Sprouts	2 cups	18.0
Green Peas	1 cup	14.0
Minestrone Soup	1½ cups	14.0
Navy Beans, Cooked	1 cup	13.5
Split Pea Soup	1/2 cup	10.0
Lima Beans, Cooked	3/4 cup	9.5
Black-eyed Peas, Cooked	1 cup	9.0
Kidney Beans, Cooked	1/2 cup	8.5
Vegetarian Burger	4 oz.	8.5
Beans, Cooked	3/4 cup	8.5
Lentils, Cooked	1 cup	8.0
Lentil Soup	1/2 cup	8.0
Garbanzo Beans, Cooked	1/2 cup	8.0
Baked Beans	1/2 cup	7.5
Black Bean Soup	1 cup	7.5
Soy Milk	8 oz.	7.5
Soybeans, Cooked	3/4 cup	7.0
Pinto Beans, Cooked	1/2 cup	6.5
Lentils/Rice	1 cup	6.5
Lentil Curry Soup	1 cup	6.5
Adzuki Beans, Dry	1/4 cup	5.5
Bean Enchiladas	1/2	5.5
Tofu	1/2 cup	5.0
Vegetarian Hot Dog	1	5.0
Bean Chili	1/2 cup	5.0
Soybean Nuts	1/2 cup	5.0
Sunflower Seeds	1/4 cup	4.5
Bean Burrito	1/2	4.0
Butter Beans	1/2 cup	4.0
Bean Dip	2 T	3.5
Refried Beans	1/2 cup	3.5
Boston Baked Beans	1/2 cup	3.5
Pumpkin/Squash Seeds	1/4 cup	2.5
Trail Mix	1/4 cup	2.0
Three Bean Salad	1 cup	1.5
Peanuts, Unsalted	25	1.5

Nutripoints of Food

MILK/DAIRY

Nonfat Dry Milk, Prepared	2 cups	11.5
Nonfat Light Yogurt	1 cup	10.5
Skim Milk	1 cup	9.5
Evaporated Skim Milk	1/2 cup	9.5
Skim Buttermilk	1 cup	9.5
Nonfat Plain Yogurt	1 cup	9.0
Lowfat (1%) Milk	1 cup	8.0
Lowfat (2%) Hi-Calcium Milk	1 cup	7.5
Lowfat Plain Yogurt	1 cup	7.0
Egg Whites	6	6.0
Lowfat (2%) Milk	1 cup	6.0
Dry Cottage Cheese	1/2 cup	5.5
Buttermilk	1 cup	5.0
Lowfat (1%) Cottage Cheese	1/2 cup	4.5
Low-cal Cheese	2 oz.	3.5
Lowfat (2%) Cottage Cheese	1/2 cup	3.0
Low-cal Pudding	1 cup	3.0
Whole Milk Plain Yogurt	1 cup	2.5
Whole (3.3%) Milk	1 cup	2.5
Lowfat (1%) Choc Milk	1 cup	2.5
Lowfat (2%) Choc Milk	6 oz.	2.5
Whole (3.7%) Milk	1 cup	2.0
Frozen Yogurt	1/2 cup	1.5
Goats Milk	1 cup	1.5
Cottage Cheese	1/2 cup	1.5
Lowfat Ricotta Cheese	2 oz.	0.5
Yogurt Dressing	2 T	0.5
Lowfat Mozzarella Cheese	1 oz.	0.5
Parmesan Cheese	1 oz.	0.5
Lowfat Swiss Cheese	1 oz.	0.5

Nutripoints of Food

MEAT/FISH/POULTRY

Raw Clams	6 oz.	13.5
Ray Oysters	12	13.0
Baked Venison	4 oz.	8.5
Tuna, Canned/Water	1/2 cup	8.0
Baked Pike	6 oz.	7.5
Baked Salmon	3 oz.	7.5
Baked Halibut	4 oz.	7.5
Baked Red Snapper	6 oz.	7.0
Baked Bass	6 oz.	7.0
Baked Abalone	3 oz.	6.5
Baked Swordfish	3 oz.	6.5
Quail w/out skin	4 oz.	6.0
Baked Sole	6 oz.	6.0
Pheasant w/out skin	4 oz.	5.5
Baked Sturgeon	4 oz.	5.5
Chicken Gumbo Soup	3/4 cup	5.5
Baked Moose	3 oz.	5.5
Lean Baked Ham	4 oz.	5.0
Baked Trout	3 oz.	5.0
Sardines, in Oil	3	4.5
Baked Rainbow Smelt	4 oz.	4.5
Baked Ocean Perch	4 oz.	4.5
Baked Turkey w/out skin	3 oz.	4.5
Baked Chicken Breast w/out skin	3 oz.	4.0
Lean Beef Round Steak	3 oz.	4.0
Lean Beef Flank Steak	3 oz.	4.0
Baked Scallops	6 oz.	4.0
Baked Orange Roughy	5 oz.	4.0
Baked Mackerel	3 oz.	4.0
Lean Beef Top Loin	3 oz.	4.0
Lean Veal Cutlet	3 oz.	3.5
Seafood Gumbo Soup	1 cup	3.5
Baked Lamb Roast	3 oz.	3.5
Baked Flounder	3 oz.	3.5
Baked Cod	4 oz.	3.5
Beef Tenderloin	3 oz.	3.5

PEST CONTROL IN THE GARDEN

Pest control in the garden is far easier than in the greenhouse. Most people today want to go "organic" which means using no pesticides on the garden. Thus, the only option they have is to bring in predator insects that will eat the destructive insects. This is one place where ladybugs are your real friends; they will eat aphids and many of the other parasites that can suck the juice and life out of plants. In Appendix B, we recommend a book which deals with natural pest control.

On the other hand, if you decide to go with insect sprays to control the insects and parasites in your garden, you are going to want to read the labels even more carefully than you read the labels on cans of food. Some of these will say that you should not use them "within five days of harvest," while others might say "within 24 hours of harvest." The shorter the time they can be used before harvest, the milder they are. You would certainly want to start with the mildest one possible, to see if that would handle your particular problem, before trying something stronger.

Something else that is significant in curtailing pests is keeping your soil healthy. Healthy soil that is not deficient in nutrients needed by the plants and that has the desirable acid-alkaline balance helps to foster strong, healthy, disease-resistant plants. In many communities, you can take soil samples into the local Extension Service to have them tested. There are innumerable books available on the subject of soil and gardening where you can get more information about how to build up your soil and how to maintain good, healthy, well-balanced, rich soil. There is a video tape by Master Gardener, Dr. Barbara Fair, as well as some books, listed in Appendix

B that can be very helpful concerning maintaining rich, healthy soil.

When you clean the mixture of hay and manure out of your chicken, sheep and goat barns or sheds, you can put it on your garden in the fall and plow it under. This helps put the vital nutrients back into the soil.

WEEDING AND MULCHING

As important as any other aspect of gardening is the necessary weeding. Particularly the first month and a half or so while the plants are small and just getting established, it is critical to try to weed around them about once a week. If you do not, and you have nice sunny weather and lots of rain, invariably you will find that the weeds have a way of taking off faster than many of your fledgling seedlings. However, a few minutes once or twice a week with a hula hoe close to the plants, and a rototiller when needed between the rows, can keep your garden clear of weeds.

A hula hoe is a wonderful invention, having a thin metal piece about an inch wide that very easily slips under the soil with a little pressure to uproot small weeds. With it, you can cover a lot of ground fairly rapidly, compared to hand weeding. However, if you go too long without weeding, then the weeds will get too big for the hula hoe to take care of and you will need to pull them up by hand, if they are close to the young plants, in order to get the roots out.

We plant in tilled rows about 3 feet wide. Between these, we dig about a 4-inch trench with a special blade for that purpose that fits on our rototiller. This is for any excess water to drain off, if the garden gets too wet or we have too much rain. In these 3-foot beds between trenches, we may plant 2 rows, about 18 inches apart, of peppers, beans, corn and other vegetables of this approximate size in mature-plant diameter. We only plant one row of tomatoes down the center of one of these beds, actually two seedlings close together, so that we can later put on tomato cages, when the plants get to be about 1 foot high. This gives the tomato vines something to grow on and it also makes picking the fruit much easier later. This type of planting arrangement is pictured in Figure 7.1.

Tomato cages can be fabricated out of field fencing by cutting off sections large enough to form a cylinder of fencing about 2 feet in diameter. Then wire the edges together and you have a very useful tomato cage that can be affixed over the plants before they get too large by threading 4-foot stakes through and pounding them solidly into the soil. These are about 3-feet high and we find that our tomato plants easily grow that high and higher, before the season is over, and they are loaded with luscious fruit in great abundance.

Also, somewhere along the line in this garden-maintenance phase, if you plant pole beans or snow peas, you will want to pound in some poles or stakes and attach twine to allow for easy climbing.

Something that we have found very successful is to plant all of our squash and melon-type plants in a separate section of the garden from the regular rows. This area we lovingly refer to as "Vineland." In freshly-tilled soil, we insert tall stakes in a grid pattern, about 9 feet apart in each direction. Then we plant a small circle of about 8 or 9 seeds or 4 or 5 seedlings around each stake in a circle about 1 foot in diameter (as shown in Figure 7.2). That

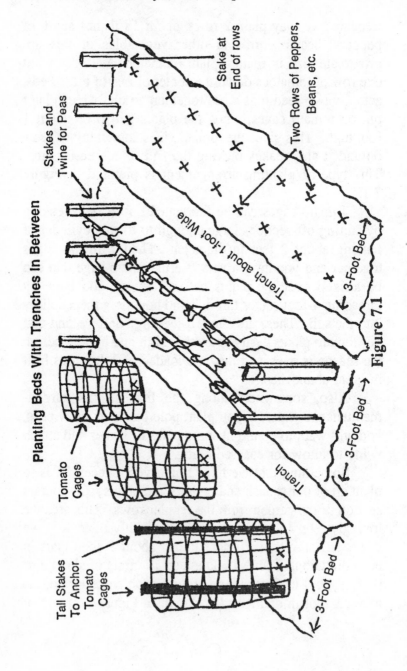

Planting Beds With Trenches In Between

Stakes and Twine for Peas

Tomato Cages

Tall Stakes To Anchor Tomato Cages

Trench about 1-foot Wide

Trench

Stake at End of rows

Two Rows of Peppers, Beans, etc.

3-Foot Bed

3-Foot Bed

3-Foot Bed

Figure 7.1

way, it is very easy to weed this whole vast area, while the plants are small, using the rototiller to go first one direction between the stakes and then 90 degrees in another direction. However, as anyone who has ever grown zucchini, pumpkins, cucumbers or other squash knows well, these have a way of spreading out and taking over the whole garden, as they mature and begin to produce. That can be a problem, if you plant them in regular rows. The way we do it, they can spread out all they want, and eventually the large leaves they produce help to keep the weed population down.

Aerial View of Stakes In "Vineland"

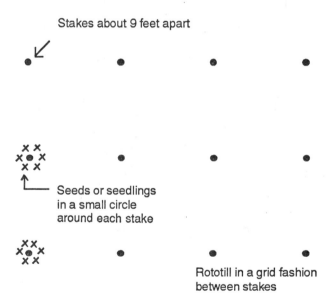

Figure 7.2

Many people successfully employ a gardening method called "mulching" to aid in their weed control. Mulching refers to the use of some sort of a protective covering of something like sawdust, wood chips or hay that is spread or left on the ground for the purpose of reducing evaporation, helping to maintain an even soil temperature, prevent erosion, control the weeds or to enrich the soil.   Again, there are many books available that give further instruction on this method, if it is something you wish to pursue.   Some people even use black plastic over their garden area, such as in raised beds, and then poke holes through the plastic in which to plant their seedlings.   This certainly does curtail weed growth.

One idea for planting potatoes is to initially put an old automobile tire around each plant and fill it with dirt. Then as the potatoes grow, you can put another rubber tire around your plants after they get to be a foot or so high. You can even add still another tire on top of this, as the plants grow taller.   Then when you go to harvest them, you just remove the tires, instead of digging potatoes.

However you take care of it, weed control is an integral part of having a successful and productive garden. A little time invested weekly makes all the difference.

FERTILIZING THE GARDEN

We have never used a commercial fertilizer on our garden.   Spreading the hay and manure from the goat, sheep and chicken stalls, as well as plowing under the corn stalks, zucchini vines and the rest of the garden plants keeps our soil healthy and full of nutrients.

However, if we did not do this, then we would purchase and apply some appropriate fertilizer to the garden annually. The type of fertilizer that we would use would depend on the results of a soil test to find out what deficiencies our soil had.

Chemical fertilizers are compounds generally mined from rocks. Twelve of the thirteen essential plant nutrients man can regulate originate in the rocks and are mined.

Nitrogen starts in the atmosphere. It is allowed no rest in the soil but is chemically changed from one compound to another until the cycle is completed and the element (N_2) returns to the atmosphere to start the cycle all over again.

Here is a list of the essential plant nutrients that man can regulate:

Nitrogen	Magnesium	Copper	Zinc
Phosphorus	Manganese	Molybdenum	Chlorine
Potassium	Iron	Sulfur	Calcium
Boron			

Through years of experimentation, man has been able to determine how much of each compound a plant will require to mature a specific crop yield. He has also learned the chemical equations that the separate compounds must be in before plant assimilation takes place.

For every crop, if you supply the soil with the proper amounts of the separate essential chemical compounds, you instantly produce healthy, flavor-filled, high-yield crops. Fortunately, soils never wear out (although they can become depleted in essential plant nutrients). The same quality and high yield crops can be produced forever on the same land.

Critics who condemn chemical fertilizers on the basis that they destroy soil structure mistake the facts. The breakdown of soil structure is due to the lack of organic residue. Of necessity, crops are being grown on land nearly devoid of organic materials. This, however, is not that serious. Common vegetable crops and others have a fantastic ability to grow in extremely hard clay soils, if the essential nutrients and moisture are adequate. So whatever kind of soil you may have, fertilizers can help you to produce good crops.

HARVEST TIME

You plant your garden and you keep it weeded during the months when it is growing, either by hoeing or by using a mulch system. Then the time comes when tomato vines are loaded with bright red fruit, the bell peppers are big and green, the cucumbers are nice and hard and green, and the tassels on the corn have turned brown, showing that it is ready to be picked. Everything is ready and in full production except the pumpkins and a few of the winter squash that take longer to mature.

Harvest time is the joyous time of year when people through the centuries have celebrated the goodness of God. Man can plant and water, but only God gives the increase.

It is fun to pick from your garden and consume what you have produced from your labors. This brings a deep satisfaction; anyone who has grown their own food will understand what we mean by this. Producing a surplus allows you to share with others out of your abundance, which is immensely gratifying, as well as being a blessing to other families in need.

Actually, not everything in the garden ripens at once. If you put your cooler weather crops in on your first planting, hopefully you will have peas and pea pods to harvest early, before the summer sun gets too hot. Green beans and wax beans are fun to grow, because they are quick to germinate and poke their heads up above the soil, and soon they are producing an abundance of beans. With many plants, such as beans, peas, peppers and tomatoes, the more you pick them, the more they produce!

Lettuce particularly will soon begin going to seed once it reaches maturity. For this reason, it is a good idea to do several plantings of lettuce, several weeks apart. That way, once you have about used up your first planting, the second one will be reaching maturity, and so on. Your lettuce crop can be encouraged to keep producing for a few weeks longer, if you break off the seed pods when you see them beginning to form on a stalk in the center. However, after about a month of this, the lettuce leaves will begin to get less tender and that is when it is nice to have a new crop just reaching maturity. This is also true of green beans. When the initial planting of beans begins to get a little tough, it is great to have a second planting just beginning to produce.

Tomatoes will begin to ripen a few at a time, but with them and much of the rest of the garden, there will come a time when they are in full production, the plants will be loaded with ripe produce. At that point, you will likely have more than you can use or even give away. At the end of the season, you may have lots of green tomatoes yet on the plants that will not have a chance to ripen before the first freezing. These can be made into a delicious relish called "Chow Chow" (the recipe is given on the video entitled "Canning is Fun!" listed in *B). Or you can even make "green fried tomatoes" dipped in egg batter, which are delicious.

Once the garden is in full production, then along with the fun time, a time of hard work begins in preserving this abundant harvest, so it will last you until the same time the following year.

The winter squash, pumpkins and zucchinis need to be cured (dried) for about three weeks before storing them. We have found that an old bedspring is an excellent place to dry these, since the air can then get to all sides. This will harden the skin and help in their preservation. Ones that are not hard when they are stored will not last through the winter and should be used up within a month or so.

When it is time to pick the excess ripe ears of corn, hopefully you will have several bushel baskets full of these for preserving. They all need to be shucked, which we find easiest to do right there in the garden, leaving the corn husks in the compost pile. Then they need to be washed and the corn cut off of the cob, to prepare the excess corn for freezing or dehydrating.

This takes us to the subject of preserving excess output of the harvest, so I will turn the pen over to my lovely wife, Jeani, who is the expert in this area.

FOOD PRESERVATION

If you provide your own vegetables from a garden, as we have indicated, preserving the excess of your produce through the winter becomes an important consideration. If you do so, you can then use foods you have preserved until the next garden is harvested. Also, you will find that when various crops come into production, you will likely have more than you can eat of the foods that are in season. There are a number of methods that can be used to keep food: freezing, canning and dehydrating are three primary ones.

Preserving your excess garden produce is an important part of your food preservation considerations, but you will likely also have excess fruit to preserve if you have an orchard or berries as well. That is the subject of the next chapter, but we will include the preservation of fruits in our discussion here on canning, dehydrating and freezing, because it applies to both the garden and the orchard, as well as to meat preservation.

Why Dehydrate?

Dehydrating has a number of advantages over other methods of preserving.

1. *It is economical.* Many people buy dehydrated foods these days, especially fruits. It is much cheaper to do your own with a home food dehydrator.

2. *It is fun and easy.* Dehydrating is the easiest method there is to preserve, and it is much less messy than canning. You can teach even fairly young children to help and make it a fun family project. It does not have to be a major production. Small amounts can easily be dried at a time, if a small quantity is all you have to preserve. With canning, I (Jeani) always feel it is more worthwhile to at least do a full cannerload, if I go to the trouble of getting out all of my canning equipment.

3. *Dehydrating best preserves the nutritional value.* This is perhaps the most important reason that we would favor dehydrating over canning and freezing: *20-30 percent* of the nutrients are saved in *canning, 40-60 percent in freezing,* and over *95 percent of the nutrients are saved in dehydrating!*

Table 7.1, on the bottoms of this page and the next, show a nutrient comparison between some foods that are canned, dehydrated and frozen. This is discussed on a video entitled *Dehydrating Made Easy* (*B), which is an excellent tool, actually showing you how to dehydrate and giving recommendations on dehydrators.

Dehydrating is by no means a new method of preserving food. The two important factors in order to dehydrate foods are an even, warm temperature—but not hot enough to cook the food—and air flow to draw the moisture out

Comparison Chart of Types of Preserving

Preservation type and amount	gm. protein	mg. calcium	Total gm. carb. & fiber	mg. vit. C	mg. iron
100 gm. apricots					
canned in syrup	.6	11	.4	-4	0.3
dehydrated	5.6	86	.8	15	5.3
frozen, sweet	.7	10	.6	20	.9
100 gm. peaches					
canned in syrup	1.8	18	91.2	13	1.4
dehydrated	21.8	81	399.2	63	15.9
frozen, sweet	1.8	18	102.5	50	2.3
100 gm. peas					
canned	15	---	56	40	7.7
dehydrated	109	---	273	20	23.1
frozen	24	---	58	60	9.1
100 gm. carrots					
canned	2.7	---	113	2	3.2
dehydrated	3.8	---	367	15	27.2
frozen	29.9	---	115	4	4.9

Table 7.1

of the foods. Sun drying is an age-old method, but you have no control over the heat and airflow, and if foods are not completely dried by the time the sun sets, they can reabsorb moisture at night. Oven drying (at a *very low* setting) is a possibility, but there is no air circulation in an oven, which hampers even drying of the foods.

By far the most reliable and desirable method is to have your own dehydrator. Fortunately, there are numerous good brands now available which make home dehydrating easier than ever. Addresses for some of these are given in Appendix B.

Canned, Dehydrated and Frozen

Preservation type and amount	mg phosphate	I.U. vit. A.	mg. potassium	mg. ribr.	mg. niacin
100 gm. apricots					
canned in syrup	15	1,740	234	.03	0.4
dehydrated	139	14,100	1,260	.10	3.6
frozen, sweet	19	1,680	229	.04	1.0
100 gm. peaches					
canned in syrup	54	1,950	590	.11	2.5
dehydrated	685	22,680	22,680	.43	35.2
frozen, sweet	59	2,950	562	.18	.18
100 gm. peas					
canned	---	2,010	---	---	---
dehydrated	---	4,010	---	---	---
frozen	---	3,020	---	---	---
100 gm. carrots					
canned	---	45,360	---	---	---
dehydrated	---	453,600	---	---	---
frozen	---	49,200	---	---	---

Analysis charts, U.S. Department of Agriculture Research

Table 7.1

How to Dehydrate at Home

Fruits lend themselves particularly well to easy preparation for dehydrating. Bananas are perhaps the simplest. You can either slice them across, in rounds about 1/4-inch thick, or cut them in half and then slice each half lengthwise in about 4 pieces of about the same thickness. Then simply lay them out on a dehydrating tray with room for air to flow between the pieces. Understandably, most of us will not be living in a part of the country where growing our own bananas is a viable option. I mention it first because it is an easy way to begin to get comfortable with your dehydrator and children can easily be taught how to prepare bananas for dehydrating, which they can eat as a substitute for candy.

Apples and pears can be cut across the core in about 1/4-inch slices. These can be dipped in water with some vitamin C powder dissolved in it, to prevent them from turning brown, before spreading them out on the trays.

Except for tomatoes, most vegetables should be blanched briefly before dehydrating them. Be sure to use clean and healthy produce for dehydrating, as well as any other method of preservation. Uniformity is important in your slicing, so that all of the pieces get dry at approximately the same time. Large cuts facilitate easier dehydrating. For example, if you cut across the core of an apple, rather than the other direction wherein the outside pieces would have apple peel covering one side, the apple will dry faster and more consistently. Something without any cuts to expose the moisture inside, such as raspberries or blackberries, will take a very long time to dry.

When testing for doneness, the main rule of thumb is to dry until the pieces are somewhat brittle. Fruits that you intend to eat in a dried state (such as dehydrated bananas or apples, which are delicious!) can be left a little chewier (with a little more moisture). Charts to use as a guideline for suggested drying times can be found in any good dehydrating book (*B).

Dehydrated foods can be stored in clear glass jars, in zip-lock baggies, or in Seal-a-Meal vacuum-packed bags. Always be sure to date them (with a permanent marker preferably), so that you can use up the oldest first.

The potential uses of foods you have dehydrated are many. Some fruits (like bananas, nectarines, apples, apricots, pears) make great snacks right out of the jar. Some can be reconstituted (soaked in water for an hour or two). Soaked berries can be added to muffins and cooked cereal. Fruit leathers (made from a blender puree of whatever fruits you have on hand) make terrific snacks and packed lunch treats for kids (or adults!). Vegetables can be reconstituted and cooked. Dried herbs make great seasonings. In addition, dried vegetables, such as onions, garlic, shallots and tomatoes, can be powdered in the blender and used as seasonings. Powders such as these can also make easy tomato sauce, tomato paste or baby food—just add boiling water, any desired seasonings, stir well and voila!

The advantages are well worth taking the time to learn to dehydrate. The easiest way to learn to dehydrate is to watch someone else do it. Again, the video *Dehydrating Made Easy* offers a practical demonstration, showing you how to get started dehydrating (*B).

Freezing

As long as it is operational, the freezer is a handy place to preserve some of the output from your garden.

If at some point you can no longer buy electricity, and you are not able to provide your own, you could not depend on food stored in a freezer for long. It is preferable to have a top-opening freezer because cold air will sink (drop), since it is heavier than room temperature air. With a front-opening freezer, the cold air is flowing down and out of the freezer as long as the door is open. With a top-opening freezer, the cold air stays in the freezer. Thus, your food will stay frozen longer in a top-opening freezer, should you lose power to run your freezer.

If you raise corn, this is one vegetable that is very easy to prepare and store in the freezer. After shucking it and washing it, the kernels can be cut off the cob with a good knife on a large cutting board. The corn should then be "blanched" (steamed for about five minutes) in a vegetable steamer or covered pot with just a little bit of water) to eliminate any harmful bacteria. (Alternatively, this can be done by placing the corn in a covered glass casserole dish without water and heating in a microwave for five minutes.)

After blanching, spoon the hot corn into Seal-A-Meal bags, expel the air (preferably with a Seal-A-Meal sealer machine that has a vacuum for the purpose of removing the air), and seal. Heavy duty zip lock bags can be used if you do not have a Seal-A-Meal machine, being careful to expel as much air as possible before closing the bag. After the bags have cooled, you would date them with a permanent pen and store them in your freezer. *Dating food items is important, so you can be sure to use up the oldest first.*

A similar process can be used for other vegetables such as peas, beans, broccoli and brussels sprouts. Zucchini can be ground up in a food processor and placed in freezer bags for later use in zucchini bread.

Canning

Personally, I (Jeani) prefer frozen and dehydrated vegetables, for the most part, to canned ones. Exceptions to this would be vegetables used in relishes, tomato-based sauces, and pickled vegetables. All of these can be done in a water bath canner, whereas a pressure canner is needed for regular canned vegetables, such as green beans, corn or squash. Frozen and dehydrated vegetables, such as beans and corn, just taste so much fresher than those that are canned, because they are not cooked for long periods of time like vegetables canned in a pressure canner. (On the front cover, I am pictured with some of the produce from our garden and some of the sauces and relished that I had canned one year.)

On my video entitled *Canning is Fun* (*B), I take you through two of my favorite water bath canning recipes. If you have never canned before, this video will teach you how. Even if you have, you can pick up some new, good recipes to try out with your own garden. Also listed in Appendix B is a book I have written on nutrition and health, *Fit As A Fiddle*, in which I give my recipe for "Chili Sauce," an easy, sweet tomato sauce, that our family and friends love, which can be used with innumerable dishes.

Fruits, such as peaches, pears and blackberries, do lend themselves very well to canning and they can be processed with a water bath canner. A tablespoon per quart of frozen orange or apple juice concentrate can be used in place of sugar or honey as a sweetener, with delicious results. As always, be certain to date what you can, so that you can use up the oldest jars first.

Preserving Meat

Like fruits and vegetables, meat can be preserved in numerous ways. It can be dehydrated, canned, or frozen. In addition, a small smoker can be purchased in which to smoke the meat. Meat can also be preserved by soaking it in a salt brine.

When we butcher our sheep and chickens, we usually freeze this meat and store it in frozen food lockers that we are fortunate to have nearby.

Canning is a good method of preserving meats, fish and poultry. You would need to have a pressure canner for this. Canning with cans is another alternative to using jars. You can get cases of cans and a can sealer, and then process the sealed cans in your pressure canner according to instructions. I have canned fresh tuna in cans, along with a little sea salt and herbs, and it was so delicious that it did not even taste like fish! See Appendix B for a source for cans and a can sealer.

One nice thing about canned meats is that you have already done your cooking and major preparation time in the canning process. They can essentially be eaten from the can as an instant meal, particularly if you add seasonings to your cans or jars while you are canning. Canned salmon, tuna, and chicken go great on salads or in casseroles. Canned beef or lamb is ready to warm and eat or to put in a sandwich.

A Root Cellar

As we mentioned earlier, root vegetables (carrots, beets, potatoes, turnips and such) will tend to keep for the year if stored in a cool, dry place, such as a root cellar or a cool basement.

A good way to store these root vegetables is to place a layer of straw between the layers of vegetables. Constructing bins about 3-feet by 3-feet by 3-feet helps keep the vegetables all in one place.

Apples can also be stored this way for months. Do not let the apples touch each other, because if one goes bad, it will affect the others. (The saying, "One rotten apple spoils the whole bunch" has great validity!) Old apple cartons are good for this or even old egg cartons with about three apples per carton.

Winter squash can also be stored quite well for many months in a root cellar, provided it is dry enough. This would include the large, overgrown zucchinis that we mentioned earlier. Be sure to cure them before storing them. To cure them, you lay them out to dry in the sun for about two or three weeks after picking them, rotating them occasionally so that all sides get dried. For years, we have used an old wire bed springs to lay them on, which is ideal to allow the air to get to all sides and to keep them up off the dewy grass. If the rind is hard to the touch, they are ready to store. If you can still dent it with your finger (especially with the overgrown zucchinis), then you know it will not last too long, and it should be used up within a month or so.

When you store squash in the root cellar, you want to lay them out so they are not touching each other. If one starts to spoil, it will cause others to spoil, if they are touching. We have found that it is helpful to first put down a piece of visqueen or some other piece of plastic. That way, if there is any spoilage before you use all of them up, it is easy to clean up.

If the concept of a root cellar is new to you, may we suggest reading Chapter 10 of *Preparing For Emergencies*, the first book in this series on "Preparation" (*B).

It deals with the subject, including ways to go about building a root cellar (which may also be used as a fallout shelter or storm cellar, should the need for one ever arise).

In our era of fast foods and convenience foods, much of the food value is lost in the processing and unfortunately a lot of undesirable chemicals are often added. There is an excellent book mentioned in Appendix B, *Eat, Drink and Be Ready—For Tomorrow You Will Live*, that deals with all aspects of food written from a Christian perspective. The authors warn of coming troubled times, advise a food storage program (giving details), and discuss health, weight and proper eating habits.

A WAY TO GET FREE FOOD

Something that can be of benefit, as well as an enjoyable hobby, is to learn about the edible plants that grow wild in your area. Walt and Jane Fellows Gullett make these comments about why it is worth being knowledgeable about the subject of wild plants as a potential source of food:

> Americans are only a few years removed from the necessity of eating wild edibles, both vegetation and animals and certainly some people are dependent on wild edibles today. You too can take part in this enjoyable feast.
>
> American Indians are, of course, our teachers in this natural cuisine. Many ate a diet with plenty of acorns *(Quercus spp.)* and chia seeds *(Salvia columbariae)*. They made mush out of the acorns and ate chia seeds as a staple while traveling. Indians used lamb's quarters *(Chenopodium album)* for greens and shepherd's purse *(Capsella Bursa-pastoris)* seeds for snacks much as we eat peanuts today.

Gold miners avoided scurvy and created very elegant salads with miner's lettuce *(Montia perfoliata)*. They found licorice flavor from a wild fern plant *(Polypodium vulgare)* and they preserved numerous varieties of berries. Roots and tubers from many plants are tasty, full of proteins and vitamins, and can replace potatoes, carrots, and turnips in a diet.... There is a whole outdoor grocery store just waiting for you....

In short, wild edibles are a sensible choice for the self-sufficient person or family.

—*Food Self-Sufficiency*, pp. 134-135
Naturegraph Publishers, Inc.

There are entire books on this subject (*B), if you wish to pursue it. One with good pictures can help you identify the various plants. Be certain not to try eating any plants without a positive identification. Even better, you may find someone in your area who teaches a course on identifying local plants and their uses. That can be very helpful and interesting, as well as a lot of fun. It could make an enjoyable family outing to go for a hike together and a picnic and to learn about the native vegetation in your locale at the same time.

A PLACE OF FUN,
LOVE AND HARD WORK

The garden is a wonderful place. Most people enjoy getting back close to the soil. They love producing their own healthy foods.

As you work in the garden with your hands, it is a time when you can meditate and reflect, as well as enjoying beautiful scenery and fresh air. It is really very therapeutic. It is a time when your family can work outside together and share the bonding that comes from such an experience of producing your own food.

But make no bones about it! It is a place of hard work! Bending over planting seedlings or picking beans can be hard on the back. If you spend several hours hoeing weeds, your muscles will feel it.

But just like a woman with labor pains, when the baby comes, the joy is so great that the labor pains were worth it. The "work pains" that you may go through preparing the soil, planting and harvesting in the garden are well worth it when compared to the joyous result that you will have in partaking of wholesome, fresh *home-grown* foods.

In her book, *Fit as a Fiddle*, Jeani recommends that we eat foods that are:

1. as whole as possible
2. as unprocessed as possible
3. as fresh as possible

Frequently, she will go down in the late afternoon and pick vegetables from the garden that we will have for dinner that evening. You cannot get any fresher, more whole or less processed than that! It is an ideal way to eat; there is no substitute that brings the same satisfaction.

Up until now, we have been talking about vegetables. We also need to look at the orchard, the vineyard and any other fruit that you may also wish to produce.

Chapter 8

THE ORCHARD
AND THE VINEYARD

Man does not live by vegetables alone. He wants and needs fruit as well. Fruits are naturally sweet, delicious, and well-liked, and they can satisfy a certain desire that our taste buds have for something sweet. Fruits can be used instead of desserts in many cases. They are superb when eaten fresh, and they are still delicious when frozen, canned or dehydrated. Therefore, not only will you want to produce enough fruit for your family to consume right off of the trees (and are they super that way!) but also enough so you can freeze, can or dehydrate the surplus and enjoy your preserved fruits all year long.

By definition, a *fruit* is an edible seed covering. About the only fruits that you will produce in your garden are tomatoes and melons. However, most people do not consider a tomato a fruit, so we will ignore that in our discussion and limit our meaning of *"fruit"* to be the sweet, succulent variety, such as apples, pears, plums, cherries, apricots, nectarines, peaches and so forth, along with melons, such as cantaloupe and honeydew. In the more southern climes, you could add oranges, tangerines, lemons, bananas and pineapples as well. It makes such a delicious fruit salad to take all the different kinds of fresh fruit that are ripe at one time and to cut them up and mix them together in a big bowl, possibly with a little bit of dressing, if desired! (Nonfat plain yogurt with orange juice or some frozen orange juice concentrate makes a nice fruit salad dressing.) Fruit salads are one of our favorites. Sometimes we even make an entire meal of fruit plate with a few graham crackers.

Since we can produce only melons in the garden, which are quite perishable and cannot be stored for long periods, this means that, for other types of fruit, we are either going to need to plant an orchard or a vineyard, or preferably both. And we need to plant plenty of trees or vines, if we want to have enough fruit to last us through the winter. These are somewhat different in nature, so let us take them one at a time. Let's look at the orchard first.

PLANNING AND PREPARING FOR YOUR ORCHARD

When I say planting *your* orchard, I deliberately mean to add that emphasis on "your." You should plant the trees that will produce the fruit that *you* and your family like. If you are not particularly fond of cherries, then skip the cherry trees. On the other hand, if apples are your favorite, be sure to plant extra apple trees. This way you will have ample for yourself and to keep for the winter, as well as some surplus to give away to your friends.

There has been a significant change in the planting of commercial orchards in recent years. In the old days, trees in a commercial orchard were planted on 12- to 15-foot centers and allowed to grow up round, like a ball perched on a stick. However, in commercial orchards today, the rows are planted still about 10 to 12 feet apart, but frequently the trees within a row are planted about 5 or 6 feet apart and pruned in more of a fan shape instead of like a ball on a stick. This improves the total productivity of the acreage as well as making it far easier to harvest the fruit. For more details on this, visit some local orchards or buy a good book on the subject (*B).

In planning out your orchard, if you are going to have trees that grow very tall, such as almond, pecan and walnut trees, as well as some giant varieties of fruit trees, you should plan to plant those on the north edge of your orchard, so they will not block the sunlight from the rest of the trees. Just as with the arrangement of plants in the greenhouse, you would want the medium height trees in the middle, and the short dwarf trees on the south side of the orchard.

If your orchard is going to be planted on ground that is sloping, then it is a good idea to get a cat (a caterpillar tractor with a front blade) to come in and terrace your orchard area. Be sure to make each terrace at least 10 feet across. This will allow for both the planting of the trees on the upside edge, as well as giving you ample room to drive a tractor down to mow the grass in between the rows of trees.

When actually planting the trees, you are going to want to dig a hole about the size of three 5-gallon buckets. In the bottom of the hole, you can put some water, or water with nutrients, to give the young trees a good start. I realize it is a lot of extra effort to dig a hole considerably larger than the rootball on the young tree, but the extra growth of the tree in the ensuing years, due to the loose soil around its roots when transplanted, will be your reward.

You will most likely be planting bare root trees, and this is okay; this is the way it is usually done. They will look a bit like dead sticks with a few roots poking out the bottom and maybe a branch or two. The nurseryman where you purchase your trees will probably take out his shears and cut the trees about in half. All of a sudden, this nice 4-foot tree that you are buying is only 2-feet tall. I realize that it may be a little bit shocking, but this is by far the best way, so trust the nurseryman.

When you get home, plant the trees up to the level the nurseryman indicates. This may mean that you may have to fill the hole back up partway with loose soil, but that is what these young trees need. Be sure that the trunk of each little tree is absolutely vertical when you fill in the soil around it, because at whatever angle you plant it, that is the way the tree is going to grow from then on. (As the twig is bent, so grows the tree.)

Trees are normally planted during the very early spring while the sap is still down, before any of the trees in your area begin to put out leaves. Once you have planted them, follow your nursery's instructions about frequency of watering and fertilizing, and then have patience to wait a few months until these "sticks" begin to sprout. You may lose one or two trees and have to replace them the following winter/spring, but that is okay; it happens even in commercial orchards, so do not worry about it.

Another thing you need to take into consideration when planning and planting your orchard is that some of the species, such as apples and kiwi, have "male" trees and "female" trees. You need to have both in order to have the blossoms fertilized. A good method is to plant one male tree for every eight female trees. You could plant a female tree on either side of each male tree, and a row of female trees between each row containing male trees, such that each male tree would be surrounded by a large square of female trees. This is pictured in Figure 8.1.

**A Method For Planting
Male and Female Trees**

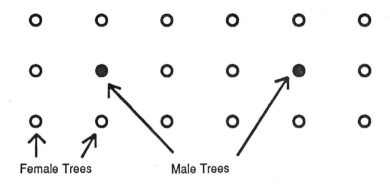

Female Trees   Male Trees

Figure 8.1

The Long Wait
And Caring For the Trees

After all the hard work of planting the trees, you are going to have to wait approximately four years before you have fruit to eat from your orchard. The Bible tells us about this:

> **23** 'And when you enter the land and plant all kinds of trees for food, then you shall count their fruit as forbidden. Three years it shall be forbidden to you; *it* shall not be eaten.
> **24** 'But in the fourth year all its fruit shall be holy, an offering of praise to the Lord.

25   'And in the fifth year you are to eat of its fruit, that its yield may increase for you; I am the LORD your God....'

—Leviticus 19

Because of the long wait for the trees to mature enough to really begin to be productive, this is why one of the first things you are going to want to do, if you buy some acreage with no structures on it, is to fence in an area and plant an orchard. It may be four or five years before you intend to move there, but this would guarantee that you would be able to begin to harvest fruit at the time you actually move to the property. Depending on the climate and the situation, you may also have to arrange for some type of irrigation, or someone to water those young trees, at least for the first two or three years. If it is close enough to you, it may be that you take weekend trips to the property at times to water them yourselves. Obviously this means that you will need water on the property at the time you plant your orchard.

Many books would stop their discussion here, assuming that everything is going to go well. Unfortunately, this is not real life. You are going to need to fertilize these trees about once a year. But, more importantly, things can go wrong. There are diseases, pests, and other factors that could damage your orchard.

For example, leaf curl is caused by a tiny insect. During one season, the leaf curl can kill just about any tree. Thus, it is wise to have someone check the orchard at least once a week. Then if something like leaf curl appears, you would want to spray immediately. I realize that "spray" is a bad word to environmentalists, but if you are trying to live in a self-reliant way and to rely on these trees to produce fruit for you, there are times when it is necessary in order to save the tree.

Similarly, apple trees can get infested with worms, as you may be aware. Worms in apples can be controlled by spraying the apple trees in the fall and then again in the spring. The details of which sprays to use and when to spray can be obtained from your local agricultural extension department or the local seed and feed store where you can buy seeds and fertilizer.

There are other diseases that can wreak havoc in an orchard. We had some pests come into one of our pear trees that stripped all of the green part off of every leaf and simply left the little tiny center stem of the leaf. Had they spread to all of our other pear trees, we would have lost them all. Yet, since we quickly spotted this problem and sprayed, we were able not only to save the rest of the pear trees but ultimately even to salvage that one affected tree.

There are many other diseases and problems that could be addressed that are beyond the scope of this book; just be prepared for them and keep a watchful eye on your orchard while it is maturing. Remember that "a stitch in time saves nine." Or, in this case, you could say "a stitch in time saves replanting half your orchard"! For books on this subject see Appendix B.

One thing that we passed over lightly is that there are a variety of pecan trees. From our experience, we would advise being certain to get the "paper-shell" pecans. Avoid the little, hard pecans; they are not worth the effort. Similarly, there are paper-shell walnuts and there are hard-shell black walnuts. Be sure to get the kind that are light tan on the outside, not the ones that are black on the outside. Those must be broken open with a hammer or a sledge hammer. The same thing is true with almonds.

We planted the wrong kind of almond trees. By the time you use an anvil and six hammers to get the almond out of the center of the seed (it looks like a peach pit), it is really no fun to eat it. Be sure you get the trees that will produce the kind of almonds that are easy to crack open.

In addition to planting the type of fruit trees that will produce fruits you enjoy, it is very wise to talk to people in the area to ascertain which trees do well there. If you learn from the wisdom of others, then you do not have to repeat their mistakes. There are a lot of wise people in your area who would love to give you advice. In fact, they are flattered when you ask them for their advice. So ask freely and they will give freely. In addition to gaining much helpful working knowledge, letting them share their accumulated wisdom with you will help to establish a friendship and a good neighbor relationship with them.

We hope that you enjoy your orchard and eating the fruit of your labors. It takes time, effort and patience, but it is well worth it. Fruit is a wonderful addition. It is ready to eat straight off the tree or it can be preserved more easily than most vegetables. Eating fresh fruits can help flush out toxins and aid in keeping your bowels regular. It has so many other benefits, we could not begin to name them all.

Harvest time is especially fun in the orchard. It can be a family affair, with everyone gathering around concentrating on a tree, with some standing on the ground picking the lower fruit, little kids picking up the fruit that falls down, and a few people on three-legged fruit-ladders picking the fruit at the top of the tree. You are going to need many, many baskets for your harvest. We happen to use the stronger plastic laundry baskets like you can buy at the supermarket for picking fruit like apples and pears. A few holes drilled in the bottom of them will let water out of them if these baskets get rained on. The smaller plastic baskets with two handles are good for smaller, more perishable and softer fruits, such as plums and peaches.

Small, 2-gallon plastic buckets work well for those who are climbing the ladders to use. Hooks for these can be formed from pieces of coat-hanger wire and attached to the bail. This can then hook over your belt or in a belt loop to allow both hands to be free for climbing and picking.

Once you pick the fruit, you will need to keep the baskets of fruit covered or enclosed some way, so that the friendly chickens, raccoons, deer and other hungry animals will not be able to get at them until you are able to squeeze them into juice, freeze, can, dehydrate or otherwise utilize them.

Speaking of squeezing fruit into juice, most years we squeeze much of our apple crop into juice. For us, this, too, is a family affair. Everyone gathers around and finds a task, as we load the apples into the grinder, which drops them down into the slatted wooden cylinder of the press. Once that gets full, then two of the stronger people turn the crank on the press which lowers a plate the size of the inside of the cylinder. This squeezes all the juice out of the pulp, which then drains into a waiting container below. Someone else will then use a funnel to pour this freshly-squeezed juice into 1-quart, half-gallon, or gallon plastic jugs, leaving some air space for expansion when it is frozen. Someone else will tighten down the lids and date each jug with a permanent marker. Then they are ready for freezing (or drinking fresh).

One year, we got a hundred gallons of apple juice from our apple trees! This apple juice is by far too sweet and strong to drink by itself! You have to dilute it at

least 50 percent with water, or it will curl your hair! For
this reason, we find the 1-quart plastic containers the most
practical for our use. This way, it is a smaller amount to
thaw, if frozen, and each quart really makes about a half
gallon of juice when diluted. The best-tasting juice is
made by mixing varieties of apples together.

We go through the same process in squeezing our
grapes into juice for freezing. But we have not talked
about grapes yet, so let us do that now.

PLANNING AND PLANTING
YOUR VINEYARD

When Noah got off the ark, the first thing he did
was to plant a vineyard. It must have been four years
later before he had fruit from it to make wine. Then,
according to the Bible, immediately he got drunk, which
was not a good idea.

You can divide grapes into two categories in two
different ways. Of course, there are red grapes and white
grapes (actually a light green). Another way to divide
grapes is into table grapes and wine or juice grapes.
Table grapes are grapes such as Concord, Red Flame,
Thompson Seedless (a white grape), and other varieties of
white seedless grapes. One of the reasons these are table
grapes is that they are bigger and therefore more appealing to the eye. However, if you squeeze them, you
get very little juice. They are delicious to eat, and they
give you lots of excellent fiber (especially if you eat the
seeds, too) but they are not the best for producing grape
juice.

There are many white juice (or wine) grapes as well
as many red juice (or wine) grapes. Out of all the grapes
that we have tried, we have found that Cabernet Savignon

grapes give by far the most juice and the vines are the most prolific, at least in our location. This juice is delicious to drink just as grape juice, as well as being an appealing, robust reddish-purple color. Of course, if you are so inclined, you can use the juice from the Cabernet Savignon grapes to make Cabernet Savignon wine.

You should give some careful thought to choosing which variety of grapes you will plant. I do not understand why, but the Bible admonishes us to plant only one type of grape in a vineyard:

> **9 "You shall not sow your vineyard with two kinds of seed, lest all the produce of the seed which you have sown, and the increase of the vineyard become defiled...."**
>
> **—Deuteronomy 22**

We have violated this rule and have Concord and Thompson Seedless table grapes growing along one fence, as well as Chardonnay juice (or wine) white grapes and Cabernet Savignon juice (or wine) red grapes in the same vineyard area. We basically have four varieties in our 200-vine vineyard.

We planted three additional types of grapes and found out that they did not give nearly the amount of juice nor produce nearly as many clusters of grapes as the Cabernet Savignons. We asked our agricultural extension people if we could cut these off and graft Cabernet Savignon onto them, and they told us no.

It turns out that this was incorrect information. By that time, the grapevines had a nice, thick trunk approximately 1 inch in diameter, and we could have instantly grown incredible Cabernet Savignon grapes from them, had we grafted them in during the winter while the sap was down in the roots. Unfortunately, because of the erroneous information we had received, we deliberately killed them by cutting them off at ground level and we planted new Cabernet Savignon grape "sticks" in their place, starting over. Jeani and I are pictured on the front cover standing by some of our Cabernet Savignon grape vines (Cabs) while they were in production.

Allow me to explain the term "grape sticks." Each year you will prune the juice/wine grapes, but not the table grapes. If you have a nice, heavy cutting that you pruned off that has at least three buds on it, you can plant this and it will grow into a mature grapevine. You plant it so that two of the buds are in the ground and one bud remains above ground level. These cuttings look like a bunch of dead sticks, and it is with these that you start a vineyard.

Some people make a living by planting these dead-looking grape sticks in rows like in a garden, about 6-inches apart. They then leave them there for a year to let them root. Rooted grape "sticks" can be sold for significantly more than the initial prunings themselves. Since many people are impatient and want to save a year, they will buy the rooted grape sticks from another vineyard to use in starting their own vineyard.

Some people recommend planting grapes about 6-feet apart, while others say to plant them about 12-feet apart. We would highly recommend 12-feet apart. The only time that the 6-feet apart planting has any advantage is the first and possibly the second years when you get a slight amount of increased production due to a greater number of vines. After that, as the vines mature, you would be better off having them 12-feet apart.

The object with the juice or wine grapes is to let one stem grow up along a grape stake. The grape stake is a treated 2-by-2 post about 6 feet in length, pointed on one end, that you drive into the ground near the grape plant. You tie the stem to this stake. There is plastic tying material available in rolls, made for this purpose that will stretch and not damage the vines. The object, ultimately, is to have the stem grow straight up the stake and have a left and right branch about 3 or 4 feet above the ground, and another left and right branch about 5 or 6 feet above the ground. At those two heights, you stretch wires between your grape stakes, and these horizontal branches will grow along those wires (of course with your help by tying them to the wires).

At the end of each row of grapes, you need to put a fence post in the ground that is slanted away from the rows. It is to these that you will attach the ends of the two horizontal wires that run between the stakes.

The first year or so, pruning is not all that critical. The main thing you want is to get one major vertical stem going up the stake, while trimming off all the side-shoots and off-shoots. Eventually, when you get your four horizontal branches going, then you will annually trim all of the vines that grow off those horizontal branches, leaving one or two buds on each branch. A diagram of a typical grapevine grown in this manner is shown in Figure 8.2, both unpruned and pruned.

This discussion about planting, pruning and stringing wires in the fashion described is primarily for juice grapes. The table grapes are quite a different matter; they do not need the individual pruning. We simply planted these along one fence in the vineyard and let them grow. After several years, we did trim the lower branches off, because it was a nuisance to stoop way down to pick the lower grapes. After they got too bushy, we trimmed them back with hedge clippers. We have found that the Con-

Unpruned and Pruned Grapevines

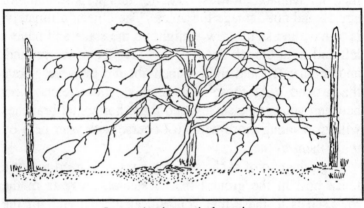

Grape vine in need of pruning

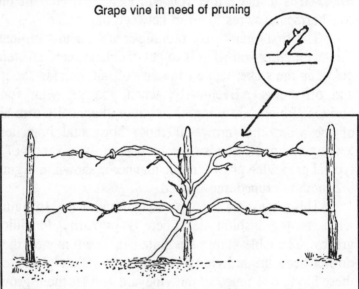

A well-pruned grape vine

Figure 8.2

cords are by far the most disease-resistant of all the grapes we have grown.

Other varieties of grapes can get leaf-mold and bugs of all sorts that will literally suck the juice out of each grape. If you run into these problems, you will need to consult the local agricultural extension or your seed/feed store for the proper thing to use on the grapes. In many cases, sprinkling them or spraying them with sulfur will get rid of many of the problems.

Grapes put down a taproot, much like a tree does, and after a few years it is hardly necessary to water them. If you do water them, it is better not to water them with overhead sprinklers, but to water them from the ground level once a month and really soak them. Then with patience, wait another full month before you water them again. Of course, this can vary somewhat with the climate and the soil conditions, which you would have to investigate locally.

Four years after you plant them, your grapes will start to really produce and, of course, you will want to eat some of them. One of the differences between the table grapes and the juice grapes is that the juice grapes are quite small, even though the cluster may be big, as compared to the individual grape of table grape varieties. Therefore, especially if you do not eat the seeds, eating the juice grapes can become quite a chore. Just like some animals were designed for one purpose and other animals were designed for a different purpose, so it is with grapes. You need to plant the kind or kinds that will fit your specific desires and requirements.

As with the orchard, if you are going to plant your vineyard on a sloping area, you will want to have a cat come in and terrace it, with each terrace being at least 10 feet wide.

It is advisable to make provisions to buy ample grape stakes, because some of them will break when you try to drive them in. Others may break after a few years' wear and tear and they will need to be replaced. The ideal is to drive in all the grape stakes to a consistent height so that the top wire can be stapled to the top of the grape stake and the lower wire can be laid across a nail that has been driven into the side of the stake. This makes for easy replacement of a faulty stake. All you have to do is to remove one staple, get rid of the old stake and drive in the new one. I have also found that it is better to plant the grape *beside* the stake, rather than in front of it. If it is planted in front of it, it could get in the way of your tractor when you are mowing the grass in the vineyard.

When planting new grape starts, one nice way to plant them is to cut the top and bottom out of a gallon milk carton and plant the stick within it, so that the carton is half in the ground and half out of it. This will protect the grape start, from weeds and from too much cool air, as it takes root and buds.

After the plant has matured, you may well want to use some type of mulch around the bottom of the grapevine to keep down the weeds in the immediate area. Grapes also need to be fertilized each year.

All this may sound like a lot of work, but remember that the fruits of your labor are well worth it. Grapes are delicious eaten fresh off the vine. They can be washed and frozen as individual grapes on a cookie sheet, so they do not stick together. Once frozen, they can be stored in ziplock baggies in the freezer and eaten frozen like candy all year long. Also, we find that the juice from the grapes is very strong and sweet and can be cut close to 50 percent with water to make a tasty, refreshing beverage all through the winter months, if you freeze it or can it.

Grapes are not only delicious, but they are also high in nutrition. The grape seed extract (leucoanthocyanin) is one of the most powerful antioxidants yet discovered. Antioxidants neutralize free radicals in the body, which are the cause of seventy-one major diseases, including cancer and heart problems. (See Chapter 12 for more on antioxidants.)

LET THE BERRIES BEGIN

Another very useful and popular type of fruit, that you do not find in a vineyard nor in an orchard, is berries. If you want to raise raspberries or blackberries, you may want to plant these around a perimeter fence. These things are prolific, and once they get started they spread. In fact, if you find some blackberries on your property in an undesirable place, they can be very hard to get rid of, like a weed. However, planted along a perimeter fence, they also provide security. Someone may climb a bare fence, but I guarantee you, he will not climb a fence that is covered with blackberry vines! They have too many harpoons all over them!

Lewis Hill gives the following good description of pruning bramble fruits in his book on fruits and berries:

> If pruning is neglected when you grow the bramble fruits, the planting will deteriorate rapidly. The brambles, both raspberries and blackberries, are unusual in that while their roots are perennial, their canes are biennial. So while the roots of these plants often live for many years, each cane sprouts and grows to its full height in one year, bears fruit the following year, then dies.

Because of this, after a few years wild raspberries and blackberries become a jungle of dead canes, and soon the entire patch dies off. Cultivated canes that are neglected will do the same.

This is fairly simple to avoid: Simply cut off each dead cane to ground level after it has finished bearing in late summer. You'll recognize the dead ones by their pallid color and brittle appearance. Hand-held clippers are ideal tools for this job, and you'll probably want to wear thick gloves to handle the thorny canes.

—*Fruits & Berries For the Home Garden*,
pp. 188-189, Garden Way Publishing

Figure 8.3

Figure 8.3 shows one free standing method of supporting bramble bushes, if you choose not to plant them along a fence.

Strawberries are normally grown in a separate spot that is neither part of the garden nor the orchard. It takes about two years to get a good strawberry crop growing. Once it catches on well, then it will produce year after year for you, but it does take some attention. One of the nice things about strawberries is that they come to fruit late in the spring; thus, you can be enjoying them while the rest of your fruit is maturing.

Apples and pears come to maturity much later on, with many of the other fruits, including grapes, maturing sometime in between the strawberries and the apples.

LET THE BEES DO THE WORK

In our chapter on the greenhouse, we point out that normally bees are necessary to cause lemon blossoms to be fertilized. Since we have dwarf lemon trees in our greenhouse, we therefore have to duplicate the work of the bees by going from blossom to blossom with a small artist's paint brush. Outside, in the orchard and berry patch, you will need bees to do this pollinating for you. There may be a neighbor close by who has bees and his bees will gladly come over and take the pollen from your blossoms back to their hives.

Since we like honey and use it in baking bread especially, we decided that we would put in our own beehives. Bees have a radius of approximately 10 miles. Not only will they take the pollen and nutrients from blossoms in the orchard and blackberry patch, but also from the pumpkins and squash in the garden. We found it interesting to learn that they also take pollen from cedar trees and other evergreen trees. On the average year, we get about 100 pounds of delicious, unpasteurized, nutrient-rich honey from our four hives.

There are two ways to go in caring for the beehives. One is to learn to do it yourself and to get some equipment (clothing, a smoker, a honey extractor and so forth). Beekeeping is certainly a valuable and useful skill to develop, if you are so inclined. Another alternative is to contract with a local beekeeper to come in and take care of your hives for half of the honey. The majority of the years, we have gone the second route, which works out well for everyone.

No one has ever "tamed" bees; they are still "wild." However, they are very useful and advantageous on a homestead and something that should be considered seriously. Let them do the work of going from blossom to blossom and enjoy the delectable honey that they produce from this effort. Such a deal I could not get for you anywhere else!

SUMMARY AND CONCLUSION

The desirability of having fruit in addition to vegetables should be obvious. They are sweet and, thus, they gratify our sweet tooth. In addition, they are nutritious, easy to digest, and they provide a good source of dietary fiber. If you want to produce fruit other than that in the garden (watermelon, cantaloupe, honeydew, and so forth), you will want to have an orchard, vineyard and/or a berry patch or a berry "fence."

We discussed selecting the kind of trees that will produce fruit that you enjoy and that grows well in the area where your acreage is located. Take extra time when planting the trees to dig a big hole, so that you will have a lot of loose soil surrounding the tender young roots. Then be sure to care for the young trees by fertilizing them and keeping them free of pests and diseases. If you treat your trees well, they will reward you with a manifold harvest of enjoyable fruit for years to come.

To produce grapes, of course, you will need a vineyard. Some people may be interested just in growing table grapes, if they are not particularly interested in grape juice or grape wine. The grapes from the table grapevines can be eaten immediately and the excess can be preserved. You can make jams and jellies out of them, or you can freeze the individual grapes, as we mentioned, then use these as a frozen candy treat throughout the year.

If you want to produce grape juice and/or grape wine, then you will want to plant the juice- or wine-type grapes. These require much more care and need to be pruned annually.

In addition to an orchard and/or a vineyard, you may also wish to have a berry patch or berry bushes planted along perimeter fences. Blackberries are one of the most hardy of all berries and they will thrive in many climates. Raspberries are a little more fragile and may not have quite the same productive capacity that blackberries do depending on your conditions. But, of course, they are delicious and they do grow prolifically.

If you want to grow strawberries, you would want to have a separate strawberry patch that could be left to produce strawberries year after year.

Books on the subject of planting and caring for orchards and vineyards are listed in Appendix B (*B), along with the sources of the publishers and where they can normally be purchased.

The various types of fruit discussed in this chapter will make a welcome addition to the other types of food that you will be producing.

Some of you "yippeeio" cowboys might be thinking, "Enough about all of these plants and trees—let's get on to the animals!" I am with you, so let's saddle up, round 'em up, and take a look at what animals might be best for your little home on the range.

Chapter 9

ANIMALS
FOR FOOD AND FUN

Many people reading this book might have images of saddling up the trusty horse, galloping down to the lower forty and rounding up the cows to bring back to be milked. We have probably gotten this from movies and from novels that we have read. However, in reality that would probably be the least efficient way possible to have animals on your little piece of paradise.

Let us start at the beginning and see why this is true. Animals can be pets and fun (yes, I said *fun*). You can have a good romp with your dog or fun hand-feeding and training your llama, or your children might even enjoy making pets out of some of the other animals, like a lamb or an orphaned goat kid. But fun is not the primary reason we want animals on our acreage. We primarily want them for six things:

1. milk
2. meat
3. eggs
4. wool
5. guard service
6. skins or hides

We will examine each of these six vital areas one at a time. As we go, you can decide which of these six reasons are more important—and which are less important—to you personally. Then you can get the animals that best meet your specific needs. Some animals are also good for weed control (goats eat poison oak, for example) which helps in fire protection. But before we look at these six fundamental considerations, we need to cover a basic subject first.

BIG VERSUS SMALL

Larger animals, like cows and horses, have some advantages but they also have some major disadvantages. One of the disadvantages of having a horse is that, in most cases (unless you are a full-time cowboy), it is basically a pleasure animal. It does not produce milk, meat, eggs or wool. A horse can also ruin a good pasture, because it tends to pull up the grass by the roots rather than biting it off higher up like other grazing livestock. It also costs a couple of thousand dollars a year to keep a horse, if you have to buy hay to feed him. This would include all of his shots, grain, a salt lick and other expenses involved in maintaining a horse. Horses are great to have and they can be a lot of fun, but you should realize that they are purely a luxury item and treat them accordingly.

If you have the acreage and the finances to afford horses, and you can take the time to ride them two or three times a week, to groom them, and to train them, then be my guest. I grew up in Texas around horses, and Jeani and I both happen to love them. They are terrific animals. However, since they are a luxury, they would be about the last animal that I would recommend for someone to invest in on a homestead property.

Cows are quite large, in the 1,000-2,000 pound range, and they are expensive. If you had one milk cow versus four milk goats and you were to lose your cow, you essentially would have lost your entire investment. On the other hand, if you lost one of your goats, you still would have three left that could continue to produce milk and offspring for you.

One other real preference of milk goats over cows is the size. A woman can easily handle a 100-150 pound goat, but it would be far more difficult for a small woman to handle a huge cow of 1,000 pounds or more. Since chores around the property will need to be shared by various family members, it seems wise to favor animals that women and older children can easily handle, as well as men.

PRODUCING YOUR OWN MILK

One thing I did not realize, when we moved to our place in the country, is that for a cow to give milk on an ongoing basis, she has to be "freshened" every year—that is, she has to give birth to a new calf. What this means is that there will be a time during the year when her milk production will dry up during the terminal months of her pregnancy. Also, you are also going to have to give a portion of her milk to the calf during its first few months after she gives birth. (All of the milk should go to the calf for the first few days; during that time, it is called colostrum and it is high in protein and immune-building nutrients that are important to a newborn animal.) Therefore, if you wanted continuous milk production year round, you would have to maintain a bull and two cows. This is quite an expensive investment just for milk.

On the other hand, you could have a buck goat and four or five doe goats which could easily provide you with milk year round for the cost of just one good cow. Again, if you lost one of these smaller animals, your entire production of milk would not be shut down by the loss.

This brings up the age-old question about the taste of goat's milk. At the mention of it, many people shudder and instantly rebel. Sometimes this may be for a valid reason. Perhaps they were in Switzerland or on a farm someplace where they drank some warm goat's milk right out in the field where the shepherd was milking the goat and it tasted very different from the cold, pasteurized cow's milk that they were accustomed to drinking.

I should interject here that there are six breeds of goats. The kind that we have and would recommend are Nubians. Their milk has more butterfat content and it tastes much more like cow's milk than that of the other breeds.

I would like to relate a story to you. A pastor friend of ours had regularly bought goat's milk from us. At first, the children would not drink it, because they *thought* they did not like it. Then the parents started pouring it into empty cardboard half-gallon containers left from the cow's milk they had bought at the store. Then the children drank it very readily and enjoyed it.

One evening, we were having dinner at their house and another couple dropped by. The discussion turned to goat's milk. This other couple had the typical "ugh" reaction. The pastor told them that he did not believe they could tell the difference between cow's milk and goat's milk. He then disappeared into the kitchen and brought back two glasses of milk. He told them that one contained goat's milk and the other cow's milk. This couple tasted both glasses, pointed at one and said, "That is definitely cow's milk." Pointing to the other, they said, "That is definitely goat's milk." The pastor had the last laugh because both glasses he had brought in for them to sample were cold, delicious goat's milk!

If you are accustomed to drinking unhomogenized cow's milk, then a cold glass of unhomogenized goat's milk is just as delicious and you really cannot tell the difference in taste. In fact, goat's milk is much better for you and much easier to digest than cow's milk, as the following article points out. This article, "Nutrition's Unsung Hero," by Roger D. Jones, gives a descriptive snapshot of the valuable dairy goat, an ideal addition to a homestead:

> Despite common misconceptions, goats are beneficial to those who raise them. Under proper care and maintenance, goats provide complete protein substances in their milk and meat. After making a careful choice of the breed of goat, a nanny makes a lovable, productive and easy-to-care-for pet.
>
> Suppose you were to consume 1 pound of lean beefsteak, 3-1/2 pounds of oysters, 3-1/5 pounds of chicken, 1-2/3 pounds of peas, 8 eggs, 7 oranges, 5 pounds of spinach, 6 tomatoes and 6 bananas. The nutritional value of all these foods combined is equal to one quart of goat's milk. Yet the dairy goat has been the most underrated animal on earth.
>
> Many...rare base minerals are contained within the goat's milk....The fat globules of goat milk are so much finer than in other milk that one gets all the milk, which also explains why goat milk is so difficult to separate. Separating is seldom necessary anyway, for the whole

milk used in coffee isn't much different from the ordinary cream. Moreover, the milk goat can and does release into her milk the epithelial (health) cells and is the only animal known to do so. These cells, when taken in the human system, encounter dangerous disease germs in the bloodstream, and destroy them. That is the secret of the nanny's product being a major disease preventative.

Likewise, the meat itself is a complete protein food. There is so very little fat content in the meat that oil is needed to grease the pan when frying burgers. It is similarly compared to lamb. Taste the meat and you will find it tender, sweet, and easily digested.

Common misconceptions about goats are that they all stink, and eat tin cans. It's the buck, "Billy," that smells; not "nanny." Furthermore, you will never find a goat that eats tin cans! The paper maybe, but not the cans.

When choosing the right goat for you, consider the breed and its temperament, as well as the cost. Basically, there are six breeds of goats. Saanans are white goats with passive temperaments. They are the "holsteins" of the goats. Toggenburges also have a passive temperament, and come in brown to beige colors. Alpines goats feature short, upright ears and longer coats. They, too, are passive in nature. Nubians have long, droopy ears and a definite Roman nose. These goats make good pets, being the most lovable breed.

LaMancha's are those creatures that have mouselike ears and make lovable pets also. Grade goats are mixtures of any two or more of the above breeds.

Your use of the nanny also would determine your choice of breed. Show goats need to be registered with the American Dairy Goat Association. Strictly milking for home use, choosing a grade goat could save you money. The thing to look for in choosing a milker is the length of the teat, and how the bag feels. The bag should not be hard, but pliable when massaged. For best results, the teats should fit the width of your hand. Also, the teat holes should not be too small or too large. By this I mean—when the teats are too small, you are liable to bruise them upon each milking. Because of the pencil lead size stream of milk, milking takes longer and requires more work. When the hole is too large, the milk will drip out, and there will be a constant problem of udder diseases. For the best results on buying your first milker, purchase a nanny that already has freshened so you can see how the bag is attached when full. Know first hand how she milks by doing it yourself. Also make sure you test the nanny's milk for taste by drinking some already chilled from the previous milking. A milk goat is unlike a cow in that she requires less room, feed, or medical care.

Nanny's home must consist of a clean, dry, and properly ventilated area. The size, shape, and color of the shelter depends only on the individual's taste. One ton of good alfalfa hay a year feeds approximately five goats. Goats also make good lawn mowers. Caution—keep them away from trees and flowerbeds. The milking goat should receive a good dairy grain mix at each milking, morning and evening.

There is nothing that will rip open a goat's udder faster than another goat with horns. Goats rarely are born hornless. Therefore, the horns should be burned off within the first two weeks of birth. At this age and done properly, it is painless.

Nanny rarely needs medical attention if properly taken care of, although, the unexpected such as neighborhood dogs mauling the goat, a leg torn by a fence, or breach birth will mean a call for a veterinarian.

When you have chosen the goat for you, and have provided the proper care and maintenance for her, years of enjoyability and productivity await you.

—*Northwest Magazine*, August 27, 1978

Researcher of vibrant health, author and centurian Norman Walker (who died in his sleep at the age of one hundred and twenty-two) makes these comments about goat's milk:

> Whenever milk, other than mother's milk, is needed, *raw goat's milk* is the most logical and beneficial milk for humans of all ages to drink....
>
> The goat is probably the cleanest animal we have. Its eliminative organs are close to perfect.   Hence her disposition is friendly—almost loving....
>
> The quality of goat's milk is far superior to that of the cow, being naturally homogenous, having more non-protein nitrogen, better quality of proteins, with much higher amounts of niacin and thiamine than almost any other food or food product.
>
> —*Fresh Vegetable and Fruit Juices*, pp. 86-89
> Norwalk Press, 2218 East Magnolia
> Phoenix, AZ 85034

We would concur with Norman Walker's comment that goats are clean animals. In fact, if they pull their hay out onto the ground, they will not eat it, as other animals will. For this reason, it is highly desirable to build some sort of a "keyhole" feeder for goats. One possible type is pictured in Figure 9.1. The slot is wide enough for their neck (about 4 inches) but not wide enough to pull their head out. The keyhole part should be 7 or 8 inches, wide enough for the head to come out. This forces a goat to lift her head up each time she wants to leave the feeder and usually prevents her from taking out a mouthful of hay to drop on the ground. (Illustrations in this chapter are from *Country Women—A Handbook for the New Farmer* by Anchor Books, pp 189, 226, 228, 278, which is now out of print.)

Keyhole-type Feeder For Goats

Figure 9.1

There has never been a case of tuberculosis (TB) found in a goat. Therefore, its milk does not need to be pasteurized (heated, which kills the enzymes) like cow's milk does.

Other than cows or goats, the only option you would have for fresh milk would be milk sheep. People raise these all over Europe, but our dairy lobby has convinced Congress that they should be illegal to be imported into the United States. Thus, unfortunately you cannot get milk sheep here in the United States.

Some people with allergies to dairy products make a milk substitute out of soybeans or nuts, like almonds, for "soy milk" or "almond milk." These can be used on cereal and for certain other such uses instead of milk. However, if you wish to raise animals for milk, goat's milk is the closest thing to mother's milk, the most easily-digested, and the least likely to cause allergic reactions.

From this discussion alone, I trust you realize that we prefer the smaller animals over the larger animals for a number of very valid reasons. Goats are also very easy to milk. You can build a milking stand with a stanchion at one end to secure the goat's head above a grain box while you are milking. They are very easy to train to come when you call them and to hop up on the platform. A free-standing milking stand is pictured in Figure 9.2

A Milking Stand With Grain Box on Stanchion

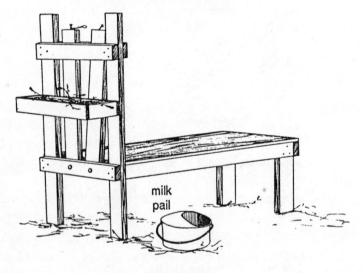

milk
pail

Figure 9.2

Jeani is shown on the front cover milking one of our Nubian goats (they can be brown or black or multicolored). In building our milking stand, we included a side piece where the person milking can sit. (Otherwise you would need a stool.)

A good freshened goat will give about a gallon of milk a day, with two milkings. If you wish optimum milk production, you would want to milk twice a day, preferably at about the same times each day. However, it is not necessary to milk twice a day. After four years of doing so, we decided that the trade off in time was more important to us than the difference in total milk production and we dropped down to milking just once a day, which worked out just fine. Goats are very adaptable animals. They are also very friendly and love to be petted. They like people and if you handle them a lot when they are kids, they may like to follow you when you go on walks.

ANIMALS FOR MEAT

God appears to have created various animals for various purposes. Horses are great for riding and cows are not. Cows are great for giving milk, but horses are not. Goats are great for milking, but are not really well designed for meat production, while sheep give lots of meat per animal. This is not to say that you cannot eat goats—you can. Particularly if eaten while very young, they are delicious, but the amount of meat per animal is not nearly that of a sheep.

Therefore, in the four-legged animal category, the most productive and reasonable options for meat would be cows, sheep and pigs. Because of size, we chose to shy away from cows. However, one year we bought a baby calf. Some friends of ours had some extra pasture land, so we left it down there all summer. Then, just as our garden was finishing up, we brought it up to glean out of the garden. Then we had it butchered, cut up, and frozen. This meat lasted us well over two years. If you do decide to raise a cow for meat, you could do a similar thing.

Sheep can be an ongoing source of meat, as well as producing wool that you can either sell or spin into yarn for making woolen clothing. We have a very small flock of sheep. In the winter, we narrow our flock down to one ram and 15 ewes. Then in the spring, actually beginning in January or February, the ewes will begin lambing. Many of them will have twins, but some of them will only have one. The average is about one and a half lambs per ewe. Thus, our flock grows during the summer to between 30 and 40 sheep.

We let them graze all summer by rotating which pastures we have them grazing on. Rather than allowing the sheep to graze all over one large pasture, if you subdivide that pasture into four smaller areas, and let them graze in one section for a week and then move them onto the next section, this means that each section will lie fallow for three weeks to allow a good grass growth between times. You can raise at least twice as many sheep on the same amount of pasture this way, as you can if you let them graze the entire larger pasture area at will.

As long as the sheep can graze and feed themselves, we essentially leave them alone. We have found them to be a very hardy animal that requires little care and pampering. But come October or so, when the grass ceases to rejuvenate itself as quickly and the potential of hay feeding arises, then we usually butcher, or give away to poor families or pastors, about 20 of the sheep. Each of the lambs will weigh out between 50 and 100 pounds and for sure we will butcher the male lambs. (If we need a new ram, we will buy or trade for one from a different bloodline.) We may keep a few of the new lamb ewes with good bloodlines and characteristics to replace some older ewes that are past their prime. Therefore, we usually end up butchering an old ewe or two which we make purely into lamburger, since the mutton is not as nice to eat in other forms, such as steaks and chops, as is the tender lamb.

Most communities have what they call a "farm kill" company. They will actually come out to your ranch, kill, skin and butcher the sheep, hang them up in a refrigerated truck and take them back to their place, where they let them hang for three or four days in a walk-in refrigerator. If you wish, you can come in and be there when they cut up the meat, telling them how thick you would like the lambchops and steaks, which roasts to keep, how much you want converted into lamburger, and so forth. Then you are going to need a great deal of deep-freezer space to keep your packages of meat frozen for a year or more while you use them up.

Pigs are an animal that some people shy away from because of biblical admonitions. Other people shy away from them because of their heavy fat content. In general, we find that they are not as popular on people's individual homestead ranches as are sheep for meat. Pigs do have one advantage; they are "rooting" animals. If you turn them loose in your garden after you are finished harvesting for the season, they will dig out the roots of all of the vegetables as well as digging out the roots of the weeds. They really scour a place clean.

One of the big disadvantages is that pigs only have one stomach, and whatever "garbage" they might eat goes almost directly into their meat. In contrast, ruminators, like cows, sheep and goats, chew the cud and have more complex digestive systems with three- or four-chambered stomachs that more thoroughly digest what they eat. (Incidentally, it is an interesting sidenote to realize that the animals that the biblical dietary laws prohibited the Hebrews from eating, and labeled as "unclean," were the scavenger and "garbage eating" animals, birds and fish.)

One other advantage of pigs is they will have litters of some 6 to 10 piglets, so you get more production per sow than you would per ewe. Therefore, if you decide to raise meat for sale, pigs would be very high on the list because of their high productivity.

For us, turkeys are a specialty item. Each year we get about six turkey chicks to raise. We frequently lose one or two along the way, but that still usually leaves us with at least four to have one each for our celebration at Thanksgiving and Christmas, and then a couple left in the freezer that we can use on other special occasions. Turkeys are the most stupid animals on the ranch (sheep are a close second). If they are outside and it is raining, they have been known to look up, open their beaks, and drown themselves. In spite of this, it is nice to have these big turkeys around during the fall before they are butchered. Every time we see one, it is a pleasant reminder of Thanksgiving and Christmas and an opportunity to say an extra thanks to the Lord.

We have mentioned raising rabbits in an earlier chapter when we discussed producing meat in the city. There are many homesteads that maintain a rabbit hutch with quite a few rabbits. They can provide a nice, additional source of food, that tastes something like the dark meat on a chicken. But, in our estimation, a far more important consideration is that of raising chickens.

"HERE, CHICK-CHICK"

Without a doubt, chickens are *the most important animal* to have for self-reliant living. You can produce a continuous supply of protein without killing the source. Chickens are much more disease resistant than rabbits. Without chickens, no homestead would be complete.

Chickens are usually one of the favorite meat animals on the entire ranch. People tend to love fried chicken and other delicious chicken dishes.

Let us pass on to you how we raise our chickens. In early February, we purchase about 100-125 Cornish-cross chicks. This breed is purely designed for meat production and not for egg laying. They grow extremely rapidly, but because they develop such huge bodies so quickly, sometimes their legs simply will not support their rapid weight gain and you wind up with some limpy, gimpy-looking chickens close to butchering time. We raise these for about 8-10 weeks, and then have them butchered, cut up and frozen. They are very delicious to eat with thick, meaty breasts.

When I say we "have them butchered," I mean that literally. There is a service not too far from us, where we take the live chickens in crates. They butcher them, dress them, double-bag them and freeze them for a very reasonable fee per chicken. We pick them up ready to store in the freezer! These people have automatic machinery to do the plucking and it is well worth the small fee.

One year we butchered all of our own chickens. There were five of us working who butchered, cleaned, and dressed 75 chickens. We had a production line going where one person would catch the chicken and cut off its head. He would put it in a barrel to flop around. The next person would dip it in very hot water and then pluck out the feathers. The third individual would then gut the chicken, cut off its feet, and save the liver, heart and, sometimes, the gizzard. A fourth individual would go over the fine-tuning and pick off or cut off any remaining undesirables on the chicken. The fifth person would then put it in a plastic bag for freezing. It took us a solid nine hours to complete 75 chickens, and we were all totally exhausted! If the necessity arose, we would certainly be willing to do that again, but personally we have found that the modest cost in having them butchered for us is well worth the savings in time.

Butchering one chicken is not all that bad. You can cut off its head with a sharp hatchet or axe (or wring its neck) and let it flop around on the ground. (Our preference is to put it in a barrel to flop around.) When it stops flopping, dip it in very hot water (if it is boiling, that will pull the skin off too), remove the feathers and then dress it out. The only negative to doing just one chicken at a time is that you have to get a pot of water boiling that is big enough to hold a chicken, all for just one chicken. However, this is the way people did it before the freezer age. They would butcher a chicken or two every time they needed one. Fresh is always best and so delicious! But having some in the freezer is a handy convenience.

After we have butchered our Cornish-cross meat chickens, we clean out and sterilize the area where they have been, and immediately bring in a brooder full (100-150) of Rhode Island Red chicks. This breed is better designed for egg production than for meat. We start these under our brooder (a metal hood with two lights under it for heat) as baby chicks and gradually raise the height of the brooder as they grow up. One type of a brooder is shown in Figure 9.3. These chickens are full grown and usually laying by about October. This is also about the time that the Rhode Island Reds we raised the previous year are beginning to molt and their egg production is dropping so much that the cost of the feed is worth more than the eggs.

A Brooder For Chicks

Figure 9.3

So, around that time, we have the Rhode Island Reds from the previous year butchered into stew chickens (they are a little bit tough to be fryers), and we move the new Rhode Island Red chickens into the area where we have had the previous egg layers. These chickens can produce an egg a day apiece. A little arithmetic lets you know that we can get up to 100 eggs per day when all of the chickens are at maximum production. This is obviously far more than we can consume, so we sell the surplus at a nearby store.

Thus, for meat from the chickens, we have both the fryer chickens that we raise from chicks and the stew chickens from the previous year's layers. This provides the major portion of our meat.

Many of us like eggs, at least occasionally, for breakfast. But eggs are also a called-for ingredient in making many other dishes, pastries and some desserts. Even the old standby of eggnog (alcoholic or non-alcoholic) requires them. By far, the best source of eggs on your homestead would be chickens.

Now let me warn you that there are chickens, and then there are chickens, and then there are chickens! There are quite a number of breeds of chickens. Some breeds lay white eggs, while others lay speckled eggs and some brown eggs. Among the health-food crowd, the brown eggs seem to be by far the most preferred. Our Rhode Island Red chickens lay brown eggs. Since we keep a rooster for every 15 hens, these are fertile eggs, which are supposed to be even more healthful than non-fertile eggs.

Some breeds of chickens lay an average of an egg every day, especially in the spring. Some lay small eggs, some lay very large eggs. We would encourage you to do your own research, but the end result of our research was that the Rhode Island Reds were by far the best all-around for egg production, in our opinion.

If you wanted to raise just a single breed of chicken to use for **both** meat and eggs, I would recommend Barred Plymouth Rocks. These are the chickens that are black and white striped. Like other chickens, if you order them the regular way, you would get about 1 rooster for every 15 to 20 hens. If you order a "straight run," this means that they are not sexed and you will get about 50 percent roosters and 50 percent hens. Of course, you would use the majority of the roosters for frying and preserving.

The Barred Plymouth Rock is a non-hybrid breed of chickens. Thus, they would faithfully reproduce their own kind. You would need to incubate the eggs, however, since most of the chickens that you buy as chicks come from many, many generations of incubations and the "setting" instinct has been bred out of them. If you want hens that will actually set on their eggs, you are going to have to go to one of your country neighbors who has chickens that have been hatched from setting and buy some from him.

Whichever breed you choose, we feel that chickens are an absolute must if you are going to move into a rural area and live self-reliantly. Someday we may not have the convenience of all the refrigeration that we have today. With chickens, you could keep the meat alive "on the foot" until you needed it, and then slaughter a chicken hours before you needed to cook for a meal. In the meantime, if you are raising predominantly hens, hopefully you would be getting daily egg production from them, providing protein and flavor for your diet.

Some people have tried to use ducks for egg production with varying degrees of success. That may be a viable option, but in our opinion this is not the best way to go.

The type of feeder and waterer you would need for baby chicks, as well as that needed for grown poultry, are pictured in Figure 9.4.

After you read the following article from *Time Magazine*, you will really want to put in your own meat chickens, wherever you live:

SOMETHING SMELLS FOWL: The good news about chicken is that thanks to modern processing techniques, it costs only about a third of what it did two dec-

Needed Equipment For Chickens and Turkeys

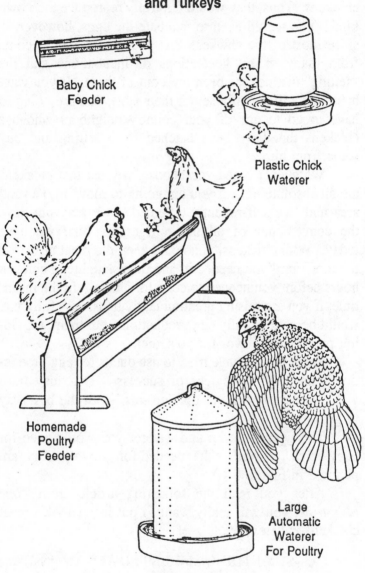

Baby Chick Feeder

Plastic Chick Waterer

Homemade Poultry Feeder

Large Automatic Waterer For Poultry

Figure 9.4

ades ago. The bad news is that an uncooked chicken has become one of the most dangerous items in the American home. At least 60% of U.S. poultry is contaminated with salmonella, camphylobacter or other micro-organisms that spread throughout the birds from slaughter to packaging, a process that has sped up dramatically in the past 20 years. Each year at least 6.5 million and possibly as many as 80 million people get sick from chicken; the precise figure is unknown since most cases are never reported. Whatever that number, the conservative estimate is that bad chicken kills at least 1,000 people each year and costs several billion dollars annually in medical costs and lost productivity.

The man who made promises to clean up the U.S. poultry business quit abruptly last week. The rotten system he leaves behind will be much more tenacious. Agriculture Secretary Mike Espy will leave office at the end of the year because he accepted too many goodies from the industry that he was supposed to be regulating....

Since 1940, the number of chickens slaughtered annually in the U.S. has grown from 143 million to more than 7 billion. By the mid 1970's, this trend posed a crisis for the poultry industry. Unless the industry was allowed unrestricted automation, supply could never meet demand. Under the regulations at that time, chickens moved slowly through the slaughtering process, and those birds noticeably contaminated with fecal matter were either trimmed or discarded altogether.

Everything changed in 1978. Based on a single study now considered flawed by independent experts, the Carter Administration's USDA allowed the poultry industry to wash rather than trim chickens and also to speed up the production lines. "It was the worst decision I ever made," says Carol Tucker Foreman, then the official in charge of food safety at the USDA. "They had that study, and I was convinced the consumer would benefit from lower-cost chicken." Many studies since then have shown that washing is ineffective, even after 40 rinses. (Trimming is still required for beef, "because the meat industry doesn't have poultry's clout," says a USDA official.) Simply put, the slaughtering process in which washing is the integral component merely removes the visible fecal matter while forcing harmful bacteria into the chicken's skin and body cavity—and therefore out of the sight of inspectors who supposedly guarantee the product's wholesomeness. In a typical plant, three inspectors work a processing line, each examining 30 birds a minute, or one every two seconds.

The slaughtering process today further increases the likelihood of cross-contamination as dirty birds mingle with clean ones. If they haven't already become contaminated by the rapid defeathering and evisceration processes, which spread bacteria virtually everywhere, the birds lose almost any chance of emerging clean when thousands at a time bathe in the "chill tank" in order to lower their temperature prior to packing.

The industry has a good reason for resisting changes in this cold bath, known to critics as "fecal soup": the process allows chickens to become waterlogged. Regulations allow as much as 8% of a chicken's weight to be water, which consumers pay for as if it were meat....

Poor working conditions, too, have an impact on food quality. Antoinette Poole, 40, quit last month after working at a Tyson plant in Dardanelle, Arkansas, for five years. Her job: scooping up chicken breasts that fell off the processing line and onto the factory floor—and rinsing them off with cold water. Poole claims she was so overworked that chicken parts sometimes sat on the floor for as long as half an hour. "Sometimes it stinks to high heaven, but who cares? Once it's frozen it ain't gonna smell bad. But I wouldn't want my family to eat that chicken," she says. If the chicken parts seemed bad, Poole was permitted to trim or condemn them. But "I got intimidated by supervisors if I threw too much into the condemned barrel," Poole says. "Supervisors get bonuses for saving as much chicken as possible. The USDA inspectors make their rounds, but they can't be two places at once. And we couldn't say anything to them or it would be our jobs."...

The American poultry-processing system looks even worse when compared with safeguards in other countries, especially in Europe, where governments impose much tougher inspections. The U.S. process is "actually quite insane," says Martin Weirup, who has overseen Sweden's successful salmonella-eradication program. "We have an entirely different process that begins with separating birds at the start of the process so the diseased ones, if there are any, are slaughtered last." European food safety begins on the farm, where sanitation is rigorously practiced. Says Willem Edel, a Dutch expert on salmonella: "You [Americans] don't really do anything there, so you're doomed from the start. The fact is, if you let birds come to the slaughterhouse infected, there is virtually nothing you can do. The Americans tell us privately that it's because of your industry's political influence." The social cost of infected chicken, argues Edel, is far higher than the price of imposing a cleaner system. "But industry has to care about those costs, or it has to be made to care about them."

—*Time*, October 17, 1994

PULL THE WOOL
OVER YOUR CHECKBOOK

If you are interested at all in providing your own clothing, in most areas of the country wool from sheep would be your number one choice of material. Sheep grow a new fleece every winter and come May or June, you have them shorn so they do not roast all summer long in that heavy wool coat.

We have never shorn our own sheep. We have always had a local shearer come in who does it for a certain amount per sheep. The wool from each sheep is tied with dissolvable twine and normally placed into a huge wool bag, which is like a gunny sack except about 7 feet long. This wool can be sold collectively, as we do here in the Rogue Valley at a once-yearly "wool pool," or it can be sold to individuals who wish to process the wool themselves and spin it into yarn and ultimately knit or make clothes out of it. There is quite a bit involved in going from the raw wool to yarn. First it has to be boiled, cleaned and carded, before it can be spun into yarn. Most people would rather sell their wool and buy the yarn later. But if you want to be totally self-sufficient, this process and skills are ones that you could pick up.

We have one llama that we got to guard our sheep. Llama wool is bought by the ounce, whereas sheep wool is bought by the pound. It is very, very valuable.

Speaking of guarding the sheep, we have had predators such as coyotes come onto the ranch and kill a number of our lambs. Therefore, it is wise to have a good animal to guard your livestock. By and large, llamas are good guard animals for sheep and they will tend to scare away dogs, wolves and coyotes.

Another good guard animal for the sheep would be a well-trained sheep dog. Our preference is an Australian shepherd. It is advisable to acquire one as a puppy and to raise him with the sheep, so that he does not chase them or try to kill them. To introduce a full-grown, untrained dog with the sheep, we have found to be a major disaster.

Unless you have a full-time shepherd with your sheep, which would be unusual if you have a small flock like we do, then a guard llama or a guard dog may prove to be highly advantageous.

A FRESH LOOK AT DOGS

What I am going to cover in this section may seem repulsive to many readers, but to a great number of people from Indonesia, Asia Minor, China and other countries, it would seem to be a very normal thing. So please let me apologize beforehand and, if anywhere in this section you get to feeling a little squeamish, then skip the rest of it and go on to the next section.

I think that it is a good idea for every homestead to have a pair of good quality dogs. And when I say a pair, I mean a male and a female. Dogs can be very useful as watch animals for the homestead. They can hear and smell things coming way before you can, and they can alert you to any intruder—whether it be human or a wild animal—and allow you the leeway to take appropriate action in time.

Dogs are also good at guarding children, as well as providing playmates for children, which can be a valuable asset, especially in a rural setting. I have seen a dog keep a child away from a snake that could have bitten and killed the child. Dogs are very protective of those that they love, and this is one of many wonderful characteristics that they have.

Now I would like to look at an aspect of raising dogs not normally considered. When a dog has a litter of puppies, she frequently has 6 to 8, very similar to the number of pigs in an average litter. In the East, people will raise most of the litter up, just like they would the offspring from a pig, with the plan to eat the dogs when they get to be a fairly good size. The mere thought of eating a dog, to most of us in the West, is highly repulsive, though we must realize that this is purely a cultural thing and not because dog meat tastes bad.

If you were going to raise dogs both for guard duty and for meat, you would want fairly large dogs, such as German Shepherds, that would provide you with an adequate meat source if the need arose—about like that of a small goat.

Even if this idea is repulsive to you (and I can certainly understand if it is), if you think that someday you may have to live in survival conditions, it would not hurt to have a good pair of dogs. You could always give away the offspring until you were in a time of desperation for food, and then you would be able to make your decision at that time, but at least you would have that option of a possible food source.

SKINS FOR LEATHER

If you choose to raise a cow for meat, when the cow is butchered, the farm kill people will ask you if you want the skin. If you say, "yes," they will gladly leave it for you, sans head; otherwise they will take it away and just throw it away with the trash.

Similarly, when the farm kill people come out to butcher the sheep, they will ask you if you want the skins. Again, you have the option of retaining them or letting them be taken away with the rest of the refuse. These sheep skins are usually from one-year old lambs and the wool is relatively short, quite uniform and nice.

If you butcher a goat yourself or a deer from hunting, then you have the same option of whether or not you wish to retain the hide.

If you retain any of these hides, they will need to be tanned. There is an entire process to tanning that is interesting to learn and could be a valuable skill to develop. It involves scraping the meat off the inside, washing the skin using tannic acid, making it pliable and flexible, and so forth. This tanning process is a necessary step if you are going to utilize the skin for coats, tents, hats, car seat covers or anything else.

I heard of one instance, which I cannot verify, where a man had a sheep butchered and kept the skin, threw it over a fence with the meat side up, and the flies went after it. The resulting maggots ate all of the meat down to the last minute particle, and it was claimed that the sheep skin was left very flexible and soft and totally free of all meat. It is a little hard for me to imagine this happening, but I can see where it would be possible. So if you butcher an animal during the summer when the flies are heavy, you might give it a try. If you butcher in October or later when the flies are just about gone, this would not work.

See Appendix B for books with further input on tanning.

FISH FOR FUN AND FOOD

Many people enjoy fishing as a recreational sport. However, in most cases the cost per pound per fish can be quite high. A friend of mine bought a boat, with a good Johnson outboard motor, a boat trailer and fishing gear. At the end of the first year, he estimated that the fish that he had caught cost him well over $100 per pound! But the recreational value was worth it to him.

However, this type of expense in a self-reliant lifestyle probably does not fit in with most people's budgets. If it is possible to have a small pond or lake on your property that you can stock with fish, this is an ideal way to go. We have been fortunate and have a small, approximately 2- to 3-acre lake which we have stocked with 2,000 rainbow trout. There are times when some of our guests wish to go down and just fish for recreation and so they "catch and release" anything that they reel in. Other times, we have gone down early to catch our breakfast. However, there could be a time when that small lake could be a major source of protein for us, in addition to providing recreation.

If you are a dyed-in-the-wool fisherman, then one consideration in looking at potential places to purchase would be if there was a possibility of putting in a small pond or lake. An alternative is to have a river or a lake nearby that you could walk to or drive to very easily and be able to simply cast off of the shore.

For many people, fish would not be a consideration, however we have found that the meat from fish is delicious and not fat-laden like some of the meat from land animals. Therefore, just keep in the back of your mind that there may be fish in your future as you go to a more self-reliant way of living.

HUNTING AND TRAPPING FOR MEAT

Hunting is a "sportsman's" way to acquire meat for the table. Many men enjoy hunting and have hunting rifles (or even bows and arrows) with which they enjoy hunting. However, hunting is very time consuming. If one really needs to *rely* on wild animals for meat production, then trapping is by far the superior method.

My only piece of advice here is that if you intend to use either hunting or trapping to add meat to your diet, I would recommend getting whatever weapons, traps and training that you need *now*, and begin to practice so that it would be second nature to you, rather than something novel, and unfamiliar, about which you are very uncertain.

SUMMARY AND CONCLUSION

We have covered a great deal in this chapter about the role that animals can play in your efforts to become more self-sufficient. We saw initially that we need animals for milk, meat, eggs, wool, guard duty and skins. People who do not drink or use milk can eliminate concern about milk production from their consideration. Others who may be concerned about cholesterol and do not eat eggs can eliminate egg production from their consideration. The point is to give thought to these various areas and then to get the animals that will meet the needs that *you* really have.

We discussed the advantage of having small-sized animals versus very large animals—of having a buck and five milk does (goats) versus a bull and two cows. Not only is the cost per unit much higher with large animals, but also the loss per unit is just as high, if you were to lose one. In addition, they are much harder to handle. Most women or teenagers can take a 100-150 pound goat by the collar and get it to go wherever they want it to go. So we highly recommend small animals over big animals.

Concerning milk production, we recommended Nubian goats. They are fun, intelligent animals to have around and they can make enjoyable pets for children, as well as contributing to your food supply.

For meat, sheep are an excellent source of red meat, and chickens and turkeys can be delicious poultry sources, particularly valuable in their contribution of white meat with low fat. Pigs would be a much less desirable choice because of the heavy fat content and their single-stomach digestive system. However, they might be valuable as a "cash crop" if you were raising meat for sale.

If you want eggs, chickens are an obvious addition. We prefer the Rhode Island Reds which produce brown eggs. We love our brown fertile eggs and they are also very popular at the store where we sell them. In fact, people have been known to follow us back into the store when we were delivering a load of eggs just to purchase some, when the store had temporarily run out!

Wool is a very natural and easy thing to acquire from sheep, because they should be shorn every spring-time and there are usually ready markets for the wool. Your local Grange Co-op or feed store could likely tell you if there is a wool pool in your area or other buyers interested in purchasing wool.

The actual use of skins for hats, coats, tents, and so on is probably about at the bottom of the list of priorities for most homesteaders. However, if you plan to use some of your own animal skins, you will need to tan them properly and to acquire ahead of time the materials that you will require for this process.

We then discussed guard animals for the sheep, such as llamas or a good Australian shepherd dog. Our Australian shepherd is called Ringo Rand and he comes from championship lines. He is very bright and alert; we love him very much and he takes good care of our sheep.

We observed why it would be a good idea for every homestead to have a good pair of high quality dogs. We recommend that you acquire these one at a time. *Do not* acquire two new dogs at the same time; that is a mistake that we made once. It makes it too difficult to train the dogs, because they are more interested in each other than in obedience training. Acquire one dog, get him trained well, loyal, and bonded to you, and then bring in a second dog.

Of course, hunting is another way to add meat to your diet. This was the primarily meat source for the early American Indians, and evidently they were very successful with this method. As far as a more assured way of obtaining meat, trapping seems to be a better and easier way to acquire meat from wild animals because the traps are working for you twenty-four hours a day, even when you cannot be there.

All in all, we think the addition of animals to your homestead will be welcome and beneficial, not only as food for the table, but also as fun pets and to help guard your place.

Speaking of guarding your homestead, for most people, some kind of a weapon would be desirable, so let's take a look at that aspect of rural living.

Chapter 10

SOME WEAPONS
ARE NECESSARY

When we speak of weapons in this chapter, we are not speaking of weapons for self-defense. We are speaking of weapons that are necessary in the normal operation of a self-reliant piece of property.

You may be thinking, "I would like to move out to the country to get away from guns and knives." What you really mean is that you would like to get away from the city where a lot of people have guns and knives for the purpose of hurting other people. Guns and knives needed for self-reliant living (totally apart from self-defense) are of a different sort. You will need these weapons for a variety of different reasons.

CONTROL OF PREDATORS

During two different years, about five years apart, we had one or more coyotes come down from the hills and kill some of our sheep. It is possible that a good guard llama or guard dog would have prevented this, but we did not have either one at the time. Let's just say that you were raising sheep, goats, pigs or some other domestic animal, and a predator started coming in and killing one of your livestock every second or third day. What would you do?

It is obvious that you would have to get rid of the predator. I have found that sitting down with a coyote to have an intellectual discussion and reasoning with him about the evils of eating other people's property does no good whatsoever (if you could get one to hang around for such a bawling out). Trying diplomatic negotiation is doomed to failure with coyotes, wolves and bears, so what is the alternative?

One way or the other, the predator must be killed. Even if you trap the beast, you are still going to have to kill it once it is trapped. You cannot take it a mile or ten miles down the road and release it, for—believe me—it will easily find its way back to your convenient food source (your livestock).

The better and more efficient way to get rid of the predator is by shooting him with a good quality hunting rifle. You need to realize, though, that the predator may be two or three hundred yards away and it can be relatively small, as in the case of a coyote. Most "Sunday shooters" are not that accurate at that distance. Therefore, it would be advisable to have a rifle which has the maximum shots legally allowed in a clip, because if you miss on the first shot, you may have to take several shots as the critter starts to run away. (Unfortunately, they don't tend to stand still and let you practice your target shooting.)

Let me relate to you an experience of my own that helps illustrate this. On Living Waters Ranch where we live, our home is located about 100 yards from the building where we have our offices. We had lost a sheep to a coyote a few days earlier and from the balcony of my office, I saw the coyote come up to the flock of sheep in the pasture below my window. There I was with an ideal view and the perfect time to site in and squeeze off a round to get rid of that predator. But there was just one problem—my rifle was over at our house. By the time I left the office—trying to walk carefully so as not to disturb the coyote—went into the house, unlocked the rifle cabinet, got out the rifle and got out on the balcony of our home, the coyote was no place to be seen.

Well, momma didn't raise no idiot, and so I purchased a second hunting rifle to keep in my office, which I kept propped up over in the corner, in case that coyote came back while I was in the office. I thought nothing of this, particularly since there were no children around, but keeping a hunting rifle in my office apparently got translated by some disgruntled ex-employees into the juicy rumor that we were an "armed camp" where everybody had a gun with him at all times. (Once I found out about the rumors, I moved the gun over into my closet, but by then the damage had been done.)

A few days later, the coyote reappeared, so I grabbed my hunting rifle. (Some may call it an assault weapon, and perhaps they are right; in this case, it was an assault against an animal that was threatening our food supply, so it was in self-defense.) I quietly went out on the balcony, took careful aim, fired and missed. The coyote started running for the fence and I was peppering him with lead, shooting some a little high and some a little low, not knowing how much the bullet might drop, some quite far in front of him, some just a little bit in front of him, not knowing exactly how fast he was running. In all, I probably fired ten shots at that beast. Somewhere along in there, one of them got him. (Being a careful hunter, of course I was sure that there was nothing in that gunsight except that coyote and green grass.)

There are those who claim that hunters only need three bullets if they are going to hunt properly. That may be true for the super marksman, but for those who are an average shot like myself, a few extra bullets can come in very handy for taking care of predators.

I should relate to you another story about something that happened before this event with the coyote. Some friends of ours nearby had quite a large ranch and they invited us to go deer hunting there with them. Jeani and I set off hunting with them one day as soon as the light was good. We hunted and waited, and hunted and waited, and hunted and waited, and did not see anything for about three or four hours. We decided to call it a day and headed back down the hill towards their house and barn area. I had a 30.06 into which you load the bullets one at a time, and you can put in about five or six. Since we were through hunting for the day, I unloaded my rifle and put the bullets in my pocket. Just as we were approaching their barn, this gorgeous buck with five points on each side stepped out from behind the barn. The others did not even see him (their guns were not loaded anyhow). While I was frantically reaching into my pocket trying to grab a bullet to load into the gun, the deer casually bounded away into the woods, never to be seen again. The moral to that story is, it does not do you any good to have a gun if it is not loaded when you need it.

The very next day I gave that gun to a friend and I got myself a hunting rifle that had a clip in it! If I had a rifle with a clip on that particular day, we would have had about 150 pounds of deer meat in our freezer. The second moral to that story is to get a hunting rifle that has a clip with as many bullets as you are legally allowed to have.

So it is useful for both you and your spouse to have a hunting rifle. Also, realizing that all sorts of things could go wrong, it might not even hurt to have a spare for each of you that could be used in the event that you had to put one of your rifles into a gunshop for repair.

Let's look at another predator situation that is not nearly so dramatic. Raccoons love to kill and eat chickens and, believe me, a feisty, shrewd old raccoon can squeeze through the tiniest hole. There is nothing more "thrilling" at 2:30 a.m. than to have some chicken screeching, squawking and flapping outside your window while being attacked and killed by a raccoon. It does not make for a very peaceful night's sleep, to say the least.

Now, raccoons are very wiley animals. We have tried all sorts of traps for them, but only once have we been successful in trapping one. They will even come up and steal the bait out of a trap and escape like Houdini or "the Shadow." We finally fixed a setup that took care of Mr. Raccoon. We have a tall wire gate that does not close too tightly. We set a spotlight on this gate, hung a gunnysack full of tin cans on it, and also a gunnysack with some raw meat in it. We went to bed, then about 2:00 a.m. when I heard the tin cans rattling, I slipped up, quietly opened the door and was able to dispose of Mr. Raccoon while he was clawing at the gunnysack with the raw meat in it.

We also had another coyote another year that we never saw; we simply saw the carnage where he had taken a small lamb, killed it and then ripped its stomach from top to bottom. We finally had to resort to traps to catch that clever coyote. We did not use the leg traps; we used the wire-loop-type traps set in two or three places where he could come under the fence. With this type of trap, a coyote gets his front legs through and the wire loop begins to tighten like a cowboy's rope around a steer's neck and he cannot get his hind feet through. Then he is stuck there in this wire loop which is wired to the fence.

One Sunday morning, we had just gotten dressed for church and we heard an awful yelping and racket. I went outside and saw that this especially troublesome coyote had been trapped. So, dressed in my Sunday best, I took my trusty .45 (1911-model Colt), went down and put the poor coyote out of its misery. I had to shed his blood in order to save the rest of the sheep. Since it was a Sunday morning when I was writing this, it reminded me that Father God had to have the blood of Christ shed in order that all those who would believe in His Son, Jesus Christ, could become His sheep and be saved from an eternity in the lake of fire, and instead have an eternity of joy with Him (see John 3:16; Luke 15:3-7; Revelation 20:15; 1 Peter 1:17-19).

CONTROL OF VARMINTS

I classify as "predators" things that will eat your animals. I classify as "varmints" things that will eat your garden, your grain and your other non-animal foodstuffs. There is probably another category of "pests," such as an army of pesky squirrels, but we will leave the "pests" alone for now and talk primarily about "varmints" in this section.

There is almost nothing more disheartening than to have a beautiful garden growing and then to go down one morning and find that the top third of each cabbage head has been munched off by some pesky varmint. These varmints could be anything from opossums or porcupines to raccoons, rabbits, or even deer. All of these are varmints that would love to get at your garden. To them, it is just one big inviting, "all-you-can-eat" salad bar!

Of course, rats, squirrels, mice and other varmints of this nature like to get into your stored grain, animal feed, dog food and so on.

Obviously, the type of weapon that is appropriate for shooting a varmint in a garden may not be appropriate for dispensing of a varmint in the kitchen. In the garden, you can use anything from traps or poison to a rifle or a handgun for dealing with intrusive varmints. If someone saw a person walking around a farm or ranch with a pistol strapped to his waist, he might be inclined to think of that individual as a red-neck or some kind of a "bad hombre." However, let me share with you something that I have done both on Catalina Island and here on the ranch, and I do not apologize for it.

I have an old .357 magnum Colt revolver that I have had for at least thirty years. In the revolver, I keep two .357 magnum shells which will take down a good-sized deer. In fact, I have killed a 300-pound wild boar with it. I also keep in it two .38 special bullets, which would be handy for getting rid of raccoons, opossums, porcupines, rabbits, and so forth. There is a .38 caliber shell (they come in various calibers) that has birdshot in it and a transparent blue cap on the tip of the bullet instead of a single piece of lead or brass, and I also keep two of those in my revolver. I use the birdshot for rattlesnakes (we have seen three in eighteen years here at Living Waters Ranch) or for very small varmints like a rat that may be scurrying around and hard to nail precisely with a single bullet.

I call this set-up a "dial-a-shot" system. If the pest is a snake, a pesky bluejay pecking at apples on our apple trees, a rat or a squirrel, I will fire one of the birdshot bullets, which is the first thing that comes up if you cock the hammer. On the other hand, if I see that the problem is a somewhat larger varmint, I will simply rotate the revolver cylinder up two notches so that a .38 special is ready to be fired, take careful aim and eliminate the intruder. On the rare occasion where something bigger may crop up (such as the wild boar when I was living in a secluded cove on Catalina Island), I can always dial the revolver on two more notches and bring up a .357 magnum round. To give you an idea of the relative power the .357 magnum has, police say that a .38 will stop a man, a .45 will knock the man down and a .357 will knock a man across the room.

As far as I am concerned, for a person on a self-reliant piece of property carrying something like my "dial-a-shot" revolver or a .45-caliber, semiautomatic (1911 model) pistol, when out on the property away from the house, makes good sense. It is *not* for use on people, it is not to scare anyone, and it is not to prove that you are macho or tough; it is simply that you may run across a predator, a varmint, a snake or, during hunting season, an animal that is volunteering to be meat on your table. I also now lean to the .45 because it has a clip.

You cannot use a weapon unless you have it with you, and you cannot use it unless it is loaded (of course with the safety on).

THE FOWL THING ABOUT SHOTGUNS

Up until now, we have primarily discussed rifles and handguns. The third category of explosive-type weapons which could be useful on a ranch is a shotgun. In fact, in the early days of America, if most farmers were only going to have one weapon, it would have been a shotgun. The shotgun can be used against varmints and pests and for bird hunting. In addition, in some cases, it can be a more effective defensive weapon against a mob than even a machine gun.

Possibly you have seen and read stories about the kick of a shotgun, and this is true for many of them. However, there is one shotgun that you can hold out at arm's length and fire that simply does not have that kick, and that is a 12-gauge Remington 1100.

For a shotgun, you can buy a wide variety of shells, everything from small birdshot or duckshot up to shells that have two slugs in them and even shells that have just one big single slug in them. In fact, there was a case in which there was a criminal hiding in a motel which had cement block walls. The police kept trying to get him out one way or the other. I believe they had even fired a few rounds from a pistol or a rifle, but the criminal still would not come out. They took a 12-gauge shotgun and put one of these shells in it with a single slug and fired it. The single slug went through the block wall in front of the motel room, through a piece of furniture, and through the cement block wall at the back of the motel room. Immediately, the criminal came out with his hands up saying, "When you bring in the 'heavy artillery,' I'm coming out!"

Because of the wide variety of shells available, a shotgun can be a very versatile weapon and have many practical uses on a self-reliant homestead.

AIR- AND GAS-POWERED WEAPONS

When you think of an "air rifle," you probably think of the BB guns that some of us had when we were children. The air guns of today are a far cry from that. They shoot pellets and are powerful enough to kill a rabbit at 100 yards. There are also air-powered or compressed gas-powered bow guns which shoot arrows (like you would use in a bow and arrow) with deadly force and accuracy. One advantage of these weapons is that they are silent. Thus, you could kill a varmint and not have a loud recoil echoing up and down the canyon. A source for these air weapons is listed in Appendix B (*B).

We will not cover conventional bows and arrows in this chapter, nor some of the more exotic weapons such as crossbows and blowguns. If a person is particularly intrigued with these types of weapons and wishes to take the time to get very proficient in their use, we know from observing natives in South America and other places, that one can become very efficient in employing them for hunting and for disposing of varmints and predators. Reference is made in Appendix B to a source where you can get these types of weapons, if you are interested.

WEAPONS FOR DEFENSE

Good people never use weapons in an aggressive attack manner, but in my opinion, sometimes it is necessary to use them to defend oneself, one's family or perhaps even one's property.

We will not spend much time on this subject here, since I hope to write a future book on "Survival." This book is not designed for the "survivalist;" it is designed for the individual who wants to get out of the city and into a more rural, self-supporting life-style.

In thinking of defensive weapons, there are basically two categories: (1) defending oneself at a distance and (2) defending oneself up close. For distance, one is obviously going to need a rifle and/or shotgun.

To defend oneself up close with a gun, one would need a handgun. I prefer a semiautomatic with a clip. The police say that the average gunfight takes place at 15 feet and lasts an average of 5 seconds. Therefore, if someone has broken into your home, and you hear him and are afraid that he is about to do you and your family physical harm, then to me there is nothing for a close-contact self-defense weapon like the .45 automatic that the military has been using since 1911. These are readily available, as are ammunition and parts, and there are millions of them out there.

An alternative to the .45 are some of the new 9-millimeter semiautomatic handguns. Some of these we do not recommend and some of these we would recommend highly. The laws of the United States and ever-improved technology and advances could change our recommendations.

I might just say this about the 1911 .45 caliber semi-automatic. If you buy one directly from Springfield or Colt or one of the other manufacturers, it is almost a "kit from which you can make a gun." You will very likely need to take it to a good gunsmith to have him fine tune it and perhaps make certain modifications to it. So if you buy one, it would be wise to take it to an expert gunsmith and follow his recommendations.

As of the beginning of 1995, here is a list of guns, given in the sequence of recommended acquisition for homestead self-reliant living:

- .357 magnum revolver (Colt or Smith and Wesson)
- 12 gauge shotgun (Remington 1100)
- .223 rifle (with a clip)
- .45 caliber semiautomatic pistol (1911 style)

- .308 rifle (with a clip)
- 9mm semiautomatic (Sig-Sauer)

Some discussion could be made as to whether or not this is the proper sequence. One could argue that a rifle should be purchased before a shotgun. This is true if you are concerned about long-distance self-defense, but that was not a major consideration in making this list. I could even disagree with myself, if I knew your habits, characteristics and skills, but I felt that a rough list would be helpful to the average reader of this book.

SUMMARY AND CONCLUSION

We have seen that around the homestead, your self-reliant piece of acreage or whatever you want to call it, some weapons can be very useful in the everyday running of your place.

First of all, you need weapons to dispose of predators that want to prey on your sheep, goats, chickens and so forth. A good rifle or shotgun is one of the better tools for this task. However, at times it is necessary to use traps in order to get a wiley predator to hold still long enough for you to dispose of it.

We also saw a need for weapons to dispose of varmints that want to eat the lovely produce out of your garden. We can just imagine some of these varmints walking by our garden and thinking, "Oh boy! A salad bar just for me!" Then they go in and sample a little of everything. Such critters do not eat all of anything; they just take some bites out of every head of broccoli or cabbage, for example, so as to ruin the whole lot! A shotgun, pistol, rifle, traps, or even poison are fair weapons to use to "dissuade" these food robbers.

It is also possible that you might have poisonous snakes in your area and other things of that nature for which you would need a weapon in order to dispose of them. Snakes can be killed with a hoe or a shovel. However, with poisonous snakes, I personally prefer not to do "hand-to-hand" combat. I would just as soon stand a few nice paces away and fire a birdshot shell, either from a handgun or a shotgun. Also, be sure not to leave any poisonous snakes that you have killed lying around. If a dog were to come up and start chewing on the head, the venom could easily kill him. (However, you can cut off the head and the rest of the snake is edible meat.)

We also noted that there may be a time when you could be in a situation in which you are afraid for your life and intruders are about to harm you physically. If such a circumstance were to occur, you might need to defend yourself. A semiautomatic handgun (.45 caliber or 9 mm) is the preferred weapon of choice for close range self-defense. Of course, long-range self-defense against a group of rioters or looters is another matter entirely. For that, one would need to utilize a rifle or a shotgun.

Considering how to dispose of a raccoon that you have shot, a coyote, a snake, or even how to dispose of the head, skin and intestines of a domestic animal that you have butchered, takes us to the whole subject of sewage and trash disposal. We have saved this subject for last, other than our concluding chapter and the valuable resources listed in Appendix B, because, frankly, it is not really my favorite subject! But I have put it off as long as I can, so we will tackle it in the next chapter. Before you read on, you may want to put on rubber gloves, hip-high wading boots and a filter mask with a few drops of perfume on it to mask the odor. After you are properly prepared, proceed on to the next chapter.

Chapter 11

GETTING RID OF
SEWAGE AND TRASH

When we live in the city, so many services are performed for us that we take them for granted. For example, we flush our toilets and somehow, magically, this waste gets taken away from our home, sterilized and dumped into the ocean, or some such place. We never think twice about it. We put our garbage cans full of trash out by the curbside or in the alleyway and those terrible, noisy garbage trucks come clanging along and take care of it. The next morning we find our cans empty, but perhaps one of the lids is across the alley in our neighbor's area. We grumble and go get it, but that is usually the greatest hardship or inconvenience we suffer in regard to our trash disposal. Somehow, this garbage just disappears never to be seen again and never to again bother us.

However, as you move out from the city and become self-reliant, you will find that it is *your* responsibility to get rid of your sewage and trash. This is not the most delightful topic to discuss in this book, and perhaps that is why I saved it until near the end. However, this subject must be dealt with realistically, because it is something that you will encounter.

GETTING RID OF THE SEWAGE

Assuming that your property does not have a city sewer line running past it, you will have to put in a septic system in order to get rid of the sewage. In some counties and some states, an old-fashioned outhouse is still legal. However, most of us who have been raised with flush toilets would prefer to continue to use them, so we will assume that you will want to have a septic system.

The first thing that you *must* get is an approval for a septic system from your county agency (your neighbors can tell you which agency to contact). They will require you to have a backhoe come out and dig a number of test holes which they will then come out and inspect to see how water percolates down through the soil at the bottom of these test holes. After they review these test holes, they can give you one of two types of permits.

The county can issue a regular septic permit or they can issue a septic permit that requires a sand filter. The sand filter variety is much more expensive, but I would tend to put this type in, even if I had a regular septic system approval.

Before we proceed, let me describe what a septic system is, for those not familiar with one. The water and debris from your flush toilet goes into a holding tank where, hopefully, any solid material ultimately decomposes into a liquid form. (You must only put human waste and biodegradable toilet paper down the toilet. Nothing else, not even kleenex, is acceptable.) There is an overflow pipe at the top of this septic tank, which is usually buried, that will lead to perforated pipes out in a drain field. The drain field consists of perhaps four lengths of pipe about 50-feet long running back and forth under a plot of ground that is maybe 50-feet square.

Drain rock is put on top of these perforated pipes, and on top of that is a hardware cloth or a cloth that will allow water through but not dirt. Then the remainder of the space is filled in with the soil that was taken from these ditches initially. As the liquified waste from your septic tank overflows out into this drain field, the ground beneath the drain field absorbs the water and as this sewage water percolates down through quite a few feet of soil, it is purified. Frequently, the county will require that you fence off this drain field area and not let animals graze on it, unless it has a sand filter.

In a sand filter septic system, you have exactly the same thing, except between the holding tank and the drain field there is a giant sand filter about 16-feet square and about 4-feet deep. The water is percolated up through pipes in the sand filter and then it percolates down through the sand to purify it. It is my understanding that water coming out of the sand filter is potable (can be drunk). If you install this type of septic system, you do not have to fence off your drain field and animals can graze on that area.

One thing you will want to do is to be sure to use toilet paper that is "approved for septic systems." This type of toilet paper will ultimately liquify. It is similar to the toilet paper used in airplanes and motorhomes. *Do not use regular toilet paper in your septic system.* It will clog it up and cause all sorts of problems.

To initialize a septic system, there are starter packets that you can flush down your toilet which put the right biological agents into the holding tank to liquify the solids. Of course, that means these agents will liquify the solids from human waste and biodegradable toilet paper. You do *not* flush sanitary napkins, kleenex, paper towels or any other such item down the toilet.

After quite a number of years of use, the holding tank of most septic systems will gradually fill up with solids that did not dissolve. When this occurs, you will need to call Roto-Rooter or some other sewer-drain service that pumps out septic tanks with their "pooper scooper" to come out and pump out your tank. After they do this, you are good for another five to ten years. We have used such care with what we flush down our toilets that in all the years we have lived here, we have never yet had to have one of their "honey dipper" trucks come out.

I have only touched briefly on septic systems here. The details about them are far more than a book like this would allow us to cover. But if you build your own home and have to put in a septic system, you will become aware of all the details about them. I just wanted to forewarn you this is something that you may need to address.

GETTING RID OF TRASH

In a self-reliant living setting, getting rid of trash is something that you will need to do and it may be surprising to you how much trash you accumulate even in just one week.

When I lived out in the cove on Catalina Island for a year, we divided our trash into three types:

1. the edibles
2. the burnables
3. the rest (cans, bottles, plastic, etc.)

The edible remains off of our plates and spoiled food from the refrigerator I took up the canyon and dumped out in the same place. At that time, Catalina Island had 30,000 wild boar on it and a number of these lived in our canyon. They got to where they would come down regularly to this lovely smorgasbord that I was providing for them. Then if I wanted pig for dinner, I simply dumped the smorgasbord out, went over to the side and concealed myself with my trusty hunting rifle and waited until they came down. It usually took five or ten minutes to line up on the exact one that I wanted before I squeezed off a shot.

Today at Living Waters Ranch here in Oregon, we give edibles, like carrot tops, plate scraps and other kitchen scraps, to the chickens to eat and they love it. They eagerly come running when they see the bucket coming that contains the fresh edible food. (They don't like banana peels or citrus rinds though.)

Meanwhile back on Catalina Island, all the burnable stuff, including labels from cans, we took up the canyon to a burn barrel and burnt it as often as necessary. Here in Oregon, we can burn things like this during the winter months when it is wet, but we cannot burn trash during the summer when it is dry and the risk of forest fires is high. So check your local regulations to see about what is allowed in your location concerning disposing of the burnable trash. During the summer, it is likely that you will have to make some other provision to get rid of the burnables. It may be that you store them up and burn them when it is again legal in the fall. Another possibility is to get permission from a gas station, a restaurant or a grocery store to put some of your burnables in their big trash dumpster during the summer.

By and large, the edibles and the burnables are not a problem. The biggest waste disposal problem is with the metal, glass, plastic and anything else that you collect as trash that is not readily burnable or edible. On Catalina Island, we washed out any tin cans from food, cut out both ends and flattened them, so they would not take so much space in the trash. (Remember, we had no electricity and, therefore, no trash compactor.) About once a week or every other week, I would take these objects out into the ocean in my boat and dump them overboard. Any bottles that floated, I would use as target practice for my trusty .357 magnum.

Here in Oregon, we have two choices in disposing of this type of garbage. We can either take it to a nearby landfill, which is what we do or, as some of our neighbors do, we could find a large, depressed area on our property and begin our own type of landfill, dumping this type of refuse in there and eventually burying it. Of course, it is possible to take things like pop cans and return them for recycling and make a few extra pennies. The same is true of newspapers (but you will also want to save a good supply of these for starting wood fires in the winter).

In order to haul off your nonburnable garbage, you will most likely need a pick-up truck. To bury it, you will need at least a tractor with a bucket on the front, if not a small caterpillar tractor with a blade on the front. (We will have more to say about this type of equipment in the next chapter.)

The bottom line is that you are going to spend *time* doing services like this for yourself and your family that someone else did for you in the city, for a very small fee, and that you probably took for granted.

WHAT TO DO WITH THE MANURE

There is another thing that you will encounter in your self-reliant homestead that you did not face in the city when you had no animals. That is what to do with all the manure that these animals produce, and do they produce it in large quantities!

Periodically, you will need to clean out the stalls for the sheep and the goats. This will usually be manure mixed in with hay and straw. This is excellent fertilizer. We dump it on the garden in the winter months and plow it under either then or in the spring. During the summer, when our garden is in production, we have a compost pile where we dump this type of waste. Actually we have two of them that are 8 feet by 8 feet. When our garden has been completely harvested and is ready to be plowed under, then we put this accumulation of manure on the garden before we plow it under.

The chicken house will also need to be cleaned out periodically. Most of the chicken droppings are underneath the place where they roost. We designed our chicken house so that there are giant, outside flap doors opening into that area, so that we can easily shovel this manure out directly into a tractor bucket. Chicken manure is "too hot" to put straight onto a garden—that is, if you put it around existing plants it will tend to burn and kill the plants. Therefore, it is wise to let it sit in a compost pile for six months to a year before putting it on your garden.

Cleaning out the chicken house, the goat stalls or the sheep stalls and hauling the manure to the compost piles or the garden with a tractor is not exactly my favorite job on the ranch, but it is a necessary one and these droppings make great fertilizer. People are becoming more ecologically minded and, as you can see, this completes our ecological cycle. The manure from the animals goes to fertilize the garden which grows the plants that we eat. Then we give the surplus of the plants back to the animals to eat and the cycle starts all over again.

SUMMARY AND CONCLUSION

In this chapter, we have looked at three of the messier or perhaps less enjoyable tasks that you will experience on your homestead:

1. a sewage system
2. getting rid of the trash
3. hauling off the manure

The first of these you have likely had done for you most of your life while living in the city, and you may have taken that very valuable service for granted. We flush our toilets, everything disappears and we forget it. However, on your own homestead place, you will need to have a septic system (preferably one with a sand filter) which must be maintained.

Disposing of trash can become a time-consuming chore on a homestead. You would normally dispose of the three types of garbage in separate manners. The edibles can be fed to the animals. The burnables can be burned, assuming climatic conditions and county laws permit burning. If not, the burnables must be stored until a time when they can be burned or they must be hauled off and buried with the "junk," which consists of the cans, bottles, plastics and other things that are not biodegradable and that you cannot burn.

Disposing of the manure from the sheep, goats, chickens, turkeys, rabbits, cattle or whatever animals you may have is an ongoing task that needs to be done once every six months or so. If the garden area has not been planted or is not in production, this manure can usually be placed directly on the soil as fertilizer. If there is a garden in process, then this manure needs to be stored in a compost pile to spread upon the garden area later as fertilizer.

These things take time and they are not the most pleasant tasks on your homestead, but they are well worth it. Many are the wonderful benefits that you gain from providing your own wholesome, unadulterated food and your own fresh water and great are the joys of living in a way not dependent upon the fragile distribution and service systems.

Now we will try to summarize where we have come, add a few happy thoughts and close this book with a smile on your face.

Chapter 12

SHARING AND HAPPINESS

Before I deal with the subjects of sharing and happiness, with which I will close this book, let us address a few miscellaneous but important issues and also think back over where we have come. There is an ever-increasing need to be self-reliant. The distribution system that brings us our food and other necessities is very fragile and could be shut down by natural disaster, a major union strike or many other things. A similar thing is true of our service systems which bring water to our home, take the sewage away, pick up the trash, and provide us with electricity, fire protection and police protection. All of these services could be interrupted temporarily or even permanently by a number of things.

With these very real potential difficulties, more and more people would like to be self-reliant and not depend on "the system" to take care of their every need. Being self-reliant is very important for anyone at anytime, but it is even more significant during retirement years. Thus, one's retirement planning should include a specific plan of action to move to a homestead or a self-reliant living piece of property. If you are already retired, then you know the value that you place on being "independent" and not having to depend on other people for life's necessities.

It is possible to become relatively self-reliant in the city, although it is much more difficult than it is out on a rural homestead. It is possible to raise your own garden in the city. In many areas you can raise animals, especially rabbits. Of course, you can go hunting and fishing for other animal protein and, thus, provide your own food. Providing your own water is not too difficult, if the laws where you live allow for it. Of course, it is going to involve drilling a well and then having the ability to utilize that well water, even during times of electrical shortages.

By far the easiest way to become self-reliant is by getting some acreage in the country, which we have called your homestead, and building your own home to self-reliant standards. The amount of acreage that you need depends on your intended use. If you are going to have a garden only and not raise any animals, you could get by with 2 to 5 acres. On the other hand, if you intend to raise animals for food, as well, then you are going to need a minimum of 10 acres; 20 to 40 would be ideal.

We discussed the high desirability of having a greenhouse in which you could raise salad vegetables year round. We noted that heating and cooling of the greenhouse are significant considerations. Cooling it in the summer is as important as heating it during the winter. We looked at pest control in the greenhouse which is the biggest problem. However, the ability to have fresh produce from the greenhouse throughout the year is well worth the effort it takes to keep that environment free from destructive pests.

BEYOND YOUR HOUSE

After discussing a move to a more rural setting, we addressed the subject of building your own home on that property. Then we moved outside to talk about gardening. This included such things as soil preparation, companion planting, weed control and harvest time. After harvest comes the most difficult, but most rewarding task—that of preserving the harvest. We stated that there are three primary ways to preserve the abundance from your garden:

1. freezing
2. canning
3. dehydrating

Dehydrating preserves the most nutrients by far, as compared with the other two methods, but it can be supplemented by freezing and canning foods, as well.

We then discussed the obviously-desirable addition of home-grown fruit to your diet. Producing fruit on your homestead would require an orchard, a vineyard or both. Various aspects of having an orchard were addressed, including the fact that there are both male and female apple trees, plum trees and so on, which is significant to know in your planting. The primary way of preserving the fruit from the vineyard is either by squeezing it into juice and freezing the juice or by making jams, jellies, fruit syrups and other preserves.

Although there is a trend to eat much less meat than our parents did, most people are not vegetarians. Therefore, to be self-reliant, most people will want some animals on their homestead, whether they be chickens for eggs and/or meat, a cow or goats for milk, or sheep for meat. We discussed the desirability of having smaller animals (goats instead of cows, for example), since they are easier to handle and less costly if one dies.

We also discussed the consideration of weapons as a necessity on a homestead today, just as they were in the frontier days. They can be very useful in getting rid of any predators, such as coyotes, wolves, and even raccoons that want to prey on your domesticated animals. Also, if you are going to butcher some of your livestock, then putting them down with a weapon is a much nicer and easier way of killing them than other alternatives.

The last subject that we touched on really stinks! That was the disposal of sewage, trash and manure. Yet waste disposal is one of those not-too-pleasant tasks that has to be done in order to keep the homestead running efficiently and properly. Ignoring it does not make it go away! However, realizing that it is an integral part of the life cycle and, therefore, of you being self-reliant can bring a sense of satisfaction even in dealing with your own trash. Your animal manure is an important ingredient in maintaining healthy soil so that your plants can flourish and your land can be productive. And that is what you want—a productive, peaceful homestead!

SHARING IS IMPORTANT

People have often asked me if I were a "survivalist." Most of them have an image of a survivalist as being like someone sitting at the mouth of a cave with a shotgun, with a few buckets of gold coins and some cans of dehydrated or freeze-dried food behind him daring anyone to come near him. I am the furthest thing from that image that you could possibly imagine!

Unlike the isolationist survivalist, I strongly believe in sharing. It is a joy to have friends over for dinner and to be able to serve only food that you have produced on your property. (Of course, anything we produce is with God's help and blessing). Perhaps you are serving a chicken or leg of lamb that you have raised, fresh corn on the cob, green beans and a salad made from vegetables out of your garden, along with fresh fruit from your orchard for dessert. What a wonderful feeling!

It is also a joy to be able to take some of the surplus from your garden to your church or club to let people partake of the extra zucchini, pumpkins, cucumbers, tomatoes and so forth for free. The same thing holds true for the surplus of fruit from the trees in your orchard.

The Bible tells us that it is more blessed to give than to receive. Jeani and I get a tremendous blessing from giving away some of the surplus food that we grow. And the Bible is right—sharing and giving does indeed bring a blessing and happiness from the Lord.

TRACTORS, TOOLS AND TOGS

In this concluding chapter, we would like to mention a few miscellaneous items that did not exactly seem to fit in any of the previous chapters. For example, in addition to the hand tools, (hoes, rakes, shovels, and post-hole diggers), you are going to need something to help carry heavy things from place to place. A wheelbarrow is the first thing that would pop into the minds of some people. As far as I am concerned, a wheelbarrow is good for hauling sand or gravel, or mixing a small amount of cement, but beyond that, something far superior has been developed, and that is a garden cart.

A garden cart has two bicycle wheels with a box-like container fixed between them. It will carry several times the volume of a wheelbarrow and do so much more easily. Garden carts are also great for hauling produce from the garden to the house, fruit from the orchard or vineyard and so forth. The type we prefer is the metal kind that folds (*B), although those made out of plywood are very adequate and we are still using two of these that we bought sixteen years ago.

However, if the distance is great, and particularly if it is uphill, some type of a motorized carrier is highly preferable. I feel that if a homestead has two cars, one of them definitely should be a four-wheel-drive vehicle, with a large carrying capacity in the back. We personally prefer the Chevrolet Suburban. It can be used to haul sacks of grain out to the ranch, even when it is raining. There are other makes of four-wheel-drive vehicles that have a large carrying capacity in the back that would work just as well. Be sure to get one that has doors that open sideways or a single door that opens up. Do not get one where half of the back door opens down and half of the back door opens up.

However, for the really rough work, and the plowing and mowing, a homestead really needs a tractor.

The Homestead Tractor

If you have a very small homestead and a very small garden (that can be plowed easily with a rototiller), you may not need a tractor. But I believe that a tractor is almost a necessity if you are going to be truly self-reliant.

When we clean out the chicken manure from the chicken roosts, we shovel it into the bucket of our tractor. We then drive the tractor down to the garden and, if it is fall when we do this and the garden is finished for the year, we use the bucket to dump the manure in various places so that when it is plowed under it will be spread out fairly evenly. Or, if we do this chore in the spring when the garden has already been planted, we can dump it into the compost bins to the side of the garden for spreading later.

When we clean out the big area where the sheep eat and sleep, we put tines on the front of the tractor bucket to help break up this manure mixed with straw and we then scoop and pitch it into the bucket with a pitch fork. This we likewise take down to the garden. We use a combination of these two techniques in cleaning out the stalls and the area where the goats dwell. It is possible that this could be done in a garden cart (ugh!) or in the back of a nice suburban (double ugh!!) but the only sensible, reasonable way is to use a tractor.

If you have a very large garden to plow, as we do (almost two acres), then you need a tractor powerful enough to pull a rotovator. This is the only sensible way to plow such a large area, as far as I am concerned. You could also have the tractor pull a single or double-bladed plow and then come back through and harrow it, but the rotovator does it all at one time, which makes the job easier.

Then if you want to mow a large area (for harvesting hay or for aesthetic value), a mower attachment added to the tractor makes the job much easier and the results are very satisfying.

We also have an electrical generator that hooks onto the back of our tractor so that we can have electricity to run hand power tools or even our small electric-powered cement mixer anywhere that we can drive the tractor.

It may be that your neighbor will have a tractor that you can borrow occasionally, and this might be a liveable, makeshift approach, but we find we use the tractor so often that we really need our own. If you are going to buy your own, let me give you some recommendations.

You should get a reasonably-powerful tractor, not a little bitty garden tractor, and it should have a front bucket on it. On the back, it should have a 3-point hitch with a power take-off (PTO). It is the PTO that runs the generator, causes the mower blade to rotate, and drives the tines on the rotovator. We have a Ford tractor, and we are very happy with it. The other brand that we recommend would be a Kaboto. However, self-reliant implies that we may not be getting international trade in the same manner as we do today, so we would prefer to stick with American-made products in this area.

Concerning which implements to get for your tractor, the first thing I would suggest would be a rotovator with which to plow the garden. We have even used this in our vineyard in the spring instead of mowing to really take the grass and weeds down. (Do not worry; they come back!) The second implement I would recommend buying would be a mower, to take care of the grassy areas in the garden and elsewhere, where you do not want the sheep to mow. The third implement I would buy would be a brushhog, which is also sturdy enough to be used to hook a tow-chain on and to pull cars out of snowdrifts or ditches.

I would be very careful in buying a post-hole digger to go on the tractor. We had one, but it was not set up in a way that there were rails that forced it to remain vertical and it would tend to wobble all over the place, particularly if it hit a rock. If you buy a post-hole digger to go on the back of your tractor, it would be one of the last things that I would suggest buying, and it would be worth spending the extra money to get the kind that has two vertical guide rails to ensure that the post-hole digger goes in vertically.

Also, I would certainly recommend buying an electrical generator, so that if all else fails, you can always hook that onto the tractor and have electricity wherever you want it, including the house or the chicken yard.

One year our electricity went off and the lights in our brooder—which gave heat to the baby chicks—went out. When we went out with a flashlight, we found them huddled up in a heap almost lifeless in a corner. We put them in two shallow cardboard boxes, brought them into the house and set them on the woodstove. The bottom box got hotter first and it would begin to have chicks pop up to life like popcorn popping (going, "Cheep, cheep... cheep, cheep!"). When this occurred, we would switch the two boxes and place the bottom one on top. We kept rotating them this way until we fortunately were able to save about 99 percent of the chicks. If we had had an electrical generator for our tractor at the time, we simply could have backed it up to the chicken house the minute the electricity went off and plugged their lights into it.

If you have a propane-powered generator and an automatic transfer switch, as we also recommend, an electrical generator for your tractor is less important. However, we have found that there have been times when we needed electricity in a very remote area and the only way to get it there was with the tractor electrical generator.

HOME HEALTH CARE

One of the factors worth some consideration when you are moving towards a more self-reliant life-style is that of health care. In the city, with medical facilities, doctors, clinics and hospitals handy, many people give little thought to medical care until they have some kind of a health crisis. When we are looking at the prospect of living in a more rural setting where such services may not be so convenient or readily available, thoughts about what you can do personally regarding your health care become even more relevant. This would also be true for someone remaining in the city but wishing to become more self-reliant.

In the initial book in this series, *Preparing For Emergencies (*B),* there is a chapter on "First Aid" which would be pertinent to readers of this book. Acquiring first aid knowledge and skills would be valuable for anyone wishing to move toward a more self-reliant way of living. There is no telling when those skills may prove invaluable. In addition, having an extensive "First Aid Box" and "Medicine Box," as detailed in that book, would be wise and prudent.

It could be that various family members might wish to take courses in CPR, First Aid, Foods and Herbs that Help Heal, and other such health-related topics to develop some skills and knowledge to help in times of a health or medical emergency. Another equally-important aspect is for you and your family to maintain good health. There are also numerous videos that can be helpful. Keeping your bodies in shape and practicing preventative health care becomes all the more important when you are further from medical services. In the long run, it is a healthier way to live too! Some resources to help in this regard are listed in Appendix B.

Taking Supplements

Since there is much said today about taking supplements, a question that might naturally arise in a person's mind is this. If Jeani and I eat so healthy from food that we raise, do we take supplements? And if so, why? The answer to the first question is definitely *yes*. The reason we take supplements is to try to undo some of the conditions and eliminate some of the toxicity that were created by years of eating the normal American diet before we started eating a more healthy diet. The second reason we take supplements is because perhaps 30 percent of our meals are not consumed at home. When we travel, we are eating at restaurants or hotel coffee shops. The third reason we take supplements is that our modern environment (which includes everything from smog, foam rubber, radiation, and toxic cleaning agents to highly processed foods and artificial foods) depletes our bodies of nutrients faster than a normal diet can replenish them.

You might legitimately ask the question that if you live on a homestead, are you not away from the contaminants of the environment? You are certainly free from the smog of the cities, the pollution of the factories, the smoking of fellow workers and so forth. Out on your homestead, the pollution from the air you breathe is lessened, but it is still there. Even on a homestead you have elements in the air that you breathe that our ancestors of a hundred years ago simply did not have. For example, there is formaldehyde in the backing in carpets. There is formaldehyde in foam rubber. There are automobile and tractor exhaust fumes, fumes from the many cleaning agents and personal toiletries such as shampoo, hairspray and shaving cream and many other factors such as these that can erode good health.

Our forefathers of one hundred and fifty years ago did not have these things seeping into the air that they breathed. They had wooden furniture and, if it had a cushion, it was made out of cotton, filled either with more cotton or with feathers. Their only cleaning agent was soap. Their only shaving cream was more soap. If they had carpets at all, they were made out of natural materials, such as hooked rugs made of scraps of cotton material. So in today's world, even on the homestead there are contaminants that leak into the air that you breathe which rob nutrients from your system and undermine optimum health.

If we turn to the eating side of the equation, there are now many things that Nutritionist, Jill Agar, calls "fake foods" that are made from hydrogenated oils (like margarine), which are not natural molecules that the body treats more as invaders than actual food. These "fake foods" create free radicals that attack the bloodstream and the blood supply system, frequently causing structural breaks in the blood vessels. The body then sends out cholesterol and calcium to patch these structural breaks. We will have more to say about free radicals momentarily, but for now it is of importance to know that antioxidants fight and destroy these free radicals, which are basically molecules that are missing an electron.

We all know that we should exercise regularly (you will get exercise as a natural byproduct on a homestead), eat a diet that is low in fat and high in fiber, and get plenty of restful sleep so the body can rejuvenate itself. But in addition, in order to combat the added stresses of living in our modern environment, which our forefathers did not have to fight, supplements can be a valuable tool to use as weapons in this warfare and to help bolster our immune systems to maintain optimum health.

The Four Basics
Of a Good Supplement Program

The four basics of a good supplement program to help you achieve good nutrition are as follows:

1. metabolic conditioners
2. antioxidants
3. chelated minerals
4. enzymes

Let us examine these four vital areas one at a time.

METABOLIC CONDITIONERS: Metabolism or metabolic rate is the amount of energy your body utilizes doing all the things it needs to do—like feeding cells, making hormones, and regulating body temperature. Metabolism is directly affected by body composition: the more lean tissue (muscles and organs) you have, the higher your metabolism and the better your body burns fat. As we age, our metabolic rate slows down and our body retains fat: hence obesity and its attendant diseases.

Chromium picolinate, chelated chromium and L-carnitine are metabolic conditioners that promote fat utilization and help to increase lean body mass. Nutritional chromium is absolutely essential to certain functions in the human body. Experimental studies have tended to indicate that severe chromium deficiency may lead to glucose intolerance as well as other effects typically seen in clinical diabetes.

American diets of highly refined foods are very poor sources of chromium. Ninety percent of American diets contain less than the amount recommended by the National Academy of Sciences (50-200 mcg.) [G.W. Evans, "The

Effect of Chromium Picolinate on Insulin Controlled Parameters in Humans," Int. J. Biosec Med Res. 1989; Vol 11:163-80.]

Chromium picolinate was originally developed because of evidence that good chromium nutrition is vital for cardiovascular health. Many people develop decreased sensitivity to insulin which has been shown to be a risk factor for heart disease and high blood pressure and can progress to diabetes. The role of chromium is to support the insulin sensitivity of the body's tissues. The effect of chromium is to decrease storage of fatty tissue and increase its metabolism. By helping to stabilize blood-sugar levels, chromium also lessens appetite.

Dramatic research by Gary Evans, Ph.D., Trace-mineral nutrition expert at Minnesota State University, showed an increase in chromium intake helps to make the body thinner and firmer. [G.W. Evans, "The Effect of Chromium Picolinate on Insulin Controlled Parameters in Humans," Int. J. Biosec Med Res. 1989, Vol 11: 163-80.]

The same source cited a double-blind study that was conducted on male athletes for a six-week period. In the group that received chromium, body fat decreased by 22 percent.

ANTIOXIDANTS: Before we can understand anti-oxidants, we need to discuss free radicals a bit further. Alex Comfort, M.D., Ph.D., Gerontologist says, "Free radicals are produced by your body every day as by-products of metabolism, oxidation and detoxification of dangerous chemicals. Unleash a free radical in the body and it steals an electron from the first molecule it bumps into. Now that molecule needs another electron, and it steals an electron from the next guy, and the process continues like a wild game of tag. This rampage can destroy cell walls, causing chromosome damage, and hence cell death or mutation (which may lead to cancer) is more likely to occur."

One free radical hit on the body can cause a 3,000-molecule chain reaction. It is currently estimated that our bodies sustain more than 100,000 hits per cell per day! It's a wonder we are alive! Consider this:

- 75 percent of arteriosclerosis disease is due to free radicals.
- 54 percent of cancer disease is due to free radicals.

Research studies of 1973 reviewed in London in October of 1989, concluded that we need five to ten times the vitamin and mineral levels previously suggested by the RDA. Hence, most vitamin and mineral supplements at minimum RDA levels are effective in preventing scurvy, beriberi and rickets, but they are far below an effective anticarcinogenic or heart-benefiting level. [Comments by UK Conference Attendees, in the *American Journal of Clinical Nutrition* 1/91.]

Ester-C: A study was conducted demonstrating that vitamin C is the most effective antioxidant in aqueous solutions. This has probable application to blood plasma and indicates that vitamin C, if in great enough concentrations in the blood, may be able to greatly decrease the incidence of free radicals before they can attack and cause oxidative damage to cell lipids. [*American Journal of Clinical Nutrition* 54 (6 Suppl): 1119S-1124S.1991.]

Ester-C is an effective form of vitamin C that can give higher concentrations in both plasma and white blood cells than regular vitamin C. [*Research Communications in Chemical Pathology and Pharmacology* 57 (1):137-140, 1987 & US Patent# 4.822.816, April 18, 1989]

Vitamin C fights free radicals while helping to regenerate vitamin E. [Can J Chem 61:1288-1289, 1983 & *American Journal of Clinical Nutrition* 54 (6 Suppl): 1119S-1124S.- 1991]

Ester-C may be more beneficial beyond the RDA levels of regular vitamin C—especially in conditions of stress, infection, smoking, increased exercise, and others. [*Nutrition and Health* 61:1288-1289.1983 & *American Journal of Clinical Nutrition* (1 Suppl):358S-361S.1991]

Ester-C has superior bioavailability, it is absorbed 400% faster, excreted 200% slower, and has up to 500% greater potency and effectiveness than traditional vitamin C. [*Research Communications in Chemical Pathology and Pharmacology* 57(1):137-140.1987 & Life Sciences 482275-2281.]

Regular vitamin C is acidic and when it meets the alkaline environment of the intestine, it causes a neutralization reaction which produces gas, diarrhea, and discomfort. Ester-C has an essentially neutral Ph, so it should greatly reduce this type of reaction. [US Patent #4822.816 April 18, 1989.]

Researchers are now saying that the most important medical discovery since antibiotics is the discovery of antioxidants which neutralize oxygen free radicals.

CHELATED MINERALS: Chelated minerals are chemically structured so that they are readily used by the body. They have been shown to be more bioavailable than other forms of minerals. For instance:

- Calcium amino acid chelate is 60-80 percent better absorbed than calcium salts and 60 percent better absorbed than calcium in milk. Calcium is known to be important for strong bones and teeth and is instrumental in normal muscle (including heart) contraction and relaxation, proper nerve function, blood clotting, blood pressure, and immune defenses. Calcium may also help reduce the rate of osteoporosis.

- Zinc amino acid chelate is shown to be 200-300 percent more bioavailable than zinc salts and 200 percent more bioavailable than zinc picolinate.

- Manganese amino acid chelate is up to 250 percent more bioavailable to the body than non-patented amino acid chelates.

- In a study on intestinal uptake of copper, the amino acid chelate was taken in over three times better than copper oxide, almost four times better than copper sulfate, and almost six times better than copper carbonate. [D. Graff et al, address to Utah Academy Arts, Letters and Sciences, April 1970]

Just because a label lists a percentage of the recommended daily allowance does not necessarily indicate that the body is able to absorb anywhere near that percentage. The body has to change these minerals to forms it can use. This takes time and, in the process, most of the actual mineral is eliminated from the body.

With chelated minerals, you utilize more minerals because they are already in a form that can be readily used by your body. Therefore, you get more use of your minerals for your money.

ENZYMES: Stress and a high sodium content in our bodies deplete our potassium levels. A high level of potassium is required for the production of enzymes. In fact, a 25 percent reduction in the potassium in our body gives a 75 percent reduction in the enzymes! Enzymes are necessary for the breakdown of food so that our bodies can utilize it and they are regulators of metabolic processes. Enzymes are our first line of nutrition, our first line of protection, and our first line of restoration.

One important enzyme is coenzyme Q10. There have been papers and even books written about coenzyme Q10 and I could not possibly go into all of the benefits in just a brief paragraph. Dr. Julian Whitaker of the Whitaker Wellness Institute and author of the worldwide health newsletter *Health and Healing*, calls coenzyme Q10 "almost a cure-all." Dr. Whitaker is my personal heart physician and I have high confidence in his wisdom. This is what he had to say in the November 1993 issue of *Health and Healing* (*B):

> Charmaine was in the office last week for a routine check. When I first met her four years ago she was as near death as any patient I had ever seen. Her body had collected over 70 pounds of edema fluid and her legs were so swollen that the skin had split. When she wasn't in a wheelchair, she was propped up in bed breathless and disoriented for lack of oxygen to the brain. Charmaine was suffering from cardiomyopathy, and had been told she had about six more months to live.

> Charmaine was taking standard medicine for severe congestive heart failure—digitalis, Capoten, and Lasix. I simply added a nutritional regimen, including large doses of coenzyme Q10 (CoQ10), an essential nutrient for the production of cellular energy. The results were almost immediate and miraculous.

> By February of 1990, she had lost all the edema fluid and was fully functional. In November of 1991, long after she was supposed to be dead, she developed acute appendicitis and underwent general anesthesia and abdominal surgery. She was discharged from the hospital after two days. Had this happened two years earlier, lying flat on the operating table would have drowned her in edema fluid.

Today, Charmaine takes no heart medications at all and leads an active life. She does, however, continue to take CoQ10 as well as other vitamins and minerals.

Folks, vitamins and minerals are not magic, but CoQ10 stabilizes and modulates the electron transfers used by all biologic systems in the extraction of energy.

CoQ10 is also a potent antioxidant protecting cells from free radicals—the byproducts of energy production. It is made by every cell in the body, but it diminishes with age and disease, which aggravates the complications of both. When CoQ10 is low, nothing in your body works well. It is like giving your car 40-octane gas instead of 90-octane strength.

Not surprisingly, published studies have shown that supplemental CoQ10 helps with a wide variety of illnesses, including AIDS, cancer, chronic fatigue, and even periodontal disease. However, since the heart uses such large quantities of energy, the benefits of CoQ10 for the heart have received the most scientific attention.

In a study published in the *American Journal of Cardiology (AJC)* in 1985, 150 mg of CoQ10 given daily to heart patients for four weeks reduced the incidence of angina attacks from 5.3 to 2.5 per day. The researchers concluded that the CoQ10 strengthened the diseased heart, allowing it to reach higher levels of energy before pain or oxygen deprivation occurs.

In a long-term study of 126 patients with severe cardiomyopathy published in the *AJC* in 1990, CoQ10 was found to prolong life by a factor of years, not simply by months or weeks. Moreover, in some patients, the disease was eliminated entirely.

Peter H. Langsjoen M.D., a cardiologist who co-authored this study with Karl Folkers, Ph.D., has been documenting the benefits of this nutrient for 30 years. Using CoQ10, Dr. Langsjoen reduced heart and blood pressure medications by 40% to 50%; 25% of his patients have become drug-free, making a mockery of the cardiologist's refrain, "You'll have to take this drug for the rest of your life."

CoQ10 is fat-soluble—it is absorbed through fat rather than water—and Dr. Langsjoen has discovered that if taken with some oil, absorption improves, thereby doubling the effect on blood levels. Dr. Langsjoen's patients chew tablets of CoQ10 (the tablets are made by Vitaline, 800/648-4755) with 1/2 teaspoon of peanut butter or a bit of cheese. I tell my patients to open CoQ10 capsules and mix the contents with a small amount of sesame or almond butter spread on bread.

Who should take CoQ10? Anyone who has a serious illness or wishes to avoid one. The dose I recommend to my heart disease patients ranges between 180 to 360 mg per day, depending upon the severity of the problem. For instance, if you have symptomatic congestive heart failure take 240 mg of CoQ10 daily in two 120 mg doses. For the healthy, 30 to 60 mg once a day should do the trick. Be sure to take your dose with half a teaspoon of sesame or almond butter, which you can buy in health food stores.

CoQ10 is also sold in health food stores—any brand will do. Check your discount vitamin catalogs for the best prices.

In comparing prices, also be careful to examine quality. (Some vitamin companies include fillers.)

The types of enzymes are too numerous to mention, but gastric enzymes are also worthy of special note. Since enzymes are destroyed by heat, when cooked foods make up the totality of our diet, we are relying 100 percent on our body's manufactured enzymes to properly digest and metabolize that food, since the enzymes in cooked foods have been destroyed. Doing this year after year depletes the body and leads to impaired digestive functions (common among the elderly). This can then cause us to overeat in search of the nutrients we are lacking. You can only make use of what you can metabolize from your foods, and this is where enzymes play a critical role.

Since weak digestive functioning is so widespread among those on the typical Western diet, gastric enzyme concentrations containing Amylase (for digesting starches), Lipase (for fats), Protease (for proteins), and Cellulase (for cellulose) can be a beneficial addition to the diet, taken *before* meals.

Where to Get the Supplements

Many types of supplements can be purchased in health food stores, if you wish to pay retail. However, in Appendix B, we give other sources where you can get these wholesale or, if you are interested, through multi-level companies (now called network marketing), where you can not only get them at wholesale but, if you introduce your friends to the supplements as well, you can earn some income from them. This income could range from a few dollars a month to up to six figures a year.

One company worth looking into is Interior Design Nutritionals which has a package of four capsules called "Life Pak." These four capsules contain all of the major antioxidants, chelated minerals, chromium picolinate and odor-free garlic. See Appendix B for details.

Of course, one can survive without supplements, even in our modern world. It will just be more difficult to maintain the optimum, radiant health that we deserve and that can be aided by taking supplements appropriate to your personal needs. Both Jeani and I recommend a supplement program as a wise "health insurance policy" to help compensate for what is often lacking in the foods we eat. The one outlined in this chapter is a generalized one. More ideally, you could have a professional in your area develop a personal supplement program customized for you as a unique individual. But keep in mind, vitamin and mineral supplements are just that—*supplements*. They should *supplement* a good, wholesome diet that is low in fat and high in fresh, raw fruits and vegetables. They are *not* a replacement for proper nutrition, nor a cure-all.

To me, radiant health is very important, and it certainly enhances one's life, but there is something even more important. Being at spiritual peace with God is an essential to being truly happy. In Appendix A, I share with you how I found peace with God. The purpose of this book has been to give you the basics so that you can become a happy homesteader. We hope it has lived up to its purpose.

Not a Supplement But Super Food

The National Cancer Institute recommends that an individual have five servings of raw fruits and vegetables each day in order to help prevent cancer and other diseases. A thirty-five year study by the Harvard Medical School provides new support for that existing recommendation.

Even with a garden in the summer and a greenhouse in the winter, Jeani and I find it hard to meet this minimum requirement. This is especially true in the winter and when we travel and eat out. As of the writing of this book (1994), we have recently found out that by taking four capsules of "Super Food," we can meet this minimum requirement and in these four capsules, we get the nutrient equivalent of four pounds of raw fruits and vegetables every day. Thus, we can consistently meet this recommendation of the National Cancer Institute which they say will help prevent (or help our body cure) many diseases and disorders.

The name of these "Super Food" capsules are "Juice Plus+." Juice Plus+ was classified by the United States Food and Drug Administration as a *whole food* and not a vitamin or a supplement. We take two Orchard Blend Juice Plus+ capsules in the morning and two Garden Blend Juice Plus+ capsules in the evening with an 8-ounce glass of water. Most significantly, each Orchard Blend and Garden Blend capsule contains *natural food enzymes*. In fact, a glass of fruit or vegetable juice contains only a small portion of the natural food enzymes compared to one Juice Plus+ capsule.

The natural food enzymes found in fruits and vegetables release the food components in the food you eat and make them "bioavailable" to you. With these natural food enzymes, the food you eat is broken down more effectively so that your body can absorb proteins, vitamins, minerals, electrolytes and other necessary nutrients.

Fresh fruits and vegetables are your primary source of natural food enzymes. However, it would be nearly impossible to eat the large quantities of fresh produce required each day to obtain all the enzymes found in Juice Plus+. Enzymes are also useful to strengthen the immune system and to detoxify the body. Cooking destroys the life qualities of enzymes in food. For example, if you were to plant two seeds—one cooked and one not cooked —which do you think would grow? (The uncooked one, of course!) When you eat cooked food, as we said earlier, you do not get any enzymes. Your body has to produce the enzymes to digest the food. The pancreas produces enzymes, yet internal enzyme production weakens the immune system. Tests show that when people eat cooked food, the white blood cell count becomes augmented (increases), indicating that the body is defensive. On the other hand, there is no increase in white blood cells after eating raw food, which contains live enzymes. Enzymes aid digestion, taking the pressure off the pancreas.

The enzymes in Juice Plus+ were sent to Maui Medical Clinic for testing. The tests showed that enzymes boost antibody production by 350 percent, indicating support for the immune system in the body.

Chronic diseases, enzyme exhaustion and old age are synonymous. As we become enzyme deficient, we age faster. The pancreas, which dispenses enzymes, is one of the first organs to go with chronic disease. People lose enzymes when they exercise. Thus, we need to take in more live enzymes to replenish those that are lost.

Every animal on earth lives seven to ten times the age of maturity. We mature between 25 and 35—and should live to be 140 to 150 years old, but we don't. The reason is that our bodies have to produce lots of enzymes, and some age faster. We become enzyme deficient and nutritionally deficient.

Enzymes break down food in the stomach. When your pancreas does not have to work as hard, you can actually add years to your life.

I hope the following information about these Juice Plus+ capsules does not sound too positive or like a "commercial." It is just that we are excited about this and the effect we have seen on our own health and the health of others. It could help us all enjoy longer, healthier lives.

Unlike most cereal fiber, which contains only insoluble brans, Juice Plus+ has a balanced combination of soluble dietary fiber from several plant sources. Most of these beneficial dietary fibers present in fruits and vegetables have been combined in Juice Plus+ to provide a balanced complement of dietary fiber. (However, this should not be your *only* source of fiber—wholesome natural foods are still the best source and definitely recommended.)

New research shows that certain natural substances called food actives found in fruits and vegetables actually promote good health. (Scientists are now learning about natural food components such as indoles from broccoli, lycopenes from tomatoes and allicin from garlic, and additionally D-glucaric acid found in several different fruits and vegetables.) Juice Plus+ provides these important food actives at levels found in many pounds of fruits and vegetables.

In recent years, juicing has become a popular way of reducing fruits and vegetables to their nutritional essence, enabling people to consume them in larger amounts. It makes sense and, not surprisingly, millions of people went out and bought expensive juicers. Unfortunately, most of these juicers are now collecting dust, taking up space in people's kitchens. Why? Because juicing takes a serious commitment. In addition to buying an expensive juicer, you must also continuously purchase enormous quantities of fruits and vegetables and then take the time to put it to use regularly.

With Juice Plus+, there is no lengthy shopping for fresh produce, no cleaning, no cutting, no juicing and no mess to clean up afterward! You can take Juice Plus+ to work, on trips anywhere, anytime. And, because Juice Plus+ does not require a major time commitment, the chances of sticking with it are greatly increased. Juice Plus+ is far less expensive and more convenient. In addition, laboratory reports indicate that many important nutrients and enzymes from fresh juice are present in equivalent or higher levels in Juice Plus+. Also, unlike fresh juice which can contain relatively high levels of sugar and calories, Juice Plus+ has almost no sugar and only 1/2 calorie per capsule.

And keep in mind, Orchard Blend and Garden Blend are not fragmented foods, so when reconstituted by drinking an 8-ounce glass of pure water with them, you will receive most of the health benefits found in fresh fruits and vegetables. Juice Plus+ is a nutritional product which offers you the important components of fresh, raw fruits and vegetables without the inconvenience of juicing.

The following table compares the four suggested Juice Plus+ capsules to actually drinking fresh vegetable juice or fresh fruit juice (see table 12.1). Each glass in the table represents one 8-ounce glass of juice. This study was based on Independent Certified Laboratory results conducted by an unaffiliated FDA-approved analytical testing laboratory, which compared Juice Plus+ capsules to active fresh fruit and vegetable juices.

The information on how to get a supply of Juice Plus+ capsules is found in Appendix B. Just like supplements, these can be purchased at retail (but not in health food stores) or they can be purchased through network marketing where you can get them directly at wholesale from the company or, if you introduce your friends to these Juice Plus+ capsules, you can also generate an income.

Juice Plus+ contains the natural components present in fresh, whole fruits and vegetables. The naturally-occurring nutrients, fiber, enzymes and important "food actives" are retained by proprietary processing technology which makes Juice Plus+ capsules a powerhouse of good nutrition. By the unique scientific technology of "flash drying" at 68 degrees, the water and the waste are eliminated, preserving only the nutritional components of fruits and vegetables in easy-to-swallow, easy-to-digest capsules.

Jeani and I find that Juice Plus+ enhances our health and, thus, our happiness, and we all want a happy, healthy homestead.

Juice Plus+ (two capsules)
Compared To Fresh Juice (8 oz. glass)

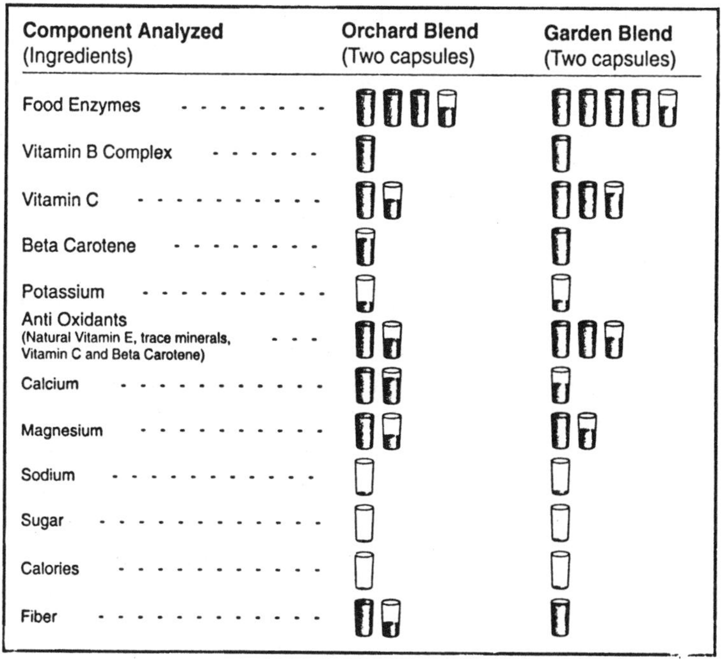

Component Analyzed (Ingredients)	Orchard Blend (Two capsules)	Garden Blend (Two capsules)
Food Enzymes	▯▯▯▯	▯▯▯▯▯
Vitamin B Complex	▯	▯
Vitamin C	▯▯	▯▯▯
Beta Carotene	▯	▯
Potassium	▯	▯
Anti Oxidants (Natural Vitamin E, trace minerals, Vitamin C and Beta Carotene)	▯▯	▯▯▯
Calcium	▯▯	▯
Magnesium	▯▯	▯▯
Sodium	▯	▯
Sugar	▯	▯
Calories	▯	▯
Fiber	▯▯	▯

Figure 12.1

Concentrated Vegetables You Can Drink

In addition to the Juice Plus+ capsules, I (Jeani) have a personal favorite food concentrate that has been available in this country since 1982, and I have enjoyed it and benefited from it for that long. It is called Barley Green, a specially-dried substance made from the first growth of young, green barley shoots. It is chock full of a wide variety of vitamins and minerals. In addition, it contains 40 percent easily-digestible protein, it is a rich source of chlorophyll (a natural healer), as well as containing plenty of all-important *enzymes*. Since many of us fall far short of eating the quota of deep green leafy vegetables that our bodies need (collard greens, kale, etc.), Barley Green can provide many of these nutrients in a palatable, easy-to-use form.

I enjoy sipping on a glass of fresh juice now and then throughout the day, but I am one of those guilty of seldom finding time to use my juicer to make fresh juices. This is the next best thing, and so convenient for travel. I carry a small bottle in my purse when we travel and put some in my apple juice on planes.

To use Barley Green, once or twice a day, you mix a teaspoon or more of the powder with juice and drink it. I prefer it with pineapple juice. I put about two ounces of juice in a glass, add the Barley Green, top off the rest of the glass with cold water (about 6 ounces), and stir well. I then sip this if I wish to have a refreshing beverage between meals, which I have found actually does give me more energy. It also freshens your breath!

Since American Image Marketing first introduced Barley Green in the U.S., in recent years they have added carrot crystals (for making carrot juice), beet crystals (for instant beet juice), and a number of other quality products.

I like to try to intake only juices one day a week, when possible, for cleansing my body and letting my digestive tract rest. Fresh juices put a minimum strain on the digestive system and the nutrients are easily absorbed into the bloodstream. These juices (Barley Green, Just Carrots and Redi Beets) have been invaluable for that purpose in the life of this busy person!

Barley Green is not available in stores; it is sold by distributors nationwide. If you cannot locate a distributor in your area, you can order it from the source listed in Appendix B.

SELF-RELIANT LIVING WORKBOOK

For years, Jeani and I have had a workbook (a three-ring notebook) with divider tabs for such subjects as:

construction ideas
farm equipment
fish farming
gardening
greenhouses
guns and weapons training
hunting and trapping
orchards
poultry
sheep and goats
solar energy
vineyards
water supply
wind and water energy

In this workbook, we include articles that we tear out of magazines and other publications on these various subjects. We also three-hole punch some of the catalogs, such as seed catalogs, and put them under the appropriate divider tab. This workbook is such a handy reference when we want to check out something, such as solar photovoltaic cells, for example.

We have created a similar notebook which we are now making available to the public as a follow-up, companion working book to go with *Self-Reliant Living*. In it, we have included some of the best articles from other sources on many of these subjects.

Also included in this workbook are a whole host of photographs and diagrams of how we have actually done things here on our ranch in Oregon. Confucius said that a picture was worth a thousand words. He was right! A picture of how hydroponic greenhouse beds can flow one into the other, for example, is indeed worth a thousand words spent trying to describe it.

Please see the last 2 pages in this book to find out how you can get a copy of this valuable workbook. It is one that you will use and to which you can add your own information, as you contact the sources and subscribe to publications that we have recommended. Even if you do not get a copy of our *Self-Reliant Living Workbook,* which we do recommend, we would encourage you at least to start your own three-ring binder so that you can organize and later find the valuable information that you will be collecting and receiving.

THE HAPPY HOMESTEAD

Living self-reliantly on your own homestead is a lot of work and, as we pointed out in Chapter 4, it takes a lot of time. When faced with a great deal of work, some people get tense and uptight, and they grumble and complain. It need not be that way. The homestead should be a haven of happiness. Tasks should be undertaken with a joyful heart, even if it is an unpleasant task, and even if you feel that you are doing more than your share of the work. Your efforts will be rewarded.

When out weeding in the garden, it can somehow lift the spirit to whistle a happy tune or even to sing. Jeani and I especially love to sing the choruses about Christ. They bring a joy and a peace to our hearts.

If peace, happiness and joy abide on your homestead, people will sense that when they visit. We have had countless visitors to Living Waters Ranch comment on how peaceful it is. That is one overriding feedback that we hear again and again.

Since Jesus Christ is the Prince of Peace, I highly recommend Him as the true source of peace for your individual heart and for your homestead. (I mentioned earlier that the story of how I found peace is found in Appendix A.) I recommend Him as a source of joy and happiness springing up from the depths of your soul. He told us that He came to give us life and *life abundantly*. I find in Him the fullness of joy.

My prayer for you is that, as you become more self-reliant, living in the city or on your homestead, you will simultaneously become more dependent on God. We can plant and we can water, but only God can give the increase. I pray that the joy and peace of Jesus will abide in your heart and will be a covering over your homestead.

Appendix A

HOW I
FOUND PEACE

By Dr. James McKeever

All the world is looking for peace and can't seem to find it. The same thing was true of me as a young person. All of my life, I had been looking for something and had not really known what it was. I vaguely called it *happiness*. When I was in college, I thought, "If I become the best dancer in college, then I will be happy." I did become one of the best dancers in college; in fact, I eventually taught dancing at Arthur Murray's, but after I achieve that, I still felt a bit of an emptiness. Then I thought, "If I get a new convertible, then I will be happy." I got a new convertible and that did not bring me the happiness I was looking for. There was a continual restlessness inside of me. It reminds me of the song that came along later entitled "Is That All There Is?"

As I continued my search for this "something," I started dating a girl who was an excellent dancer and a very beautiful, lovely companion. The major drawback was that she was a Baptist. As a good Methodist boy, I had been warned about the Baptists, that they were narrow-minded, fanatical, and they would try to convert you. She kept pestering me to go to the Baptist Student Union (BSU) meeting with her on the SMU (Southern *Methodist* University) campus. I wanted no part of that, but she kept nagging me about it. Finally, I was either going to have to go to this meeting with her or break up.

So I finally told her, "Okay, I will go to your blankety-blank meeting with you one time, if you will shut your mouth and never mention it again." She readily agreed to this. I went to their meeting and saw what I considered at the time to be the social dregs of the campus. And here I was a big fraternity man, invited to all the sorority dances and so forth. In this group, the girls had stringy hair and wore little or no makeup, and the guys were mostly pansies, not what I considered "real men." I thought, "My gosh, what have I gotten myself into?" However, I decided I could take anything for one evening, so I sat there with my arms folded, daring anyone to speak to me or even come near me.

The student who gave the talk that night, Gerry Hassel, was the only one in the group that I could really respect as an individual. He had won photographic contests and so had I. He had won a ping pong championship and so had I. He had lifted weights and so had I. Thus, we had many things in common. Eventually, he was the one who helped me find this missing "thing" that I had been looking for, which I found out was peace with God.

When the meeting started, I was amazed when these students prayed—you could tell they were really talking to God. They were not like the prayers that I had heard most of my life in the Methodist church. They had a quality about them in their relationship to God that I wanted. Being the go-getter type, I was at every meeting they had from then on, both their Wednesday night meetings on campus and the weekend youth revivals that they held in churches in the area surrounding Dallas.

I thought I was a Christian. I had been raised in the Methodist church, had taught Sunday school, had read my Bible, and even believed that Jesus Christ was the Son of God. In fact, I had done everything the Methodist church had told me to do. Gerry asked me if I had been born again. I told him, "Of course." Then he asked me the embarrassing question, "When did it happen?" I said, "I have no idea." He said, "If you don't have any idea when it happened, how do you know that it did?" This caused me to begin to wonder if I really was born again, because by then I knew that, according to Jesus' teachings, one could not enter the kingdom of God unless one had been born again.

Also being a pseudointellectual, I had a million questions for which these kids did not have any answers. I am sure they got tired of seeing me coming toward them. Then one evening at one of their youth revivals, Gerry spoke on these two verses:

16 But I say, walk by the Spirit, and you will not carry out the desire of the flesh.
17 For the flesh sets its desire against the Spirit, and the Spirit against the flesh; for these are in opposition to one another, so that you may not do the things that you please.
—Galatians 5

He depicted this as a tug-of-war between the flesh and the spirit. No one had to ask me—I knew which side of that tug-of-war I was on. I was solidly on the flesh side. Gerry pointed out that as one receives Jesus Christ as his personal Savior and becomes born again, he is then transferred from the flesh side to the Spirit side of the tug-of-war. Then he stated that it is possible to know for sure that you have eternal life, that you are on the Spirit side of the tug-of-war. He read this:

> **11 And the witness is this, that God has given us eternal life, and this life is in His Son.**
> **12 He who has the Son has the life; he who does not have the Son of God does not have the life.**
> **13 These things I have written to you who believe in the name of the Son of God, in order that you may know that you have eternal life.**
>
> —1 John 5

Gerry went on to point out that these things are written to those who believe in the name of the Son of God so that they can know that they have eternal life. It is not a "guess so," "hope so" or "maybe so" situation. We can *know* for certain that we have eternal life and thus have peace with God. He said that in order to get to the point of knowing that we have eternal life, we need to review some basic principles. He then spoke about the following ideas.

First, it is important to know that all things that God created—the stars, trees, animals, atoms and so forth—are doing exactly what they were created to do. That is, everything except man. He pointed out that there was only one verse in the Bible that told us why man was created:

> **7 "...Everyone who is called by My name,**
> **And whom I have created for My glory,**
> **Whom I have formed, even whom I have made."**
>
> —Isaiah 43

This verse says that humans were created to glorify God. Gerry stated that neither himself nor any other human being had glorified God in all their lives, in everything that they had said, done and thought. He said that this gives us the first clue as to what "sin" really is and that we could find out more about it in the following verse:

23   ...for all have sinned and fall short of the glory of God,...

—Romans 3

This verse says that all of us have sinned and we all fall short of the purpose for which we were created—that of glorifying God. There is even a simpler definition of sin. Sin is "living independent of God." Any person who has graduated from high school can choose which college to attend. If he or she makes that decision apart from God, it is "sin." This is the basic problem in the Garden of Eden. Satan tempted Eve to eat the fruit of the tree of "the knowledge of good and evil." He said that if she would do this, she would know good from evil and be wise like God. This means that she could make her own decisions and would not have to rely on God's wisdom and guidance.

Gerry said that since we all fit into this category of living independent of God and not glorifying Him in everything that we do, we need to look at the results of this sin. He asked us what "wages" were, and we could all agree that wages are what you get paid for what you do. Based on that, he then read this verse:

23   For the wages of sin is death, but the free gift of God is eternal life in Christ Jesus our Lord.

—Romans 6

This verse states that the wages of sin is death—eternal spiritual death. Spiritual death is what we get paid for the sin that we do. It also gives us the other side of the coin: that is, that through Jesus Christ, we can freely have eternal life instead of eternal death.   Isn't that wonderful?!

Gerry said that this brought us to the place where Jesus Christ fits into this whole picture. He then related a story about a judge in a small town which beautifully illustrated to me the place of Jesus in all of this:

> In this small town, the newspapermen were against the judge and wanted to get him out of the office. A case was coming up before the judge concerning a vagrant—a drunken bum—who happened to have been a fraternity brother of the judge when they were at college. The newspapermen thought that this was their chance. If the judge let the vagrant off easy, the headlines would read, "Judge Shows Favoritism to Old Fraternity Brother." If the judge gave the vagrant the maximum penalty, the headlines would read, "Hardhearted Judge Shows No Mercy to Old Fraternity Brother." Either way, they had him. The judge heard the case and gave the vagrant the maximum penalty of thirty days or $300 fine.
>
> The judge then stood up, took off his robe, laid it down on his chair, walked down in front of the bench and put his arm around the shoulders of his old fraternity brother. He told him that as judge, in order to uphold the law, he had to give him the maximum penalty, because he was guilty. But because he cared about him, he wanted to pay the fine for him. So the judge took out his wallet and handed his old fraternity brother $300.
>
> For God to be "just," He has to uphold the law that says "the soul who sins will die." On the other hand, because He loves us, He wants to pay that death penalty for us. I cannot pay the death penalty for you because I have a death penalty of my own that I have to worry about, since I, too, have sinned. If I were sinless, I could die in your place. I guess God could have sent down

millions of sinless beings to die for us. But what God chose to do was to send down one person, who was equal in value, in God's eyes, to all of the people who will ever live, and yet who would remain sinless. Jesus Christ died physically and spiritually in order to pay the death penalty for you and me. The blood of Christ washes away all of our sins, and with it the death penalty that resulted from our sin.

The judge's old fraternity brother could have taken the $300 and said, "Thank you," or he could have told the judge to keep his money and that he would do it on his own. Similarly, each person can thank God for allowing Christ to die in his place and receive Jesus Christ as his own Savior, or he can tell God to keep His payment and that he will make it on his own. What you do with that question determines where you will spend eternity.

After hearing this story, I realized for the first time why I had to receive Jesus Christ as my personal Savior and how He fit into the overall scheme of things. It was not enough just to believe in "God" in general or even to believe that Jesus Christ was God's only son. I needed to have a personal relationship with Jesus and that would get me to God. In fact, it is the only way to God. Jesus, Himself, pointed this out:

6 Jesus said to him, "I am the way, and the truth, and the life; no one comes to the Father, but through Me...."
                                                        —John 14

23 Whoever denies the Son does not have the Father; the one who confesses the Son has the Father also.

                                                        —1 John 2

Gerry proceeded to say that we were all at war with God:

10 For if while we were enemies, we were reconciled to God through the death of His Son, much more, having been reconciled, we shall be saved by His life.

11 And not only this, but we also exult in God through our Lord Jesus Christ, through whom we have now received the reconciliation.

—Romans 5

Even though we are at war with God, every human soul longs to be at peace with God. In fact, Saint Augustine said that there was a God-sized vacuum in every man's heart that could only be filled by Jesus Christ. I knew then that I wanted to be at peace with God and that the answer was in coming to Him through Jesus Christ and receiving Him as my personal individual Savior:

16 "For God so loved the world, that He gave His only begotten Son, that whoever believes in Him should not perish, but have eternal life...."

—John 3

Here we see that if we believe in Christ, we won't perish; we will have everlasting life instead. The way we do this is very simple: we believe in our heart and we confess it with our mouth.

9 ...that if you confess with your mouth Jesus *as* Lord, and believe in your heart that God raised Him from the dead, you shall be saved;...

—Romans 10

Gerry went on to say that you cannot come to Christ just as your Savior—you must also accept Him as your Master and be willing to follow Him. That night I knew that I wanted to have peace with God and I wanted to have Christ as my Savior, so I prayed a simple little prayer and asked Christ to come into my heart, to forgive my sins, to take charge of my life and I said I would follow Him.

All of a sudden, a perfect peace like I had never known flooded my entire being. That peace has been with me ever since. I have been up to the heights and have crashed down and been up to the heights again; yet I have had peace through it all. It is a peace that we can have, no matter what turbulent events we are in or what is facing us. It is the kind of peace that Jesus had the night before He was going to be tortured to death. He told this to the disciples in the upper room during the last supper:

27 "Peace I leave with you; My peace I give to you; not as the world gives, do I give to you. Let not your heart be troubled, nor let it be fearful...."
—John 14

That peace from Jesus Christ, the Prince of Peace, is something that abides with you. It is a precious gift from Him.

During the 1929 stock market crash and the 1930's, many people committed suicide because their lives were built around material things and, when these were gone, life had no meaning. I would encourage you to seek that peace with God in whatever way you want to seek it. I have found it through a personal faith in Jesus Christ and following Him.

If you decide to pray and receive Christ as your Savior—to invite Him into your heart and life, to forgive your sins and to help you turn from your sins—and you make the choice to follow him, I would love to hear from you. There is a little book I would like to give you that will help you.

If you are still sincerely seeking this peace with God, there is a minibook that I have authored, entitled *Where*

Will You Be In 300 Years?, that I will be happy to send to you as my gift, with no strings attached. So I would love to hear from you too. My address is at the end of this book.

May God bless you and give you the peace of Jesus.

Appendix B

INFORMATION, EQUIPMENT AND PRODUCT SOURCES BY CHAPTER

In this section, we will be listing equipment and companies that sell the various products that have been mentioned throughout this book, as well as other books, publications and sources that may be of interest and help to you. The last part of this appendix is oriented by chapter, for your convenience.

Some of the companies listed sell more than what we have indicated here. This is why we encourage you to get their catalogs, most of which are free.

First, however, we would like to present the addresses and information about a few of the major sources of equipment and supplies, so we do not have to keep repeating their addresses. We will also give some major sources for the books mentioned.

ADDRESS FOR EQUIPMENT
AND SUPPLIES

We suggest you first contact the following organizations to get their catalogs:

Alpine Distributors
Excalibur Dehydrators

Lehman's Non-Electric Catalog
Magic Mill/Nutriflex
Nitro-Pak Preparedness Center
Safe-Trek Outfitters
The Survival Center

Sometimes there is a small fee for catalogs from these companies and some book companies, but it is frequently. refunded with the first purchase.

These seven suppliers are listed in alphabetical order in this section, with addresses and phone numbers where you can contact them.   Following that are listed the addresses of publishers and mail-order sources of books that are listed numerous times throughout the remainder of this appendix.   In the last portion of this appendix, which is oriented by chapters, these seven suppliers will have a "■" following their name, and you can refer back to this section for their full address.

✓ Alpine Distributors■   Orders only (800)453-7453
Matthew Walker   Information (503)826-9279
P.O. Box 3100   FAX (503)826-1023
Central Point, OR 97502   catalog $5

Alpine Distributors is an official distributor for many items in the food and health realm:

Freeze-dried food
Dehydrated food
Juice Plus+
Life-Pak
Melaleuca products

Our top recommendation as a source for quality reserve foods would be Alpine Distributors, an official distributor for AlpineAire Gourmet Reserves, which produces the largest selection of great-tasting "no-cook" foods. They even carry a one-month, three-month and a one-year supply pack of these no-cook meals and foods that has a very wide variety, which we highly recommend. They carry backpacking foods in foil pouches, freeze-dried and dehydrated foods in small and large cans, as well as bulk commodities, such as beans and grains. AlpineAire is a very reputable company, in business since 1975, specializing in top-of-the-line, great tasting, easy-to-prepare foods (complete meals and individual items) which are free from artificial preservatives, flavorings, colors, white sugar and MSG.

The AlpineAire product line has been specifically developed to supply the concerned buyer in need of nutritionally-balanced, really delicious, easy-to-use, shelf-stable food reserves. They have ten complete systems that provide no-cook (and cooking-required) food for one person for a year, for three months, for one month, and for two weeks.

In addition, Alpine sells cans of individual complete entrees (meatless, seafood, chicken, turkey and beef), breakfasts, soups and desserts, as well as complete meals. You can buy a sample pack so that you can try them out.

As well as a long and stable shelf life, AlpineAire offers satisfying and familiar foods, with nutritional quality at a reasonable price. Menu items are individually packed in pouches and nitrogen-packed in number 10 cans for easy and stable storage. Their Emergency Preparedness Assortments provide the essentials for three-day or six-day emergency situations.

If you mention that you learned about Alpine Distributors through an Omega book when you call or write, they will give you a whopping *15 percent discount* on your food order. The catalog is $5, which will be refunded on your first food order.

✓   Excalibur Dehydrators–Dept. SR1■   (800)875-4254
6083 Power Inn Road
Sacramento, CA 95824

Comments about Excalibur Dehydrators are made under the Chapter 7 listing.

Lehman's Non-Electric Catalog■   (216)857-5757
P.O. Box 41   FAX (216)857-5785
Kidron, OH 44636

Lehman's carries a wide variety of supplies of interest to the homesteader, from canning equipment and wood cookstoves to butchering supplies and garden tools. They also have a wide selection of books available. Their catalog is $2.

Magic Mill/Nutriflex■   (800)888-8587
P.O. Box 45115   (801)467-0707
Salt Lake City, UT 84145   FAX (801)486-0953

See the Chapter 7 listing for comments about Magic Mill/Nutriflex dehydrators and mills.

Nitro-Pak Preparedness Center■   (800)866-4876
151 N. Main St., Ste. OM
Heber, UT 84032   FAX (801)654-0099

Nitro-Pak Preparedness Center is a customer-service-oriented company. It has become the nation's largest one-stop source for acquiring most of the preparedness items you will need for the troubling times ahead. They carry a wide line of helpful equipment for surviving short-term or long-term emergencies or crises.

As well as dehydrated and freeze-dried foods and MRE's (meals ready-to-eat), you will find in their catalog such products as:

1. Water storage containers, filters and tablets
2. Complete 72-hour survival kits
3. A selection of preparedness books and videos
4. Wheat mills and mixers
5. Emergency light and heating products
6. A wide range of first-aid supplies

Their catalog is $3, but with it they give you a $5 certificate that you can use on your first purchase. If you let them know that you heard about them from Omega, they will extend to you a *10 percent discount on storage foods* and *5 percent* on everything else.

✓ Safe-Trek Outfitters■   (800)424-7870
1716 West Main   (406)587-571
Bozeman, MT 59715   FAX (406)586-4842

Safe-Trek is probably the most complete supply center. They have an extensive line of MRE's, long-term storage foods, water purifiers, and much more. (Also see comments under Chapters 5, 11 and 12 headings.)

They handle a wide variety of things mentioned in this book, such as fallout shelters, guns, composting toilets and medical kits of every type and variety. The many things that they offer are all contained in their beautiful 103-page (11" x 15") catalog, which has a full-color cover. They charge $8 for it, but it is well worth the price for your education in knowing what is available. They will credit the $8 back against your first purchase. If you tell them you are calling or writing because you read about them in an Omega book, they will give you a *10 percent discount* off anything in their catalog.

The Survival Center, Dept 190■   (800)321-2900
✓ P.O. Box 234
Mckenna, WA 9858

The Survival Center is one of the oldest continually-operating businesses that sells storage foods in the U.S. As well as selling grains and beans in nitrogen-packed, 6-gallon buckets, mills, food dehydrators, herbs, water purification equipment, and so forth, they also have knowledge and experience in installing complete underground shelters. They have a large selection of books (including many metaphysical books). Their catalog is available for $2.

MAJOR SOURCES FOR BOOKS

Chances are that you can find books that you will need on these subjects in your local garden store, feed store, grange co-op or regular bookstore. In the event that you cannot, we wanted to first present to you here some of the major publishers mentioned in this appendix, along with their addresses. Throughout the remainder of this appendix, when we list books by the following publishers, only the name of the publisher will be listed, and it will be followed by a "♦". You can refer back to this section to get the complete address, in the event that you cannot find the books locally.

Garden Way Publishing   (800)441-5700
Storey Communications, Inc.
Schoolhouse Road, Pownal, VT 05261

HP Books
11150 Olympic Blvd.
Los Angeles, CA 90064

Omega Publications and Videos   (503)826-4512
P.O. Box 4130   Orders only (800)345-0175
Medford, OR 97501

Omega is a major book publisher. They also offer the following video titles that were recommended in various chapters:

Preparation for Emergencies
Dehydration Made Easy
Canning is Fun
Vital Food Storage

Omega Publications and Videos has an entire video series available on practical information and skills, entitled, *The Growin' Tapes*. Subjects in this ever-expanding series include gardening, canning, dehydrating, food storage, nutrition, healthy living, and other aspects of

practical preparation.   You can request their complete
listing of videos and books when you write or call.

Ortho Books   (800)822-6349
P.O. Box 5047   FAX (314)895-1146
San Ramon, CA 94583

Rodale Press   (610)967-5171
33 East Minor Street
Emmaus, PA 18098

In addition to these publishers, there are a number of
companies that specialize in mail-order books in the
general self-reliant realm.   You should contact them and
ask for their catalog.   Books obtainable from these publishers or mail-order book houses will have "♦ ♦" following the source throughout the remainder of this appendix.
These are:

Acres, U.S.A.   (504)889-2100
P.O. Box 8800   FAX (504)889-2777
Metairie, LA 70011

Home Canning Supply   (800)354-4070
P.O. Box 1158   (619)788-0520
2117 Main Street   FAX (619)789-4745
Ramona, CA 92065   catalog $1

Know More Books   (503)821-2315
P.O. Box 568   FAX (503)592-3287
Cave Junction, OR 97523   catalog $1

Nitro-Pak Preparedness Center   (800)866-4876
151 N. Main St., Ste. OM   FAX (801)654-0099
Heber, UT 84302

Safe-Trek Outfitters   (800)424-7870
1716 West Main   (406)587-5571
Bozeman, MT 59715   FAX (406)586-4842

Tattered Cover Bookstore   (303)322-1965
1536 Wynkoop Street   FAX (303)629-1704
Denver, CO 80202

Some of the books that we think are excellent are now out of print and can be difficult to locate, although they may be available in some libraries. The following company specializes in helping you locate out-of-print books for a small fee:

Book Look   (800)223-0540

Books in this category will have " ♦ ♦ ♦ " following the title.

PRODUCT SOURCES BY CHAPTER

CHAPTER 1—
THE NEED TO BE MORE SELF-RELIANT

Highly Recommended Book

There is one book that is a must. You will refer to it over and over again:

Back to Basics
The Reader's Digest Association
Pleasantville, NY

Highly Recommended Periodicals or Publications

If you are seriously considering becoming self-reliant, the following monthly publications are recommended. They are listed in order of preference:

Self-Reliant Living (no relation to this book)
Carl Krupp, Publisher   (503)476-4721
P.O. Box 910
Merlin, OR 97532

Backwoods Home Magazine   (916)459-3300
1257 Siskiyou Blvd., #213
Ashland, OR 97520

Back Home   (800)992-2546
P.O. Box 70   (704)696-3838
Hendersonville, NC 28793

Acres, U.S.A.   (504)889-2100
P.O. Box 8800   FAX (504)889-2777
Metairie, LA 70011

Mother Earth News
P.O. Box 56300
Boulder, CO 80322-6300

Special Interest Periodicals

Countryside and Small Stock Journal
W11564 Highway 64   (800)551-5691
Withee, WI 54498   (715)785-7979

Dairy Goat Journal   (800)272-4628
Route 1   sample issue $2
Helenville, WI 53137

Harrowsmith   (800)205-3687
P.O. Box 54427
Boulder, CO 83323-4431

Home Power   (916)475-3179
P.O. Box 520   (916)475-0830
Ashland, OR 97520   FAX (916)475-3179

National Poultry News
P.O. Box 1647 Dept. CS
Easley, SC 29641

Organic Gardening
Rodale Press   (610)967-5171
33 East Minor Street
Emmaus, PA 18098

Rabbits Only $15/year
P.O. Box 207
Holbrook, NY 11741

Today's Farmer   (314)876-5252
MFA, Inc.
615 Locust Street
Columbia, MO 65201

CHAPTER 2—SELF-RELIANT IN THE CITY

Appliances, non-electric

Kerns Gas Refrigeration   (916)275-6382
3929 La Mesa Ave.
Shasta Lake, CA 96019

Lehman's Hardware   (216)857-5441
P.O. Box 41   catalog $2
Kidron, OH 44636

Dehydrators, Food

See sources listed under Chapter 7 heading in this Appendix.

Drilling Rigs, to drill your own well

DeepRock   (800)633-8774
2200 Anderson Road   (205)749-3377
P.O. Box 1   FAX (205)749-5601
Opelika, AL 36802-3301

This company supplies small, portable drilling rigs for drilling your own well. You can request their free information packet and the illustrated guide *How to Drill Your Own Water Well*. They also sell a video tape showing every step of drilling a well.

Fish Equipment

Gen-Airator, Grovac, Inc.   (414)781-5020
4310 N. 126th St.
Brookfield, WI 53005

Generators, Diesel

China Farm Machinery   (909)657-0379
23985 Rolling Meadows Dr.   FAX (909)657-8120
Perris, CA 92570

China Diesel Imports   (619)669-1995
15749 Lyons Valley Rd.
Jamul, CA 91935

Troy-Bilt Diesel Generators   (800)776-8500
102nd St. & 9th Ave.
Troy, NY 12180

Minigreenhouse (made with tires)

Manufactured by:
Wayman's Lake Mount Orchards   (801)768-9705
Lehi, UT 84043

Spent tires can usually be obtained from any tire dealer. Wire ribs inserted into perforations in 14-15 inch tires provide support for the plastic to form an umbrella, secured by a rubber ring. (See Figure 2.3 in Chapter 2.) The plastic would be removed after danger of frost is past.

Pumps

Herbach & Rademan Company   (215)426-1708
401 Erie Avenue
Philadelphia, PA 19134-1187

Solar Energy Equipment

See Chapter 5 for listing of sources.

Steam Engines, Wood-Fired

The Steam Outlet   catalog $5
P.O. Box 1426
Thonotassassa, FL 33592

Water Filters

The following companies can be contacted for a water filter that would remove heavy metals, parasites and so forth.

Alpine Distributors■   Orders only (800)453-7453

Custom Pure—The Water Store   (206)363-0039
1514 N.E. 179th Street   FAX (206)363-8569
Seattle, WA 98155

Nutritionist's Choice   catalog $1
P.O. Box 1107
Eagle Point, OR 97524

Wind Power

See Chapter 5 for listing of sources.

Books and Articles for Reference

Cottage Water Systems
By Max Burns
Garden Way Publishing♦   (800)441-5700

Crayfish Farming for Food and Profit
Atlas Publications
Dept. CS, P.O. Box 639
Blairsville, GA 30512

Diesel Electric Plants
By the Staff of Ramona Works
P.O. Box 1350
Ramona, CA 92065

Although promotional, the small book listed above contains useful information on how their equipment can be integrated into solar electric, wind generation and hydroelectric power plants.

Home Aquaculture
Alternative Aquaculture Asso.
P.O. Box 109A
Breinigsville, PA 18031

"Fish Factory" Article: *Science Digest*, May 1975
P.O. Box 1568
New York, NY 10019

Hunting and Trapping Books

See book listing in Chapter 9.

Hydroponic Books

See books listed under Chapter 6 heading.

CHAPTER 3—A COUNTRY PLACE

Books and Publications

Buying Country Land
By Peggy Tonseth
Garden Way Publishing♦   (800)441-5700

Country Careers
By Jerry Germer
Garden Way Publishing♦   (800)441-5700

Discover the Good Life In Rural America
By Bob Bone
Garden Way Publishing♦   (800)441-5700

Finding and Buying Your Place in the Country
By Les Scher & Carol Scher
Garden Way Publishing♦   (800)441-5700

Home and Land   (800)277-7800
P.O. Box 5018
Tallahassee, FL 32314

Rural Property Bulletin
P.O. Box 37-C
Sparks, NE 69220

United Country Catalog   (800)999-1020
United National Real Estate
4700 Bellevue
Kansas City, MO 64112

CHAPTER 4—IT TAKES TIME, TIME, TIME

Fences

Mighty Mule Automatic Gate Opener
GTO, Inc.   (800)543-GATE
738 Capital Circle, N.W.
Tallahassee, FL 32304

Irrigation

Dripworks   (800)522-3747
380 Maple Street   (707)459-6323
Willits, CA 95499   FAX (707)459-9645

Submatic Irrigation Systems   (800)692-4100
P.O. Box 246   (806)747-9000
Lubbock, TX 79408   FAX (806)747-1800

Recreation Underground Sprinklers Ltd.
Bay 4, 811 - 51st Street E.   (306)934-6616
Saskatoon, Saskatchewan
Canada S7K 0X7

World Class Ideas   Design/Installation Guide
Suite 317 $5 and SASE
14845-6 Yonge
Aurora, Ontario
Canada L4G 6H8

Books

How to Design & Build Fences & Gates
By Ortho Books♦   (800)822-6349

The Best Fences
By James Fitzgerald
Garden Way Publishing♦   (800)441-5700

CHAPTER 5—BUILDING THE HOUSE

Fallout Shelter

Oregon Institute of Science   (503)592-4142
   and Medicine
Arthur Robinson, PhD
2251 Dick George Road
Cave Junction, OR 97523

Dr. Robinson is an expert in fallout shelters and has plans for shelter designs and consulting available. He has authored the book entitled *Fighting Chance* and publishes an excellent newsletter, *Fighting Chance.*

Preparing for Emergencies   (503)826-4512
Omega Publications♦   Orders only (800)345-0175

The subject of fallout shelters (or root cellars) is discussed in some detail in Chapter 10 of this book, another in this "Preparation" series.

Safe-Trek Outfitters■   (800)424-7870

Safe-Trek has radiation measuring devices, as well as a "ready-to-bury" fallout shelter, which is complete with everything from a toilet to a five-year food supply.

Electrical Generation

Hydroelectric power

Alternative Energy Engineering   (800)777-6609
P.O. Box 339
Redway, CA 95560

This company supplies equipment for making electricity with solar, wind and water sources, as does Backwoods Solar (listed below).

Atlas Publications
Dept. CS, P.O. Box 639
Blairsville, GA 30512

Backwoods Solar Electric Systems   (208)263-4290
8530-SR Rapid Lightning Creek Road
Sandpoint, ID 83864

Backwoods Solar's catalog includes a planning guide with applications for use of solar-, wind- and water-generated electricity.

Canyon Industries, Inc.   (206)592-5552
P.O. Box 574-C
Deming, WA 98244

Solar Panels/Photovoltaic Cells

Alternative Energy Engineering   (800)777-6609
P.O. Box 339
Redway, CA 9560

Backwoods Solar Electric Systems   (208)263-4290
8530-SR Rapid Lightning Creek Road
Sandpoint, ID 83864

Northern Hydraulics Catalog, Inc.   (800)533-5545
P.O. Box 1499   free catalog
Burnsville, MN 55337-0499

Solar products, such as 51-watt solar electric panels and rechargeable solar lights, are listed in *Northern's* handyman catalog.

Photocomm   (800)223-9580
7681 East Gray Road
Scottsdale, AZ 85260

Two to four 51-watt Kyocera J-51 solar panels can provide a source for emergency power. Contact Photocomm for the names and addresses of other dealers closer

to your home. For technical information only on these
solar panels, contact:

Kyocera (manufacturer)   (800)537-0294

Real Goods   (800)762-7325
966 Mazzoni Street   (707)468-9292
Ukiah, CA 95482

Seelye Equipment Specialists   (800)678-9430
913 State Street   (616)547-9430
Charlevoix, MI 49720

With the new "PL" style florescent light bulbs and
the direct current low voltage electronic ballast, it is now
possible to have high-quality lighting while using very
little power. PL lights draw five times less energy to give
the same amount of light as an incandescent bulb. A 5-
watt PL light equals a 25-watt incandescent bulb in both
light output and color. A PL bulb has a 10,000-hour life,
which is about ten times longer than a regular light bulb.
PL lights cost a little more but will pay for themselves in
energy savings. They will greatly reduce the amount of
solar panels required where solar-powered lighting is
being used. As well as solar electric panels, a basic PL
light system and socket adapters are available from Seelye
Equipment Specialists.

Wind Power

Alternative Energy Engineering   (800)777-6609
P.O. Box 339
Redway, CA 9560

Backwoods Solar Electric Systems   (208)263-4290
8530-SR Rapid Lightning Creek Road
Sandpoint, ID 83864

Kansas Wind Power   (913)364-4407
13569 214th Road
Holton, KS 66436-8138

Owen Publications
P.O. Box 32172-C
Charleston, SC 29417

Troyer's Windmill Sales
3981 CR 70 Rt.#2
Sugarcreek, OH 44681

Books and Magazines

Electrical Generation, Solar, Wind and Water

The Autonomous House—
Design and Planning for Self-Sufficiency ♦ ♦ ♦
By Brenda and Robert Vale
Published by Thames and Hudson, London (©1975)

Back to Basics
The Reader's Digest Association
Pleasantville, NY

Designing and Building A Solar House ♦ ♦ ♦
By Donald Watson
Garden Way Publishing   (800)471-5700

Energy for the Home—New Low-Cost Sources ♦ ♦ ♦
By Peter Clegg
Garden Way Publishing   (800)441-5700

Handbook of Homemade Power
Bantam Books
Mother Earth News
P.O. Box 56300
Boulder, CO 80322-6300

Home Power Magazine   (916)475-3179
P.O. Box 520
Ashland, OR 97520

If you want a magazine that addresses the subject of alternative energy for the home, *Home Power* is *the* magazine.

Home Wind Power
By the U.S. Dept. of Energy
Garden Way Publishing♦   (800)441-5700

The Homebuilt Wind-Generated
Electricity Handbook♦ ♦ ♦
By Michael Hackleman
Published by Earthwind
5246 Boyer Road
Mariposa, CA 95338

The Independent Home—Living Well with
Power from the Sun, Wind and Water
By Michael Potts
Garden Way Publishing♦   (800)441-5700

What To Do When the Power Fails
Garden Way Publishing♦   (800)441-5700

Wind Power For Home & Business
By Paul Gipe
Garden Way Publishing♦   (800)441-5700

Cooking with Wood

Aunt Bessie's Wood Stove Cookbook
Know More Books♦ ♦   (503)821-2315

Heating with Wood

Complete Book of Heating with Wood
By Larry Gay
Garden Way Publishers♦   (800)441-5700

Heating With Wood
By Michael Harris
Tattered Cover Bookstore♦ ♦   (303)322-1965

How to Heat Your Home
Without Going Broke: Build Yourself
An Amazing Stainless Steel Wood Stove
By John Sadler
Tattered Cover Bookstore♦ ♦   (303)322-1965

How to Heat and Eat with Woodburning Stoves
By Willah Weldon
Tattered Cover Bookstore♦ ♦   (303)322-1965

Wood Furnaces and Boilers
By Larry Gay
Tattered Cover Bookstore♦ ♦   (303)322-1965

Woodburning Stoves
By Norbert Duerichen
Tattered Cover Bookstore♦ ♦   (303)322-1965

Security

How to Make Where You Live More Secure
By Greg Dietz
Tattered Cover Bookstore♦ ♦   (303)322-1965

Solar Heating

Designing and Building a Solar House♦ ♦ ♦
By Donald Watson
Garden Way Publishing

How to Install a Solar Hot Water Heater:
Closed Loop Antifreeze System
By James Cook
Tattered Cover Bookstore♦ ♦   (303)322-1965

How to Heat Hot Water Without Going Broke: Build
Yourself a Solar Heater With a One Year Payback
By John Sadler
Tattered Cover Bookstore♦ ♦   (303)322-1965

Solar Electric
By Strong
Garden Way Publishing♦   (800)441-5700

Solar Energy Handbook
By Henry Lamda
Tattered Cover Bookstore♦ ♦   (303)322-1965

Solar Energy Owner's Guide No. 1
By Ralph Ritchie
Tattered Cover Bookstore♦ ♦   (303)322-1965

Solar Heated Buildings of North America:
120 Outstanding Examples
By William Shurcliff
Tattered Cover Bookstore♦ ♦   (303)322-1965

Solar Energy Collection and Its Utilization
For House Heating
By Austin Whillier
Tattered Cover Bookstore♦ ♦   (303)322-1965

Solar Designing 1979
By James Lambeth
Tattered Cover Bookstore♦ ♦   (303)322-1965

Water Supply

The Home Water Supply—How to Find,
Filter, Store and Conserve It
By Stu Campbell
Garden Way Publishing♦   (800)441-5700

CHAPTER 6—THE WONDERFUL GREENHOUSE

Greenhouse Companies

Arctic   (800)428-9276
Route 1-0   catalog $4
Hammond, WI 54015

Farm Wholesale Inc.   (800)825-1925
2396 Perkins St. NE   (503)393-3973
Salem, OR 97303

Gothic Arch Greenhouses   (800)628-4974
P.O. Box 1564   (205)432-7529
Mobile, AL 36633

Hobby Garden Greenhouses   (802)372-4041
Box 83-OG
Grand Isle, VT 05458

HomeStyles   (800)356-8890
275 Market St.
Minneapolis, MN 55405

National Greenhouse Co.   (800)826-9314
P.O. Box 500   (217)562-9333
400 East Main   FAX (217)562-2841
Pana, IL 62557   catalog $2

Santa Barbara Greenhouses   (800)544-5276
721 Richmond Avenue   (805)483-4288
Oxnard, CA 93030   FAX (805)483-0229

Solar Prism Mfg., Inc.   (503)472-1285
P.O. Box 29   FAX (503)434-9142
McMinnville, OR 97128

Stromberg's Chicks & Gamebirds   (218)587-2222
P.O. Box 400
Pine River 4, MN 56474

Sturdi-built Greenhouse Mfg. Co. (503)244-4100
Dept. B, 11304 SW Boones Ferry Rd.
Portland, OR 97219

Turner Greenhouses   (800)672-4770
P.O. Box 1260   FAX (919)736-4550
Hwy. 117 South
Goldsboro, NC 27533

Vegetable Factory Inc.   (800)221-2550
Sunbeam Structures Division   (203)324-0010
P.O. Box 1353   FAX (203)324-0520
Stamford, CT 06913-0663

Hydroponic Equipment

A & R Sales   (801)753-5333
P.O. Box 681
Logan, UT 84321

Hamilton Technology Corporation   (800)458-7474
14902 S. Figueroa St.   (310)217-1191
Gardena, CA 90248

Higher Yield   (800)451-1952
29211 N.E. Wylie Rd.   (206)834-6962
Camas, WA 98607   catalog $1

Hydro Gardens Inc.   (303)495-2266
P.O. Box 9707
Colorado Springs, CO 80932

Hydro Gardens is the company we use for our timers, nutrients, and other hydroponic supplies.

Indoor Gardening Supplies   (313)426-9080
P.O. Box 40567
Detroit, MI 48240

Light Mfg. Co.   (800)NOW-LITE
1634 S.E. Brooklyn
Portland, OR 97202

Plant Collectibles   (716)875-1221
103 Kenview Avenue   catalog $2
Buffalo, NY 14217

Worm's Way   (800)274-9676
3151 S. Highway 446
Bloomington, IN 47401

Thermostat

You can use any 110-volt thermostat (as opposed to the low-voltage ones usually used for heating and air-conditioning) to control the plugs in your greenhouse. It must be a thermostat where you can actually run 110 volts through it *and control both heating and cooling*. Some 110-volt thermostats have a 3.5-degree gap between the high and low condition. These are preferable to ones that have no gap. You can usually get these at your local electrical supply company. The kind we use are:

Dayton Temperature Control—Model 2E207
Dayton Electric Manufacturing Company
5959 West Howard Street
Chicago, IL 60648

Wood-Fired Hot Tubs

Snorkel Stove Company   (206)283-5701
108 Elliott Ave. W.
Seattle, WA 98119

Books

Building A Solar-Heated Pit Greenhouse
By Gregg Stone
Garden Way Publishing♦   (800)441-5700

Greenhouse Gardener's Companion
By Shane Smith
Garden Way Publishing♦   (800)441-5700

Greenhouses—Planning, Installing and Using
Ortho Books♦   (800)822-6349

Home Hydroponics
By Lem Jones
Beardsley Publishing Company

How to Grow More Vegetables
By John Jeavons
Ten Speed Press   (800)841-2665
P.O. Box 7123
Berkeley, CA 94707

Hydroponic Food Production
By Howard M. Resh, Ph.D.
Acres, U.S.A.♦♦   (504)889-2100

Hydroponic Gardening
By Raymond Bridwell
Published by Woodbridge Press Publishing Company

Hydroponic Home Food Gardens
By Howard M. Resh, Ph.D.
Acres, U.S.A.♦♦   (504)889-2100

Hydroponic Tomatoes For the Home Gardener
By Howard M. Resh, Ph.D.
Acres, U.S.A.♦ ♦   (504)889-2100

Starting Seeds Indoors
Garden Way Publishing♦   (800)441-5700

CHAPTER 7—GARDENING AND PRESERVING

Canning Equipment

Suggested Canning Equipment to Have on Hand:

1. 7-pint water bath canner with jar rack for pints
2. 7-quart water bath canner with jar rack for quarts
3. wide canning funnel
4. canning ladle
5. canning jars (preferably wide-mouth pints)
6. a good supply of extra canning lids and some extra rings
7. lid magnet
8. jar tongs (for lifting hot jars)
9. pressure canner, if desired
10. large stainless steel or enamel-coated kettle
11. large wooden spoon
12. a good canning cookbook

I (Jeani) personally prefer my pint water bath canner and I use it far more than my larger canner which can handle either pints or quarts. That is why I suggest having both. Since I more often use pint and half-pint jars in canning than quarts, this smaller-sized canner is easier to move around full of hot water and it does not take as much water, nor as long to boil the water, as with the larger canner. Time is an important factor when you are canning multiple canner loads.

I see a pressure canner as a secondary consideration to a good water bath canner and only necessary if you also wish to have the capability of canning vegetables other than relishes and tomatoes that are acid-based. Of course it would also be necessary if you wish to can meat or fish.

Lids can be boiled in any pot. A lid magnet is invaluable for fishing hot lids out of boiling water and keeping them clean.

The stainless steel or enamel canning kettle would be used for heating tomato sauces, relishes, and so forth, where you should not use an aluminum pan.

Many of these items, if not all, can usually be found during the early summer in local stores that sell canning supplies. Here are some alternative sources. If you send for their catalogs, you can compare prices and get a good idea of what is available and what would best meet your needs.

Sources for Canning Equipment

Embarcadero Cannery   (510)535-2311
2026 Livingstone Street
Oakland, CA 94606

Embarcadero Cannery is one source we know of for cans and a can sealer, if you wish to try canning meat, poultry and fish in cans. They carry institutional-sized cans down to the more common 8- and 15-ounce sizes. Cans can also be used for preserving vegetable seeds and dried foods, such as rice. As well as being utilized for boiling water bath canning or pressurized canning, their pressure canner can be converted for use as a vacuum chamber, useful to those wishing to vacuum-pack dehydrated foods and herbs.

Gardener's Kitchen
Box 412-OG5
Farmington, CT 06034

Home Canning Supply   (800)354-4070
P.O. Box 1158   (619)788-0520
2117 Main Street   FAX (619)789-4745
Ramona, CA 92065   catalog $1

Kitchen Krafts   (609)778-4960
Box 805   catalog $1
Mt. Laurel, NJ 08054

Lehman's Non-Electric Catalog■   (216)857-5757

Dehydrators

Two brands of good-quality dehydrators that we can recommend from personal experience are the following.

Excalibur Dehydrators–Dept. SR1■   (800)875-4254

Excalibur Dehydrators are available in 4-tray, 5-tray or 9-tray sizes, with or without an automatic timer (except for the 4-tray size). These are of top quality and are the best in efficiency of drying time, since the air comes from the back. Because of this horizontal air flow (as opposed to the heat/air source being at the bottom with many brands), there is no need to rotate the trays partway through for even drying. Also, because it is like an oven, you can take out every other tray in order to do larger items, like dough art or drying flowers, if you wish to use it for craft projects like that. This is my (Jeani's) favorite dehydrator.

Magic Aire II Dehydrator, available from:
Magic Mill/Nutriflex■ (800)888-8587

The Magic Aire dehydrator has an advantage in that, although the air comes up from the bottom, it has stackable trays, and you can remove unused trays, thus shrinking the size of the dehydrator on your counter if you are not drying a full load. The basic unit comes with four trays. They also offer what they call the "six-tray kit," which includes the basic dehydrator with six trays, a dehydrating cookbook, mesh inserts, and fruit leather trays. If additional trays are desired, they can be purchased in packs of two. I (Jeani) have used this dehydrator very effectively for years with up to ten trays on it. Magic Mill/Nutriflex will extend to you a *20 percent discount*, if you let them know that you are writing or calling as a result of having read this book.

Nutri-Flow (800)290-8435
14200 N.W. Melody Lane (503)645-9741
Portland, OR 97229-4360

We cannot speak from experience about Nutri-Flow's dehydrator, but it is another alternative of a large-capacity dehydrator with air flow from the back. You can call or write any of these companies for their free brochure.

Fertilizers, etc.

de Van Koek (800)992-1220
9400 Business Drive
Austin, TX 78758

Farmgard Products, Inc.   (612)864-6551
1229 Hennepin Ave.   (612)864-5774
Glencoe, MN 55336

Gardens Alive!   (812)537-8651
5100 Schenley Place
Lawrenceburn, IN 47025

Garden-Ville of Austin   (512)288-6113
8648 Old Bee Caves Rd.
Austin, TX 78735

Gilman Products   (800)847-4526
P.O. Box 327 Riverview Mill
Wilton, NH 03086

Lane, Inc.   (800)457-5013
Box 204
Charles City, IA 50616

Natural Products   (800)238-4634
1000 Oak Street
Grinnell, IA 50112

Natural Way   (800)656-4769
RR1, Box 177
Rossiter, PA 15772

Naturally Scientific   (800)248-9970
P.O. Box 500335
Atlanta, GA 31150

Peaceful Valley Farm Supply   (916)272-GROW
P.O. Box 2209 #A
Grass Valley, CA 95945

Freezing Equipment

Seal-A-Meal Vacuum Packing Machine
And Seal-A-Meal Freezer Bags

These handy and usually relatively inexpensive little machines can be purchased at most any retail store selling kitchen and canning supplies. As well as for freezing foods, they can also be used to vacuum pack and store dehydrated foods. (However, I prefer to use jars for storing foods I have dehydrated.)

Garden Equipment

Country Home Products   (800)446-8746
Ferry Road, P.O. Box 89   FAX (802)425-4017
Charlotte, VT 05445-9983

Country Home Products offers a DR Powerwagon and Field and Brush Mower that can be very helpful pieces of hand-pushed equipment on a self-reliant piece of property. At your request, they will send a free video on these, along with their information packet.

Mantis   (800)366-6268
1028 Street Road   (215)355-9700
Southampton, PA 18966   FAX (215)364-1409

Naturally Scientific   (800)248-9970
P.O. Box 500335
Atlanta, GA 31150

No-Turn Composter   (800)393-0333
Gardner Equipment   (414)386-4880
P.O. Box 106   FAX (414)386-5611
Juneau, WI 53039

Norway Industries   (608)873-8664
143 W. Main Street
Stoughton, WI 53589

Troy-Bilt   (800)366-8686
102nd Street & 9th Avenue
Troy, NY 12180

Troy-Bilt is well-known for their excellent and easy-to-operate tillers, available in various sizes, that are great to help you prepare your soil for planting. One of their garden carts, with over-sized wheels (available in two sizes), is a *must* in our opinion. It is very handy for hauling produce from the garden, orchard or vineyard, and any number of other uses. In addition to these and numerous other items in their catalog, they also offer an "E-Z Spin Composter" for producing your own fertilizer from organic wastes.

WheelAround Corp.   (800)335-CART
241 Grandview Ave.
Bellevue, KY 41073

Hula Hoe

A hula hoe is indispensable for weeding around young seedlings, as discussed in Chapter 7. They are available at any store that carries garden implements.

Hydrogen Peroxide, 35% Food Grade

Agric Health—Robert Martin   (602)326-1399
3853 E. Kleindale Road
Tucson, AZ 85716

By diluting food-grade 35% hydrogen peroxide so it is just 1-3%, you can use it in your garden to kill fungus growth, some insects, and to provide oxygen to the plants, producing faster growth, according to the author of *Best of the Best* (P. O. Box 910, Merlin, OR 97532).

Mills

Lehman's Non-Electric Catalog■   (216)857-5757

In addition to one electric mill, Lehman's catalog also offers a variety of hand-turned mills, from inexpensive varieties to ones that can be converted to power-driven from hand-turned.

Magic Mill/Nutriflex■   (800)888-8587

Magic Mill/Nutriflex produces an excellent mill and our favorite for grinding wheat and other grains. They also have a quality bread mixer called the DLX Mixer and Food Processor.

Nitro-Pak Preparedness Center■   (800)866-4876

Nitro-Pak carries the K-Tech Grain Mill and the K-Tech Wonder Kitchen Master Breadmaker/Mixer, which has attachments available for grinding meat, pressing berries, grating, and so on.

Pesticides

Garlic Research Labs   (800)510-2121
3550 Wilshire Blvd., Suite 200
Los Angeles, CA 90010

Seeds, Non-hybrid

Abundant Life Seed Foundation   (206)385-5660
P.O. Box 772
Port Townsend, WA 98368

High Altitude Gardens   (208)788-4363
P.O. Box 1048   FAX (208)788-3452
Hailey, ID 83333   catalog $3

Miller Nurseries   (800)836-9630
5060 West Lake Road   FAX (716)396-2154
Canandaigua, NY 14424

Territorial Seed Company   (503)942-9547
20 Palmer Avenue   FAX (503)942-9881
P.O. Box 157
Cottage Grove, OR 97424

Storage Foods

Freeze-dried Food Storage Systems
(Our Number 1 Recommendation For Food Storage)

Although this book is oriented more towards helping you learn how to provide your own food as much as possible, some readers wishing to become more self-reliant may also be interested in storing some reserve foods with a long shelf life for times of potential emergency. This subject is addressed in detail in the first book in this series, *Preparing For Emergencies*. Our top recommendation as a source for quality reserve foods would be the following.

Alpine Distributors■   Orders only (800)453-7453
Information (503)826-9279

Dehydrated Food Sources

Nitro-Pak Preparedness Center■	(800)866-4876
Safe-Trek Outfitters■	(800)424-7870
The Survival Center■	(800)321-2900

Low-Cost Food Storage Article

Reprints of the article by Jeani McKeever entitled "Low-Cost Food Storage and How to Use It" are available from Omega ($2 each or 3 for $5).

Videos on Food Preservation and Storage

Omega Publications and Videos♦	(503)826-4512
	Orders only (800)345-0175

As well as publishing books, Omega offers the following video titles that were recommended in this chapter:

1. *Canning is Fun!*
   By Jeani McKeever
2. *Dehydrating Made Easy*
   By Jeani McKeever
3. *Vital Food Storage*
   By Master Gardener, Dr. Barbara Fair

Omega Publications and Videos has an entire video series available on practical information and skills entitled, *The Growin' Tapes.* Subjects in this ever-expanding series include gardening, canning, dehydrating, food storage, nutrition, healthy living, and other aspects of practical preparations. You can request their complete listing of videos and books when you write or call.

Books, Booklets and Periodicals

Cookbooks

Cooking with Winter Squash & Pumpkins
By Mary Anna DuSablon
Garden Way Publishing♦   (800)441-5700

The New Zucchini Cookbook And Other Squash
By Nancy C. Ralston and Marynor Jordan
Garden Way Publishing♦   (800)441-5700

Food Preservation and Nutrition

The ABC's of Home Food Dehydration
By Barbara Densley
Horizon Publishers
Nitro-Pak♦ ♦   (800)866-4876

Back to Basics
The Readers Digest Association
Pleasantville, NY

Ball Blue Book   (Canning, Freezing & Drying)
Home Canning Supply♦ ♦   (619)788-0520

Canning and Preserving Without Sugar
By Norma M. MacRae, R.D.
Garden Way Publishing♦   (800)441-5700

*The Canning, Freezing, Curing, Smoking of
Meat, Fish and Game*
By Wilbur F. Eastman, Jr.
Garden Way Publishing♦   (800)441-5700

The Complete Book of Canning
By Charlotte Walker Pisinski
Ortho Books♦   (800)822-6349

Dehydration Made Simple
By Mary Bell
Magic Mill/Nutriflex■   (800)888-8587

Eat, Drink and Be Ready   (503)482-3800
By Monte L. Kline and W. P. Strube, Jr.
Hans Schneider, Worldwide Publishing Corp.
P.O. Box 105
Ashland, OR 97520

An Encyclopedia of Country Living
By Carla Emory
Home Canning Supply♦ ♦   (619)788-0520

Carla Emory's classic self-sufficient country life-style guide is in its 9th edition. It is a recommended addition to your library, covering cottage industries like soap making and tanning in addition to preserving foods, making butter and cheese, and a whole host of other relevant topics.

Favorite Pickles & Relishes
By Andrea Chesman
Garden Way Publishing♦   (800)441-5700

Fit As A Fiddle   (503)826-4512
By Jeani McKeever   Orders only (800)345-0175
Omega Publications♦   "Chili Sauce" canning
                                         recipe given

Fun with Fruit Preservation
By Dora D. Flack
Horizon Publishers   (801)295-9451
191 North 650 East
Bountiful, UT 84010

As well as covering drying, fruit leathers, canning, freezing, jams, jellies, juices and syrups, the preceding little book has a chapter devoted to fruit storage in basements and root cellars.

Home Food Dehydrating
By Jay and Shirley Bills
Horizon Publishers
Nitro-Pak♦ ♦   (800)866-4876

How to Dry Foods
By Deanna DeLong
Garden Way Publishing♦   (800)441-5700

Jams, Jellies & Preserves
By Imogene McTague
Garden Way Publishing♦   (800)441-5700

Keeping the Harvest
By Nancy Chioffi & Gretchen Mead
Garden Way Publishing♦   (800)441-5700

Keeping the Harvest covers various methods of preserving foods: canning, freezing, pickling, drying, curing and cold storage.

Preserve It, Naturally!   (on dehydrating)
Excalibur Dehydrators—Dept SR1■   (800)875-4254

Putting Food By
By Janet Greene, Ruth Hertzberg & Beatrice Vaughn
Garden Way Publishing♦   (800)441-5700

Putting Food Up
By Greene, Hertzberg and Vaughan
Home Canning Supply♦ ♦   (619)788-0520

Root Cellaring
By Mike and Nancy Bubel
Acres, U.S.A.♦ ♦   (504)889-2100
Know More Books♦ ♦   (503)889-2100

This book is a guide to natural cold storage of your fruits and vegetables from your garden.

Stocking Up III
By Carol Hupping and the
Staff of Rodale Food Center
Garden Way Publishing♦   (800)441-5700

Gardening

Acres, U.S.A.   (504)889-2100
P.O. Box 8800   FAX (504)889-2777
Metairie, LA 70011

Acres, U.S.A., as well as being a source for books, is also the name of a monthly newspaper giving practical information on organic farming and gardening. Their emphasis is on minimizing adverse environmental effects and promoting soil conservation and construction. They approach weed and insect control by fertility management. They will also send you their extensive book catalog upon request.

A to Z Hints for the Vegetable Gardener
Compiled by Robert E. Sanders
Garden Way Publishing♦   (800)441-5700

The Albrecht Papers, Volumes 1 & 2
By Dr. William A. Albrecht, PhD
Acres, U.S.A.♦♦   (504)889-2100

All About Vegetables
Ortho Books♦   (800)822-6349

Cold Climate Gardening—How to Extend
Your Growing Season by At Least 30 Days
By Lewis Hill
Garden Way Publishing♦   (800)441-5700

Encyclopedia of Organic Gardening
Rodale Press♦   (610)967-5171

The Experts Book of Garden Hints
Edited by Fern Marshall Bradley
Rodale Press♦   (610)967-5171

Grow the Best Root Crops
By Weldon Burge
Garden Way Publishing♦   (800)441-5700

Grow the Best Tomatoes
By John Page
Garden Way Publishing♦   (800)441-5700

Growing Fruits and Vegetables Organically
Edited by Jean M. A. Nick & Fern Marshall Bradley
Rodale Press♦   (610)967-5171

Growing Great Garlic
By Ron L. Engeland
Acres, U.S.A.♦♦   (504)889-2100

How to Grow Top Quality Corn
By Harold Willis
Tattered Cover Bookstore♦♦   (303)322-1965

How to Grow Your Own Groceries
For $100 a Year
By Clifford Ridley
Tattered Cover Bookstore♦♦   (303)322-1965

How to Select, Grow and Enjoy Vegetables
By Derek Fell
HP Books ♦

How to Succeed at Vegetable Gardening: Sound
Successful Directions for Home Gardening
By Harry Freeman
Tattered Cover Bookstore ♦ ♦   (303)322-1965

More Food From Your Garden
By J. R. Mittleider
Acres, U.S.A. ♦ ♦   (504)889-2100

The New Organic Grower
By Eliot Coleman
Acres, U.S.A. ♦ ♦   (504)889-2100

New Seed Starters Handbook
By Nancy Bubel
Rodale Press ♦   (610)967-5171

Organic Gardening Almanac
By Llewellyn's
Acres, U.S.A. ♦ ♦   (504)889-2100

Organic Gardening: How to Garden
In Harmony with Nature
By Sunset
Sunset Publishing Company
Menlo Park, CA

The Ortho Home Gardener's Problem Solver
Ortho Books ♦   (800)822-6349

*The Real Dirt: Farmers Tell About Organic
And Low-Input Practices in the Northeast*
Northeast Organic Farming Association
And Cooperative Extension
Acres, U.S.A. ♦ ♦   (504)889-2100

Rodale's Garden Problem Solver
By Ball
Rodale Press ♦   (610)967-5171

The Self-Sufficient Gardener
By John Seymour
Doubleday/Dolphin 1978

Square Foot Gardening
By Mel Bartholomew
Rodale Press ♦   (610)967-5171

Successful Small-Scale Farming
By Karl Schwenke
Acres, U.S.A. ♦ ♦   (504)889-2100

Tips for the Lazy Gardener
By Linda Tilgner
Garden Way Publishing ♦   (800)441-5700

Vegetable Gardening
Sunset
Tattered Cover Bookstore ♦ ♦   (303)322-1965

Vegetables for the Home Gardener
By Joy Lau
Tattered Cover Bookstore ♦ ♦   (303)322-1965

Vegetables, Fruits and Herbs
By Ball
Rodale Press◆   (610)967-5171

Water-Conserving Gardens and Landscapes
By John M. O'Keefe
Acres, U.S.A.◆ ◆   (504)889-2100

Western Garden Book
By Sunset
Sunset Publishing Corporation
Menlo Park, CA

Gardening—Companion Planting

Carrots Love Tomatoes
By Louise Riotte
Garden Way Publishing◆   (800)441-5700

Companion Plants and How to Use Them
By Helen Philbrick and Richard Gregg
Devin-Adair Company
One Park Avenue
Old Greenwich, CT 06870

Roses Love Garlic
By Louise Riotte
Garden Way Publishing◆   (800)441-5700

Secrets of Companion Planting
For Successful Gardening
By Louise Riotte
Garden Way Publishing◆   (800)441-5700

Gardening—Herbs

Grow 15 Herbs for the Kitchen
By Sheryl L. Felty
Garden Way Publishing♦   (800)441-5700

How to Select, Grow and Enjoy Herbs
By Norma Jean Lathrop
HP Books♦

Growing & Using Herbs Successfully
By Betty E. M. Jacobs
Garden Way Publishing♦   (800)441-5700

Rodale's Successful Organic Gardening Herbs
Garden Way Publishing♦   (800)441-5700

Gardening—Insect and Weed Control

The Bug Book
By Helen and John Philbrick
Garden Way Publishing♦   (800)441-5700

Bugs, Slugs & Other Thugs
By Rhonda Massingham Hart
Garden Way Publishing♦   (800)441-5700

Common-Sense Pest Control
By William Olkowski, et.al.
Acres, U.S.A.♦ ♦   (504)889-2100

Controlling Vegetable Pests
Ortho Books♦   (800)822-6349

*The Encyclopedia of Natural Insect
And Disease Control*
Edited by Roger B. Yepsen
St. Martins or Rodale Press♦   (610)967-5171

Garden, Insect, Disease
And Weed Identification Guide
By Smith and Carr
Rodale Press♦   (610)967-5171

The Gardener's Bug Book—
Earth-Safe Insect Control
By Barbara Pleasant
Acres, U.S.A.♦ ♦   (504)889-2100

Organic Pest Control
Hannon House
3761 East Lincolnway, Suite 204-CS
Cheyenne, WY 82001

Using Beneficial Insects
By Rhonda Masingham Hart
Garden Way Publishing♦   (800)441-5700

Weeds, Control Without Poisons
By Charles Walters
Acres, U.S.A.♦ ♦   (504)889-2100

Gardening—Seeds

Starting Seeds Indoors
By Ann Reilly
Garden Way Publishing♦   (800)441-5700

Gardening—Soil Preparation and Maintenance

The Ablrecht Papers, Vol. II—
Soil Fertility and Animal Health
By William A. Albrecht, Ph.D.
Acres, U.S.A.♦ ♦   (504)889-2100

Improving Garden Soils
By NK Lawn & Garden
BMR
21 Tamal Vista Blvd., Suite 209
Corte Madera, CA 94925

Improving Your Soil
By Stu Campbell
Garden Way Publishing♦   (800)441-5700

Rodale's Guide to Composting
By Jerry Minnick & Marjorie Hunt
Rodale Press♦   (610)967-5171

Secrets of the Soil
By Peter Tompkins & Christopher Bird
Acres, U.S.A.♦ ♦   (504)889-2100

The Soul of Soil—Guide to Ecological Soil
By Grace Gershony and Joseph Smillie
Gaia Services
Box 84 RFD 3
St. Johnsbury, VT 05819

See additional books listed under "composting" in the Chapter 11 listing.

<u>*Storage Food Cookbooks*</u>

Cooking with Home Storage
By Peggy Laton
Nitro-Pak♦ ♦   (800)866-4876

Dehydrated Food Cooking
By Stan Smith
Hawks Publishers
Nitro-Pak♦ ♦   (800)866-4876

Just Add Water
By Barbara G. Salsbury
Horizon Publishers
Nitro-Pak♦ ♦   (800)866-4876

Wild Edible Plants

Edible Wild Plants and Useful Herbs,
The Basic Essentials of
By Jim Meuninck
ICS Books, Inc.
One Tower Plaza
107 E. 89th Ave.
Merrillville, IN 46410

Food Self-Sufficiency
By Walt & Jane Fellows Gullet
Naturegraph Publishers, Inc.   (916)493-5353
Happy Camp, CA 96039

CHAPTER 8—THE ORCHARD AND THE VINEYARD

Apple Cider Press

Happy Valley Ranch   (913)849-3103
16577 W. 327th   FAX (913)849-3104
Paola, KS 66071

Books

All About Citrus & Subtropical Fruits
By Ortho Books ♦   (800)822-6349

All About Pruning
Ortho Books ♦   (800)822-6349

Backyard Fruit and Berries
By Diane Bilderbock and Dorothy Patent
Rodale Press ♦   (610)967-5171

The Backyard Orchardist
By Stella Otto
Acres, U.S.A. ♦ ♦   (504)889-2100

Berries, Raspberry & Black
By Louise Riotte
Garden Way Publishing ♦   (800)441-5700

Fruits and Berries for the Home Garden
By Lewis Hill
Garden Way Publishing ♦   (800)441-5700

Gardener's Book of Berries
By Allana Swenson
Garden Way Publishing ♦   (800)441-5700

Grafting Fruit Trees
By Larry Southwick
Garden Way Publishing ♦   (800)441-5700

Maintaining Your Dwarf Fruit Orchard
By Editors of Garden Way Publishing
Garden Way Publishing ♦   (800)441-5700

Making the Best Apple Cider
By Annie Proulx
Garden Way Publishing♦   (800)441-5700

Planning & Planting Your Dwarf Fruit Orchard
By Editors of Storey Publishing
Garden Way Publishing♦   (800)441-5700

Pruning—How to Guide for Gardeners
By Robert L. Stebbins & Michael MacCaskey
HP Books♦

Pruning Simplified
By Lewis Hill
Garden Way Publishing♦   (800)441-5700

Pruning Trees, Shrubs and Vines
By Editors of Storey Publishing
Garden Way Publishing♦   (800)441-5700

CHAPTER 9—ANIMALS FOR FOOD AND FUN

Breed Associations

The American Goat Society, Inc.
RR 1 Box 56
Esperance, NY 12066

Australian Shepherd Club of America, Inc.
6091 E SH 21
Bryan, TX 77803-9652

International Waterfowl Breeders' Association
P.O. Box 154061C
Waco, TX 76715-4061

Maremma Sheepdog Club of America
P.O. Box 546
Lake Odessa, MI 48849

Midwest Katahdin Hair Sheep Association
RR 2, Box 148
Lexington, IL 61753

Missouri Dexter Breeders Association
General Delivery, Box C
Valles Mines, MO 63087

National Pygmy Goat Association
166 Blackstone St.
Mendon, MA 01756

North American Shetland Sheep Registry
1240 N. 22nd St.
Allegan, MI 49010

Hatcheries and Poultry Farms

Blue Ribbon Chickeries   (405)324-8539
12241 Southwest 26th   after 5:00 p.m.
Yukon, Oklahoma 73099

Cackle Hatchery   (417)532-4581
P.O. Box 529   FAX (417)588-1918
411 West Commercial
Lebanon, MO 65536

Clearview Hatchery   (717)365-3234
P.O. Box 399   FAX (717)365-3594
Gratz, PA 17030

Hoffman Hatchery   (717)365-3694
Gratz, PA 17030

Inman Hatcheries   (800)843-1962
P.O. Box 616   (605)225-8122
3000 3rd Avenue SE   FAX (605)225-4836
Aberdeen, SD 57402-0616

Marti Poultry Farm   (816)647-3156
P.O. Box 27   (816)647-3157
Windsor, MO 65360-0027

Metzer Farms   (800)424-7755
26000 Old Stage Road   (408)679-2355
Gonzales, CA 93926   FAX (408)679-2711

Murray McMurray Hatchery   (800)456-3280
Box 458   (515)832-3280
Webster City, IA 50595-0458   FAX (515)832-2213

Pilgrim Goose Hatchery   catalog $1
SC-94
Williamsfield, OH 44093

Reich Poultry Farms   (717)426-3411
1625 River Road
Marietta, PA 17547

Ridgway Hatcheries   (800)323-3825
Box 306
LaRue 7, OH 43332

Stromberg's   (218)587-2222
Box 400   FAX (218)587-4230
Pine River, MN 56474

Welp's Hatchery   (800)458-4473
P.O. Box 77   (515)885-2345
Bancroft, IA 50517-0077   FAX (515)885-2345

Sheep

Sheepman Supply Co.   (800)336-3005
P.O. Box 100   FAX (703)832-2109
Barboursville, VA 22923

Books

Beekeeping

Beekeeping
By Bonney
Garden Way Publishing♦   (800)441-5700

Cooking With Honey
By Jeanne Barrett
Garden Way Publishing♦   (800)441-5700

Practical Beekeeping
By Enoch Tompkins & Roger M. Griffith
Garden Way Publishing♦   (800)441-5700

Starting Right With Bees
By Editors of Storey Publishing
Garden Way Publishing♦   (800)441-5700

Butchering

Basic Butchering of Livestock and Game
By John J. Mettler, Jr., D.V.M.
Acres, U.S.A.♦ ♦   (504)889-2100

Butchering Livestock at Home
By Phyllis Hobson
Garden Way Publishing♦   (800)441-5700

Health Care of Your Animals

The Chicken Health Handbook
By Gail Damerow
Garden Way Publishing♦   (800)441-5700

Keeping Livestock Healthy
By N. Bruce Haynes, D.V.M.
Garden Way Publishing♦   (800)441-5700

A Veterinary Guide for Animal Owners
By C. F. Spaulding, D.V.M.
Stromberg's   (218)587-2222
Box 400
Pine River, MN 56474

Raising Small Livestock

Build Rabbit Housing
By Bob Bennett
Garden Way Publishing♦   (800)441-5700

Chickens in your Backyard
By Rich and Gail Luttmann
Rodale Press♦   (610)967-5171

Country Women—
A Handbook for the New Farmer♦ ♦ ♦
By Jeanne Tetrault & Sherry Thomas
Anchor Books

Eggs and Chickens
By John Vivian
Garden Way Publishing♦   (800)441-5700

The Family Cow
By Dirk van Loon
Garden Way Publishing♦   (800)441-5700

How to Start a Commercial Rabbitry
Bass Equipment Co.   (417)235-7557
Box 352
Monett, MO 65708

Rabbit Raising for Commercial and Fancy
The American Rabbit Breeders Assoc., Inc.
P.O. Box 426, Dept. J-72   (309)827-6623
Bloomington, IL 61702

Raising Ducks & Geese
By John Vivian
Garden Way Publishing♦   (800)441-5700

Raising Game Birds
By Leland Hays
Tattered Cover Bookstore♦ ♦   (303)322-1965

Raising Milk Goats the Modern Way
By Jerry Belanger
Garden Way Publishing♦   (800)441-5700

Raising Milk Goats Successfully
By Gail Luttman
Tattered Cover Bookstore♦ ♦   (303)322-1965

Raising Poultry the Modern Way
By Leonard Mercia
Garden Way Publishing♦   (800)441-5700

Raising Poultry Successfully
By Will Graves
Tattered Cover Bookstore ♦ ♦   (303)322-1965

Raising Rabbits
By Ann Kanable
Tattered Cover Bookstore ♦ ♦   (303)322-1965

Raising Rabbits the Modern Way
By Bob Bennett
Garden Way Publishing ♦   (800)441-5700

Raising Sheep the Modern Way
By Paula Simmons
Garden Way Publishing ♦   (800)441-5700

Raising Small Meat Animals
By Victor Grammattei
Tattered Cover Bookstore ♦ ♦   (303)322-1965

*Raising Turkeys, Ducks, Geese,
Pigeons, and Guineas*
By Cynthia Haynes
Tattered Cover Bookstore ♦ ♦   (303)322-1965

Raising Your Own Turkeys
By Leonard Mercia
Tattered Cover Bookstore ♦ ♦   (303)322-1965

*Your Rabbits: A Kid's Guide
To Raising and Showing*
By Nancy Searle
Garden Way Publishing ♦   (800)441-5700

Hunting

Complete Book of Deer Hunting
Know More Books♦ ♦   (503)821-2315

Dress 'Em Out
By Smith
Know More Books♦ ♦   (503)821-2315

Game Bird Hunter's Bible
Know More Books♦ ♦   (503)821-2315

Hunter's Bible
Know More Books♦ ♦   (503)821-2315

Small Game and Varmint Hunting
By Pyle
Know More Books♦ ♦   (503)821-2315

Trapping

Beginner's Guide to Hunting and Trapping Secrets
Know More Books♦ ♦   (503)821-2315

The Book of Snares
Know More Books♦ ♦   (503)821-2315

Survival Poaching
By Benson
Know More Books♦ ♦   (503)821-2315

The Trapper's Bible
By Martin
Know More Books♦ ♦   (503)821-2315

Smoking Meat

Build a Smokehouse
By James Fitzgerald
Garden Way Publishing♦   (800)441-5700

The Canning, Freezing, Curing, Smoking
Of Meat, Fish and Game
By Wilbur F. Eastman, Jr.
Garden Way Publishing♦   (800)441-5700

Home Book of Smoke-Cooking Meat, Fish and Game
By Jack Sleight & Raymond Hull
Stockpole Books
Harrisburg, PA 17105

Tanning Hides

Back to Basics
The Reader's Digest Association
Pleasantville, NY

As well as describing how to tan hides, *Back to Basics* is an excellent resource book in general. It contains a wealth of practical information with helpful diagrams and photos about how to *raise and butcher animals, beekeeping, preserving foods, pressing apples, making cheese, fish farming, smoking meats, generation of power*, and numerous other pertinent topics to those wishing to become more self-reliant.

Brain Tanning the Sioux Way
By Larry Belitz
Star Route, Box 176
Hot Springs, SD 57747

The Sioux Indians had a way of tanning hides using the brain from the animal which contained certain acids that would break down any residual debris and soften the leather.

> *Tan Your Hide*
> By Phyllis Hobson
> Garden Way Publishing◆   (800)441-5700

CHAPTER 10—SOME WEAPONS ARE NECESSARY

Training for Use of Weapons

> Gunsite Training Center   (602)636-4564
> Box 700
> Paulden, AZ 86334

Gunsite Training Center offers on-site gun training that is head and shoulders above any other course. There are beginning and advanced courses in handguns, rifles and shotguns.

Traps

> Hav-a-Hart traps
> Available in local hardware and feed supply stores

Videos

> *Jeff Cooper's Defensive Pistol Craft*
> Video International Productions   (205)591-1119
> 4363 First Avenue North, Suite 105
> Birmingham, AL 35222

A Woman's Guide to Firearms
With Lee Purcell, hosted by Gerald McRaney
Lyon House Productions
6000 Sunset Blvd., Suite 209
Hollywood, CA 90028

In narrative form, this informative and instructional video leads you through a step-by-step, easily understood program, providing a full understanding in the fundamentals of firearms for the beginner as well as the more experienced shooter.

Weapons (Handguns, Crossbows, Rifles, Airbows)

This is the list of guns given in Chapter 10, as of the beginning of 1995, in the sequence of recommended acquisition for homestead self-reliant living:

.357 magnum revolver (Colt or Smith and Wesson)
12 gauge shotgun (Remington 1100)
.223 rifle (with a clip)
.45 caliber semiautomatic pistol (1911 style)
.308 rifle (with a clip)
9mm semiautomatic (Sig-Sauer)

A good source is Safe-Trek Outfitters:

Safe-Trek Outfitters■	(800)424-7870
Stephen Quayle	(406)587-5571
1716 West Main	FAX (406)586-4842
Bozeman, MT 59715	

In addition to a multitude of other things, Safe-Trek carries a complete line of handguns and rifles. They also carry other weapons, such as crossbows, airbows and high-powered air rifles. The owner, Steve Quayle, is a weapons expert and would be able to assist you in picking the right weapon for your situation and desires.

Books

Predators

Bugs, Slugs & Other Thugs
By Rhonda Massingh Hart
Garden Way Publishing♦   (800)441-5700

As well as slugs, snails and insects, this book addresses how to deter pests like raccoons, skunks, rabbits, gophers, bears, coyotes, deer, bad birds and others.

"SCAT"—Pest-Proofing Your Garden
Garden Way Publishing♦   (800)441-5700

Weapons and Use of Them

Principles of Personal Defense
By Jeff Cooper
Safe-Trek♦ ♦   (800)424-7870

Survival Shooting For Women
By Tom Givens
from Safe-Trek♦ ♦   (800)424-7870

CHAPTER 11—
GETTING RID OF SEWAGE AND TRASH

Composting Toilets

In some situations, a composting toilet that converts human waste to fertilizing soil might be a desirable addition to a home or a guest house. Several varieties are available from Safe-Trek:

Safe-Trek Outfitters■   (800)424-7870
Stephen Quayle   (406)587-5571
1716 West Main   FAX (406)586-4842
Bozeman, MT 59715

Books

Composting

> *Back to Basics*
> The Reader's Digest Association
> Pleasantville, NY

The preceding book gives a write-up (p. 132) on composting or converting garden trash, kitchen scraps and other organic wastes into humus—an important ingredient of rich soils. Pictured are some easy-to-build alternatives of compost bins.

> *Don't Waste Your Wastes—Compost 'Em*
> By Bert Whitehead
> Acres, U.S.A.♦♦   (504)889-2100

> *East Composting*
> Ortho Books♦   (800)822-6349

> *Fletcher Sims' Compost*
> By Charles Walters
> Acres, U.S.A.♦♦   (504)889-2100

Also see "Soil Preparation and Maintenance" under the Chapter 7 books listed.

CHAPTER 12—SHARING AND HAPPINESS

First Aid Videos

CPR: The Way to Save Lives   (800)622-5689
J.D. Heade Company

Dr. Heimlich's Home First Aid   (818)777-4300
MCA Home Video

Emergency Action First Aid   (312)404-0030
ActiVideo

How to Save Your Child's Life   (310)451-5510
Xenon Video

First Aid and Herbal Medicine Kits And Medicine Boxes

Nitro-Pak Preparedness Center■   (800)866-4876

Safe-Trek Outfitters■   (800)424-7870

Along with the many other items in their extensive catalog ($8), Safe-Trek has a great selection of first aid kits, many of them specifically designed for various conditions. They also have a vast line of medical supplies and offer a selection of books on emergency first aid.

Preparing For Emergencies   (503)826-4512
Omega Publications♦   Orders only (800)345-0175

Chapter 4 of *Preparing For Emergencies* gives details on assembling your own first aid and medicine boxes.

Garden Carts

Troy-Bilt   (800)366-8686
102nd Street & 9th Avenue
Troy, NY 12180

Also see the comments under "Garden Equipment"
under the Chapter 7 heading.

Health Videos

A Practical Guide to Nutrition
By Jeani McKeever
Omega Publications and Videos♦

A Total Approach to Health
By Jeani McKeever
Omega Publications and Videos♦

Nutrition Update: It's Not Too Late
By Dr. Mary Ruth Swope and Jeani McKeever
Omega Publications and Videos♦

Using Nutrition As Medicine
By Dr. Mary Ruth Swope
Omega Publications and Videos♦

Super Foods

Barley Green (and other food concentrates)
Available through: Information (503)826-9279
Alpine Distributors■   Orders only (800)453-7453

Interior Design Nutritionals
Available through: Information (503)826-9279
Alpine Distributors■   Orders only (800)453-7453

Interior Design Nutritionals is on the cutting edge of nutrition. Their Life Pak, which is four capsules a day, contains all of the major enzymes, chromium picolinate, chelated minerals and odor-free garlic. You can sign up as a regular customer and get these through Alpine at wholesale, or you can become a distributor and make an income from it.

Juice Plus+
Available through: Information (503)826-9279
Alpine Distributors■   Orders only (800)453-7453

Juice Plus+ is natural fruits and natural vegetables highly concentrated so that two capsules of their orchard blend and two capsules of their garden blend give you the equivalent in nutrients of about eight glasses of fruit and vegetable juice per day. In nutritional potency, it is like eating five helpings of raw fruits and vegetables each day! Again, Juice Plus+ is sold through network marketing, and you can sign up to be a distributor if you wish to make income or to get these quality products at a discounted price as a regular customer.

Nature's Sunshine Products (NSP)
Available through: Information (503)826-9279
Alpine Distributors■   Orders only (800)453-7453

Nature's Sunshine Products has a vast number of supplements and herbs, almost everything that you can find in a health food store, except that you are able to get them more cheaply, to order at your convenience, and to have their products shipped directly to your home.

Tractor and Related Equipment

In Chapter 12, we recommend a reasonably-powerful tractor with a front bucket and a 3-point hitch with a power take-off (PTO) on the back. An electrical generator can be hooked to this to run hand power tools or a small electric-powered cement mixer.

Recommended attachments, in order of importance, would be:

1. Rotovator
2. Mower
3. Tractor electrical generator
4. Possibly a post-hole digger, including two vertical guide rails (to ensure that it goes in vertically)

Tools and Gardening Implements

Brookstone Hard-To-Find Tools (80)926-7000
17 Riverside Street FAX (314)581-7361
Nashua, NH 03062 free catalog

de Van Koek Dutch Trader (800)992-1200
9400 Business Drive free catalog
Austin, TX 78755

Books and Publications of Interest

Farming

Farming: A Handbook
By Wendell Berry
Tattered Cover Bookstore ♦ ♦ (303)322-1965

Farming for Self-sufficiency:
Independence on a 5 Acre Farm
By John Seymour
Tattered Cover Bookstore♦ ♦   (303)322-1965

Farm Management: Principles, Planning, Budgets
By John Herbst
Tattered Cover Bookstore♦ ♦   (303)322-1965

How to Make Money Growing Plants, Trees,
Flowers: A Guide to Earth Friendly Ventures
By Francis Jozwik
Tattered Cover Bookstore♦ ♦   (303)322-1965

Farming books in general
Lancaster's
Box 13636-J
Roseville, MN 55113

First Aid

Back to Basics
The Reader's Digest Association
Pleasantville, NY

From the Shepherd's Purse
By Marilyn Moore
Safe-Trek♦ ♦   (800)424-7870

This book is a good botanical work on medicinal plants, written for those desiring to learn which plants may be of service to them in case of an emergency.

Survival Medicine
By Marilyn Moore
Safe-Trek♦ ♦   (800)424-7870

This is a guide to preventative and curative techniques that use completely natural means.

Health and Nutrition

The Complete Book of Natural and Medicinal Cures
By the Editors of *Prevention* Magazine Health Books
Rodale Books♦ (610)967-5171

The Doctors Book of Home Remedies I and II
By the Editors of *Prevention* Magazine Health Books
Rodale Press♦ (610)967-5171

The Doctors Book of Home Remedies for Children
By the Editors of *Prevention* Magazine Health Books
Rodale Press♦

Encyclopedia of Natural Medicine
By Michael Murray, N.D., & Joseph Pizzorno, N.D.
Prima Publishing
P.O. Box 1260MP
Rocklin, CA 95677

Foods That Heal
By Maureen Salaman and James F. Scheer
Published by M.K.S., Inc.
Omega Publications♦ (503)826-4512
Orders only (800)345-0175

Healing Children Naturally
By Michael A. Weiner, Ph.D.
Acres, U.S.A.♦ ♦ (504)889-2100

The Healing Herbs
By Michael Castleman
Garden Way Publishing♦ (800)441-5700

Health & Healing Newsletter   (301)424-3700
By Julian Whitaker, M.D.
Phillips Publishing, Inc.
7811 Montrose Road
Potomac, MD 20854

I Live on Fruit
By Essie Honiball and T. C. Fry
1108 Regal Row
Manchaca, TX 78652-0609

Nutrition Almanac—Third Edition
By Lavon J. Dunne
McGraw Hill Publishing Co.   (800)2-MCGRAW

Prescription for Nutritional Healing
By James F. Balch, MD, & Phyllis A. Balch, CNC
Published by Avery Publishing Group (1990)
Garden City, NY

This large (8 1/2 x 11) 1990 paperback is subtitled, "A Comprehensive and Up-to-Date Self-Help Guide." It offers a practical reference for drug-free remedies using vitamins, minerals, herbs and food supplements, and the handy index facilitates your researching of specific ailments.

Prevention Magazine's Nutrition Advisor
By Mark Bricklin and
The Editors of *Prevention* Magazine
Rodale Press♦   (610)967-5171

Second Opinion Health Newsletter   (800)728-2288
By Dr. William Campbell Douglass
1350 Center Drive, Suite 100
Dunwoody, GA 30338

Homesteading

Cheesemaking Made Easy
By Ricki & Robert Carroll
Acres, U.S.A.♦♦   (504)889-2100

The Foxfire Books
Garden Way Publishing♦   (800)441-5700

This highly-acclaimed series of books was compiled by students of an Appalachian high school after interviewing scores of neighbors and relatives. The books are *a lively chronicle of rural skills in practice today as they were a hundred years ago.*

The Good Life
By Helen and Scott Nearing
Garden Way Publishing♦   (800)441-5700

Homestead Your House
By Ralph Warner
Tattered Cover Bookstore♦♦   (303)322-1965

Homesteader's Portfolio
By Alice Pratt
Tattered Cover Bookstore♦♦   (303)322-1965

Making Cheese, Butter & Yogurt
By Phyllis Hobson
Garden Way Publishing♦   (800)441-5700

Homesteading "how to" books for back-to-basic living are available from:

Eureka Resource   catalog $2
P.O. Box 53565
San Jose, CA 95153

Practical books on tanning skins, raising rabbits, backyard fish production, shelter plans and more are available from:

Homestead Books   catalog $1
P.O. Box 964
Poteau, OK 74953

Other Topics of Interest

All About Trees
By Ortho Books♦   (800)822-6349

Back to the Land...for Self-Preservation
By N. W. Walker, D.Sc.
Norwalk Pres, Publishers
2218 E. Magnolia
Phoenix, AZ 85034

The Best of the First Two Years—
Backwoods Home Magazine   (916)459-3300
1257 Siskiyou Blvd., #213
Ashland, OR 97520

Build a Pond (For Food and Fun)
By D. J. Young
Garden Way Publishing♦   (800)441-5700

Cooking in the Outdoors, The Basic Essentials
By Cliff Jacobson
ICS Books
One Tower Plaza
107 E. 89th Ave.
Merrilville, IN 46410

Earth-Quake Ready
By Virginia Kimball
Peace Press, Inc.
3828 Willat Ave.
Culver City, CA 90230

Fast-Growing Firewood
By Lewis Hill
Garden Way Publishing♦   (800)441-5700

Fences, Gates and Bridges—
A Practical Manual
By George A. Martin
Garden Way Publishing♦   (800)441-5700

The Forgotten Arts: Book One
By Richard M. Bacon
Yankee Books
Camden, ME

Garden Construction
By Ortho Books♦   (800)822-6349

How to Get the Most for Your Money:
A Consumer's Guide to Year Round Savings
By Dan Petherbridge
Tattered Cover Bookstore♦ ♦   (303)322-1965

How to Save Money on Just About Everything
By William Roberts
Tattered Cover Bookstore♦ ♦   (303)322-1965

Survival, The Basic Essentials of
By James E. Churchill
ICS Books, Inc. (address listed on previous page)

CONCLUSION

Companies do move locations and change phone numbers periodically. If there was a pink slip in the front of this book giving new addresses, please take a pen and make those changes here in Appendix B.

Appendix C

THE DEFENSIBILITY
OF THE HOME

Probably the optimum layout to make a home defensible would be patterned after the forts of the old West. This layout is shown in Figure C.1. As you can see in that figure, two people with guns in adjacent towers can adequately protect one side of the structure. Their area of coverage (visibility and therefore, ability to defend) is shown by the dashed lines. Person A could cover the area between the two lines marked "A" and person B could cover the area between the two lines marked "B." The area covered by A is shown shaded. With this particular setup, it would require eight people to provide total protection coverage to the structure, two in each of the four corner towers.

I doubt very seriously if any home builder is going to build something as large and elaborate as an old western fort, so we need to adapt that concept, factoring in modern reality.

In the first place, it is unlikely that there would be eight people available to defend a home, so you would need to reduce it to where four people could defend a home. Thus, the towers on the corners would need to be something like 4-feet square, so that an individual could go from side to side by just turning around. These small towers could even be made circular instead of square,

Old Fort-type Layout

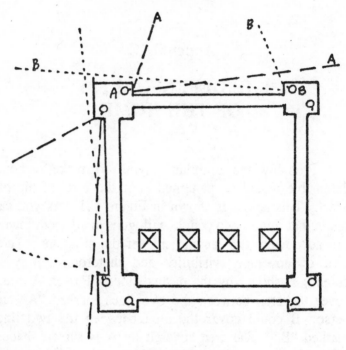

Figure C.1

which would take on a little more the look of a medieval castle. If a person is truly concerned about defense, then these small towers could have a steel lining inside each one. Something like quarter-inch steel would repel most of the ammunition encountered from civilian looters and rioters.

If this general concept appeals to you, there are two ways you could construct a defensible home of this type. One way would be to have an internal courtyard with a house surrounding it in the form of a square donut. Alternatively, the entire structure could be enclosed as part of the home.

If the internal courtyard plan is chosen, then inside the courtyard could be a greenhouse or a small intensive French-method garden, probably in raised beds. Another alternative would be to have a swimming pool in the courtyard which would also serve as water storage. Of course, this would be more expensive, if cost is a limiting consideration.

The Pentagon, headquarters of the U.S. Department of Defense, is built as a five-sided donut with a large courtyard in the middle. (The occupants of the Pentagon lovingly call that courtyard "ground zero," for they feel that it would probably be the first place hit if a nuclear war were to occur.) The Pentagon is designed such that there is the shortest distance between any two offices of any type of structure in the world. The home in Figure C.2 has similar characteristics.

Figure C.2 shows a general layout of a highly defensible house with and without an inner courtyard which could be a garden or, if covered with glass, a greenhouse.

In addition to the structure itself, if the home is to be optimally defensible, then the grounds surrounding the home need to be clear of any cover or protection that an attacker could use. (This also helps in protection against potential fires.) One way to get a picture of what should and should not surround your home is to pretend that you are head of a group who wants to attack this house. Ask yourself the questions, "How would I go about it? Where is the weakest point? Where would I put my men?" As you answer these questions, then the proper layout of the surrounding ground will become obvious.

Another thing that could add to the defensibility of a home and also enhance the heating and cooling capability is to have the home partially or totally underground, as discussed in Chapter 5.

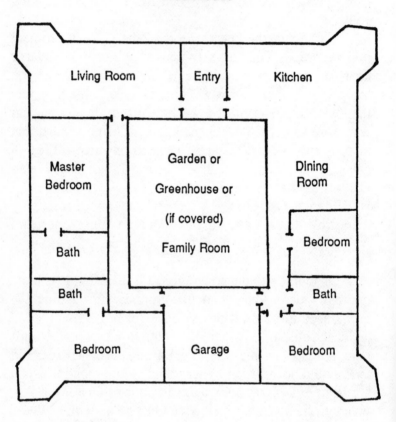

Figure C.2

Appendix D

FROSTS AND
GROWING SEASONS

City	Growing Season (Days)	Frost Period
Montgomery, AL	279	Dec. 3—Feb. 27
Little Rock, AR	244	Nov. 15—Mar. 16
Phoenix, AZ	318	Dec. 11—Jan. 27
Tucson, AZ	262	Nov. 23—Mar. 6
Eureka, CA	335	Dec. 25—Jan. 24
Los Angeles, CA	***	***
Sacramento, CA	321	Dec. 11—Jan. 24
San Diego, CA	***	***
San Francisco, CA	***	***
Denver, CO	165	Oct. 14—May 2
Hartford, CT	180	Oct. 19—Apr. 22
Washington, DC	201	Oct. 28—Apr. 10
Miama, FL	***	***
Macon, GA	252	Nov. 19—Mar. 12
Pocatello, ID	145	Sept. 30—May 8
Chicago, IL	192	Oct. 28—Apr. 19
Evansville, IN	217	Nov. 4—Apr. 2
Fort Wayne, IN	179	Oct. 20—Apr. 24
Des Moines, IA	182	Oct. 19—Apr. 20
Wichita, KS	210	Nov. 1—Apr. 5
Shreveport, LA	271	Nov. 27—Mar. 1
New Orleans, LA	302	Dec. 12—Feb. 13
Portland, ME	169	Oct. 15—Apr.29
Boston, MA	192	Oct. 25—Apr. 16
Alpena, MI	156	Oct. 9—May 6
Detroit, MI	181	Oct. 23—Apr. 25

***Frosts do not occur every year.*

City	Growing Season (Days)	Frost Period
Marquette, MI	156	Oct. 17—May 14
Duluth, MN	125	Sept. 24—May 22
Minneapolis, MN	166	Oct. 13—Apr. 30
Jackson, MS	248	Nov. 13—Mar. 10
Columbia, MO	198	Oct. 24—Apr. 9
St. Louis, MO	220	Nov. 8—Apr. 2
Helena, MT	134	Sept. 23—May 12
Omaha, NE	189	Oct. 20—Apr. 14
Reno, NV	141	Oct. 2—May 14
Concord, NH	142	Sept. 30—May 11
Trenton, NJ	211	Nov. 5—Apr. 8
Albuquerque, NM	196	Oct. 29—Apr. 16
Albany, NY	169	Oct. 13—Apr. 27
Raleigh, NC	237	Nov. 16—Mar. 24
Bismarck, ND	136	Sept. 24—May 11
Cincinnati, OH	203	Oct. 25—Apr. 5
Toledo, OH	184	Oct. 25—Apr. 24
Oklahoma City, OK	224	Nov. 7—Mar. 28
Medford, OR	178	Oct. 20—Apr. 25
Portland, OR	279	Dec. 1—Feb. 25
Harrisburg, PA	201	Oct. 28—Apr. 10
Scranton, PA	173	Oct. 14—Apr. 24
Columbia, SC	252	Nov. 21—Mar. 14
Huron, SD	149	Sept. 30—May 4
Chattanooga, TN	229	Nov. 10—Mar. 26
Del Rio, TX	300	Dec. 9—Feb. 12
Midland, TX	217	Nov. 6—Apr. 3
Salt Lake City, UT	203	Nov. 1—Apr. 12
Burlington, VT	148	Oct. 3—May 8
Richmond, VA	220	Nov. 8—Apr. 2
Spokane, WA	175	Oct. 12—Apr. 20
Parkersburg, WV	188	Oct. 21—Apr. 16
Green Bay, WI	160	Oct. 13—May 6
Madison, WI	176	Oct. 19—Apr. 26
Lander, WY	128	Sept. 20—May 15

Courtesy of National Climatic Center
The Old Farmer's Almanac 1993 Gardener's Companion

Appendix E

MEET THE AUTHORS

Dr. James McKeever is a retired international consulting economist, lecturer, author, world traveler, and Bible teacher. His financial consultations were utilized by scores of individuals from all over the world who sought his advice on investment strategy and international affairs.

Dr. McKeever and his wife, Jeani live on a 70-acre ranch in Oregon, which is basically self-reliant. They have their own water supply, long-term electricity generating capacity and the ability to live with or without electricity. Not only do they grow a garden each year, but they raise sheep for meat and wool, goats for milk and chickens for meat and eggs. They have to dispose of their own trash and concern themselves with other such services that are provided for you in towns and cities. Much of the content of this book is derived from their own experiences or, if it is not something they have tried personally, things they have thoroughly investigated. They come to this subject with a vast background of experience and have been writing about it for over twenty years.

Dr. McKeever was the editor and major contributing writer of the *Money Strategy Letter,* an economic and investment letter with a worldwide circulation and recognition. It was rated number one for three out of four years by an independent newsletter-rating service, and its model portfolio showed an average profit of over 63 percent per year over a period of eleven years.

Dr. McKeever has been a featured speaker at monetary and investment conferences in London, Zurich, Bermuda, Amsterdam, South Africa, Australia, Singapore and Hong Kong, as well as all over the North American continent and Latin America.

As an economist and futurist, Dr. McKeever has shared the platform with such men as Ronald Reagan, Gerald Ford, Henry Kissinger, Oliver North, Alan Greenspan, William Buckley, heads of foreign governments, and many other outstanding thinkers.

For five years after completing his academic work, Dr. McKeever was with a consulting firm which specialized in financial investments in petroleum. Those who were following his counsel back in 1954 invested heavily in oil.

For more than ten years he was with IBM, where he held several key management positions. During those years, when IBM was just moving into transistorized computers, he helped that company become what it is today. With IBM, he consulted with top executives of many major corporations in America, helping them solve financial, control and information problems. He has received many awards from IBM, including the "Key Man Award" and the "Outstanding Contribution Award." His books and articles on computers were translated into many languages.

In addition to this outstanding business background, Dr. McKeever is an ordained minister. He was pastor of Catalina Bible Church for three and a half years (while still with IBM) and is a frequent speaker at Christian conferences. He has the gift of teaching, an in-depth knowledge of the Bible, and has authored twenty-three

Christian books, nine of which have won the prestigious "Angel Award."

Dr. McKeever is president of Omega Ministries, which is a nonprofit organization. He is the editor of their widely-read newsletter, *End-Times News Digest,* which relates the significance of current events to biblical prophecy and to the body of Christ today. The worldwide outreach of Omega Ministries is supported by the gifts of those who are interested.

Mrs. Jeani McKeever is an outstanding individual in her own right, as well as the editor of her husband's many books and articles. She is the author of the award-winning book, *Fit as a Fiddle* and is the editor of a popular, monthly health and nutrition column, *"Temple Tips."* She has recorded two music albums of Christian songs and is in demand as a soloist at Christian events. She has made four video tapes on health, nutrition, canning, dehydrating and other vital subjects, and has practical experience in all of these areas and many more. She speaks to Christian ladies' groups on a variety of spiritual and physical subjects and has authored numerous magazine articles.

Together, the McKeevers bring you over forty years of experience in the area of self-reliant living and they are happy to share their knowledge and experience with you.

COMPANION PLANTING CHART—A Basic Guide to Plant Companions

PLANT	FRIENDS	FOES
asparagus	tomatoes, parsley	—
beans	beets (bush beans), carrots, cauliflower, cucumbers, potatoes, savory, petunias, rosemary	onions, garlic
beets	kohlrabi, onions, bush beans	pole beans
cabbage family (broccoli, Brussels sprouts, cabbage, cauliflower, kale, kohlrabi)	beets, celery, onions, early potatoes, most aromatic herbs (esp. dill, nasturtium, peppermint, rosemary, and sage)	tomatoes, beans strawberries
carrots	lettuce, onions, peas, radishes, tomatoes, rosemary, and sage	dill
celeriac	leeks or onions (alt. rows)	—
corn	beans, cucumbers, melons, peas, potatoes, pumpkins, squash	—
cucumbers	beans, corn (alt. rows), peas, sunflowers	potatoes, strong herbs
eggplant	beans	—

lettuce	carrots, cucumbers, radishes, strawberries	—
onion, garlic	beets, carrots, celery or celeriac peas, beans (alt. rows), lettuce, tomatoes, summer savory	peas, beans
peas	most vegetables, esp. beans, carrots, cucumbers, corn	onions, potatoes
potatoes	beans, corn, cabbage, peas, horseradish at corners of patch	cucumbers, squash, sunflowers, tomatoes
pumpkin	corn	potatoes
radishes	lettuce	—
raspberry	most vegetables	blackberries, potatoes
spinach	strawberries	—
squash	corn, nasturtiums	—
strawberries	borage (few), lettuce, onions, spinach	cabbage
tomatoes	carrots, onion, parsley, marigold, nasturtiums, basil, mint, borage	cabbage, kohlrabi, potatoes
turnips	peas	mustard

scattered throughout the garden: marigolds, calendulas, yarrow

Chart courtesy of COUNTRY WOMEN, p. 153 (see Appendix B, p. 373).

DETAILED OUTLINE

Index

PREPARING FOR EMERGENCIES

By Dr. James McKeever
With Jeani McKeever

We are sure you would agree that every family needs to be prepared for disasters and emergencies, but you may not know where to begin. *Preparing For Emergencies,* the first exceptional book in this series on "Preparation," tells you exactly where to begin in terms of preparation and what to do after that, step-by-step.

Major disasters, such as earthquakes, tornadoes, hurricanes, winter storms, fires, floods, riots, robberies, terrorist bombings, and nuclear explosions *can strike suddenly.* In fact, one of these disasters could strike any place on planet earth at any time. Your home is no exception.

Written in priority sequence, it gives you an easy plan to follow, to whatever level of preparedness you feel prompted to go. It helps you to anticipate emergency conditions and equips you to better handle disasters. This practical book is an invaluable compilation of years of research and down-home experience, including an Appendix that is worth the price of the book! It lists sources where you can buy numerous items you would need to prepare for emergency situations. This important book is a *must!* Order one today.

— — — — — — — — — — — — — — — — — —

Omega Publications   BC-126
P.O. Box 4130
Medford, OR 97501

Please send me _____ copies of *Preparing For Emergencies* ($11.99 each). Enclosed is $_____.

Name_____

Address_____

City, State_____ Zip _____

SELF-RELIANT LIVING
WORKBOOK

You will need this companion workbook called *The Self-Reliant Living Workbook*, which goes with this book. This is a working book in the form of a looseleaf, three-ring binder with divider tabs for subjects such as:

construction ideas	orchards
solar energy	poultry
water supply	sheep and goats
gardening	vineyards
greenhouses	farm equipment
guns and weapons training	wind and water energy
hunting and trapping	fish farming

The McKeevers have used such a book for years and find it a tremendous asset. This workbook includes some of the best articles from other sources on many of these subjects. Also included are a whole host of photographs and diagrams of how they have actually done things on the ranch. A picture *is* worth a thousand words! This information can be invaluable to you in becoming more self-reliant.

This workbook is one to which you can add to with articles out of the publications they recommend, as well as catalogs and brochures from the sources in Appendix B, as you collect information pertinent to homestead living or greater self-reliance in the city.

— — — — — — — — — — — — — — — — — — — —

Omega Publications   BC-126
P.O. Box 4130
Medford, OR 97501

Please send me _____copies of *The Self-Reliant Living Workbook* ($29.99 each). Enclosed is $_____.

Name_____

Address_____

City, State_____ Zip _____

TO THE AUTHORS

Some of the books and videos by Dr. and Mrs. McKeever and others are shown in summary on the reverse side. Please indicate your area of interest, remove this page and mail it to Omega Publications and Videos.

Dr. and Mrs. McKeever would appreciate hearing any personal thoughts from you. If you wish to comment, write your remarks below on this reply form.

Comments:

ORDER FORM AND
INFORMATION REQUEST

Omega Publications & Videos   BC-126
P.O. Box 4130
Medford, OR 97501

☐ Please send me information about other books and videos by Dr. James or Jeani McKeever

☐ Please let me know when the new book on "Survival" is available

☐ I would like to order the following **books**:
____ *Self-Reliant Living Workbook* ($29.99)
____ *The Future Revealed* (10.99)
        By Dr. James McKeever
____ *Fit as a Fiddle* ($5.99)
        By Jeani McKeever
____ *Preparing for Emergencies* ($11.99)
        By Dr. James McKeever with Jeani McKeever

☐ I would like to order the following **videos** ($19 each)
____ *Preparation For Emergencies*—Wadsworths
____ *Dehydrating Made Easy*—Jeani McKeever
____ *Canning is Fun*—Jeani McKeever
____ *Vital Food Storage*—Dr. Barbara Fair

NOTE: Please add $2 for shipping and handling for each book or video. *Prices are subject to change without notice.*

Name _____

Address _____

City, State _____ Zip _____

Charge to: ☐ Visa ☐ Mastercard ☐ Discover

Card No. _____Expires_____

Signature _____